UMBERTO'S CIRCUS

UMBERTO'S CIRCUS

By Eduard Bass

New York

FARRAR, STRAUS AND YOUNG, INC.

PART ONE

CHAPTER ONE

THE BEGINNING? When, actually, had the beginning been? Apparently it had started with that small glass of pale, thin, weakly foaming beer which had been put on the tin-covered bar in front of Antonín Karas. Hein Moesecke was the bartender's name, and the bar was called the Sailor's Bride. It was in one of those winding, dangerous little streets which in Hamburg spread out to the right and left at the end of the Reeperbahn. Some Czech workmen used to go there to eat bacon, sliced with their own jackknives, and to drink a glass of the cheapest grade of beer.

But today Antonín Karas hadn't come here for the sake of the companionship of his fellow countrymen; he had come back from Altona completely downcast in spirit. By the time he had passed the street crossing known as the Four Corners, where, in the middle of the city, the Kingdom of Prussia bordered on the free Hanseatic town of Hamburg, he had already given in completely to the streams of swarming pedestrians, and was carried along by them like a boat which has lost its rudder. They bumped into him, pushed him here and there, caught him up in their united impetus, and carried him on from corner to corner, along canals, across bridges, down the main boulevard.

And then suddenly the crowd had thinned out and he had been thrown up here at the end of the Reeperbahn. Mechanically he had made his way to the Sailor's Bride, like a shipwrecked person who crawls through the shallows onto the beach. And throughout that whole journey, deaf to all around him, he had been gripped by the dull conception that there was no work for him here, that he could no longer make a go of it. What would happen to his boy now, after he had staked everything he had on this one throw of the dice, and lost?

For almost twenty years he had been coming here during the summer for work, completely secure in the knowledge that here there was plenty of it, enough of it indeed to work yourself to death. It had all begun with that time in the 1840's when Hamburg had burned down. The fire must have been a terrible one, for he, Karas, had been kept busy for eight years helping to demolish the ruins of burned-out buildings. They told him it had razed everything for a distance of sixty blocks; even the churches had not been spared by the terrible blaze. The whole world gathered funds for the unhappy city, but most important of all, the businessmen of Hamburg themselves rose up and decided to build everything anew, to erect buildings which would be strong and worthy to live in, to create a real harbor metropolis.

Already during the first year they began to build on a rash scale. But workmen in the building trades were too few in number. Then the Lann brothers, the sailors, had brought the first news of the great opportunity to Budejovice, and in spring a whole gang of workmen left from this one village, to return next winter in complete satisfaction. There grew up a regular migration from Podsumaví to Hamburg, and from Hamburg back home. A certain Milner had formed the gang from Horní Snezná, and Anton Karas became a member.

Milner was a superb foreman. In early spring he would make the arrangements for their transportation on rafts, and in autumn he formed a band of musicians from his workmen to earn expenses for the way home. They brought money back to Horní Snezná; in its whole life the village had never seen so much. At once the villagers began to improve their huts, to buy goats, and to increase the size of their potato fields. Antonín Karas married on his earnings, and his life was happy. He had a son, Václav, a lad sturdy as a young sapling; but Márinka sickened from the time of her delivery and was often confined to her bed, so that she was scarcely equal to the demands of the household during the summer.

And then there came the present year, 1862, and it all happened as if by black magic. After the New Year Márinka took to her bed, and when Milner gathered his gang together she was so ill that Anton could not desert her. Within a week after the men left Márinka died. God grant her eternal rest! Karas provided a good funeral for her, though there were no men in the village, only women and greybeards. In the ditches and along the slopes there still lay snow; when they dug the grave the earth was as hard as stone. But Karas did not give in; with Vasek he brought a green sapling from the woods, a small larch tree, and planted it over the head of the grave, so that the dead woman's eyes wouldn't be hurt by the bright light of the sky. And then he disposed of the furniture, left something with Márinka's mother, something with his sister, and for the first time in his life he locked up the hut with a padlock and threw a sack with his tools, his trumpet, and some sweet rolls over his shoulder, took Vasek by the hand, and headed down toward Budejovice. He hadn't much money left after all his setbacks—hardly enough for the trip—and when at last the river boat docked at Hamburg and, in search of his comrades, he arrived at the Sailor's Bride to join the gang, he felt as if he had been struck by lightning. Milner was nowhere to be found, and the gang was gone.

It had happened as it usually does after a long period of prosperity: construction work had been tied up that year. The great public buildings were long ago completed, a surplus of blocks of flats had developed; in fact, for the last two years new ones remained empty. There was a hitch in something overseas, it seemed, money had become dearer and disappeared, and the local workmen sufficed for the few finishing touches and necessary building repairs. Like the other foremen, Milner had done the only thing possible: on the second or third day there he had collected his gang and struck out elsewhere, to work his way along to a happier land, and perhaps even home.

But what was he, Anton Karas, to do, with a little son and no money, he, who had been completely confident that on his arrival he would go straight to work on some scaffolding! To return to Bohemia was impossible; he could have done it only by begging. So he took Vasek to the lodgings where he always stayed, the Widow Langermann's. She too complained of hard times; both her rooms were empty. She took Vasek under her care and Karas set out to try to surmount fate. He took himself to the outskirts of the city to search for new buildings going up, he even went down to the harbor, to the docks, stopped people to ask

if there was any work—any kind of it, in brick, stone, or wood—
but nowhere was there something to turn his hand to. And if he
did find a stir of activity somewhere, people bristled up like
porcupines to defend their jobs against foreigners and save them
for the local workmen.

And so again he found himself at the Sailor's Bride. Actually
he didn't want to drink, only to stop a bit and collect himself
so that the boy wouldn't see him so disheartened and be frightened. But his head remained full of the single thought: "Can't
I find some kind of job for my two hands?"

Zum Wohlsein!" spoke the fat and sallow Hein Moesecke,
shoving at him a glass of light beer with his short fingers. Karas
hardly thanked him, and Hein Moesecke, a connoisseur of his
customers, rasped in a hoarse voice, "What's up, Anton—you
haven't found anything?"

"Didn't even get near anything," spoke Karas, and took a drink.
The beer evidently washed away some of his gloom, for out of
his mouth there came quite automatically, "Goddamnitalltohell-
anyway!"

"Well, don't lose your head, Anton," Hein Moesecke replied
to this. "Hamburg is like a sea, right? There's a living for everybody, right? Only hold out a bit. Did you talk to Karlchen here?
You must speak to him; you're a Czech, no?"

And Hein Moesecke called at once toward one corner, where
a man sat in the darkness:

"Karlchen, you have a countryman here, you might have something for him to do, no? He's a Czech, no?"

Karas walked over to the other's table. The stranger was small,
dark, curly-headed, his forehead was all wrinkles, not from age
but from the suppleness of his skin and the way he raised his
eyebrows when he looked at Karas. Beneath these two arcs there
shone sharp, dark eyes.

"You're a Czech?" he said, and offered his hand.

"Yes. From Bud'ouc."

"Bricklayer's mate, eh?"

"Right."

"And you're in the soup now?"

"That I am."

6

"And you'd like a job? You'd take any kind of a job? Sure you would, you're a Czech."

Meanwhile Karas had sat down and the other went on, not waiting for him to agree.

"Look, my name's Kerholec. Karlík Kerholec from Libuna; a letter addressed like that will find me anywhere in Europe."

"I'm Antonín Karas from Horní Snezná, a mason . . ."

"Tony Karas for short, bricklayer's mate, I know all about it. Your woman died, and you brought the boy along with you. That'll be a bit of bother, but what else could you do?"

"How did you know that?"

"It doesn't matter; I know. Anyway, Milner's gang came here to Hein Moesecke's. They headed out from here for Stettin when they got an idea of how dead it is here. But they kept explaining that a Tony Karas was going to show up with his boy. The kid's well, I hope. Stood the trip all right?"

"Oh, he's no trouble."

"Well, look, Tony, drink up that blessed beer and we'll go and see if we can't cook up some kind of deal for you. I have something up my sleeve, and if it suits you, you can pay for the beer."

And Karlík Kerholec from Libuna began to whistle a grand march, tossed on his hat at an angle, pulled some change out of his pocket—which he carried loose, in contrast to the careful way Karas kept his in a purse—threw a couple of pfennigs on the bar, and cried in German:

"Well, Moesecke, you old rascal, what'll you do when the sailor's bride gets married?"

"Heh, Karlchen, that isn't worrying me exactly. She's a bit old, no? And a fine old bag when fellows like Karlchen here come to see her, no? Come and have a drink on it, fellows. Here's to you, Anton. I won't congratulate you just yet on finding a job— that might be bad luck."

Outside in the street Karas appeared a big, strapping fellow beside the tiny Kerholec, but all the same he had to step lively to keep up with him.

"But what kind of job is it?" asked the troubled Karas. "Some kind of building?"

7

"Building and tearing down, building and tearing down, brother, always at the double, and a lot of other work besides. Everything slapdash and no end to it. The main thing is to keep on the jump. Did you ever do piecework?"

"Man, that's right up my street. I go at it so fast the other boys can't keep up with me."

"Well, that's good enough. And you know how to trim wood, cut it up, and nail bits together?"

"But I come from the woods."

"That's what I said. And do you know how to varnish and paint?"

"Of course I do, if it's part of the job."

"Milner kept wanting to wait for you. It seems you really can play the trumpet?"

"The bugle—yes, I can play."

"Of course you can, you're a Czech. I'll tell you, Anton, you'll get along fine if you just work well. Karlík Kerholec has a nose for people. Turn here, and behind that merry-go-round, and we're there."

In fact they had come to a part of the Reeperbahn where there was an open space occupied by booths, swings, merry-go-rounds, and shooting-galleries. In the midst of all this stood a bigger wooden building with a round front, bearing a gigantic sign. It stood straight in front of Karas and he could read only the letters UMBER. In vain he racked his brains to discover what it could mean while Kerholec opened the smaller door and called to some-one inside:

"Is Mr. Steenhouwer around, Carrots?"

"In the office behind the ticket window, you old villain!" a woman's voice answered.

"Thanks for being polite, Carrots."

With a smile Kerholec closed the door, walked to the next one, and turned to Karas.

"Now, man, keep your fingers crossed and step over the thresh-old with your right foot. And it might be a good idea if you were to cross yourself three times."

Karas was excited. The unexpected meeting with this experi-enced fellow, about whom he knew not a thing but whose word

8

he was ready to take from the first moment of seeing him, the sudden change in his hopeless position, the mystery of a strange job, the hope that perhaps he and the boy might be saved within the next few minutes—all this on top of his former gloom served to agitate him strongly. Involuntarily he obeyed Kerholec's advice and quickly crossed himself on his forehead, his mouth, and his breast. Meanwhile he observed above him the letters R C U.

Beyond the door there was a short passageway, papered with pictures of wild animals. Kerholec knocked on the farther door. A man's voice answered him and Kerholec nodded to Karas, implying that they should enter.

"Good day, Mynheer Steenhouwer!"

"Oh, it's you, Karl? Hello! What are you bringing me?"

A stiff, stocky man with thin light hair turned aside from his desk and put on his spectacles.

"You told me, Mr. Secretary, that we're pulling out of here before long."

"That's right. Before many more days pass. Is everything in order?"

"I could use two more tent-pitchers. One, anyway. And I've brought along one of them."

"Has he any experience?"

"No. But he's a countryman of mine."

"A Czech? Well, if he's a Czech, then take him on. The usual conditions. Does he know them?"

"He accepts everything."

"Good. He'll receive seven marks in advance. What's his name?"

"Karas . . . Anton. But there's one other thing, mynheer. He's a widower and has a boy with him."

"That's bad. We already have a flock of children, and there's still the tumbling act to come. They'll bring another half-dozen."

"The tumbling act has its own wagon, mynheer. And this boy is healthy and wide-awake; he can be taught. He can sleep with us."

"Well, if you think so. . . . How do you spell that: K-a-r-a-s? Good. Seven marks in advance. Drop in at the treasurer's office, Anton, and Karl can tell you the rest. Good-bye."

Antonín Karas was brimming over with gratitude. He would have liked to rush up to the secretary and kiss his hand, but that gentleman had already turned away, taken off his spectacles, and set to work writing. And Kerholec was pushing Karas through the doorway. Outside, for the first time the mason looked at his slip and stared in horror. On the slip were printed the very letters he had caught sight of on the building, now united into one name:

UMBERTO'S CIRCUS

Employed in a circus! He looked at Kerholec dumfounded, but the latter only grinned and broke into a chuckle.

"Kerholec . . . man . . . how could I work in the circus? . . . It's impossible . . . I don't know anything, you see. . . ."

"You know it, Tony, you do know it, only don't get scared. You know most of what you'll need, and what you don't know, you'll catch onto—remember, you're a Czech."

And Kerholec pushed aside some sort of velvet curtain and Karas saw before him a round hall, its walls lined by rows which went up almost to the ceiling, and full of windows of all shapes and sizes. Shafts of sunlight came through them like gold columns and reached to the sandy circle on the ground, where, in the midst of all this brilliance, stood a beautiful horse with a rider who wore a red bandana about his head. The horse reared up on its hind legs, its mane tossed in the air, its head, bent forward, seemed to be clenched around the bit, its forelegs beat in the air and the rider gently rapped at them.

Anton Karas, the mason, stared at this as at an apparition, as at some dream. And his curly-haired companion explained to him importantly that Umberto's Circus was one of the biggest in Europe, that it belonged to a certain Mr. Berwitz, that there were sixty pure-bred horses in it, an elephant, and a menagerie, and that the whole circus was due to start moving on the road, as it did every year from spring until winter. And for that they needed a gang of workmen, tent-stakers, as they called them, who could erect a tent in two hours and take it down again in half an hour, and that he, Karlík Kerholec from Libuna, had charge of this gang for Mr. Berwitz.

There was nothing difficult about the gang's work, only learning the tempo so that each could keep up with the other, and the men were all Czechs; they had that endurance which Czechs have for everything; it seemed that they were sought after for this work by all the circuses and did a lot of this sort of thing. They made as good grooms, stable hands, animal-feeders, musicians, and clowns as you could find anywhere. The main thing was to learn to master everything and to help wherever help was needed. But the life was a fine one, free and independent, going from place to place, seeing the whole world, strange lands and strange people. . . . And the women! Why, there were no women like circus women!

Karlík Kerholec uttered the last words in a sugary tone, perhaps in order to awaken Karas's longing, but involuntarily the mason saw in his memory the tiny larch tree on its mound. . . . What would Márinka say if she knew he had fallen among circus people! Among comedians, who travel all over the world without any real home, without a real roof over their heads, all kinds of people—perhaps even tramps—among them.

Lord, how the villagers would run to warn the others whenever they turned up! "Lock up your huts, everybody—the gipsies are coming with their dancing bear to give a show!" The police chief would show up as quickly as if he had come at a gallop and look over their passes with one eye while he squinted into their saucepans with the other to see if they weren't stewing a rabbit they had poached from some nearby estate. Probably in the village inn he had more than once announced that for tuppence he would clear the whole rabble out of the place. And now he, Karas, had joined such a guild, he, an honest workman, living an orderly existence in his own cottage, the righteous provider of a family, a father! Never had such a thing been heard of among his people.

But this fellow Kerholec—it was strange—this fellow didn't look like a gipsy; he acted like a gentleman, and Karas had unlimited confidence in him. He wouldn't have stayed a minute with riffraff of just any kind. Perhaps this circus was something a bit better than the bands the folks in Horní Snezná knew. And of course he wasn't going to act in a show, anyway: his job would be like any other kind of job. And Milner's gang—God knows how they were getting along—Krcmárík, Gerha, Vasek Zelenkayo, Jirka Opolecky, Padovec, all honest lads and fathers, and now maybe they were playing their trumpets in people's yards and collecting pennies and crusts of bread, and sleeping in stables and barns at night. At least the two of them would travel over the world, and Vasek wouldn't have to tramp on foot. Vasek, God, Vasek, what would he say to all this? He would have to buy him a better cap for the trip than the old one he had. And he could buy a good one; he'd be getting seven marks in advance. Lord, how the boys and Milner would have to sweat before any one of them would have seven marks!

"Those seven marks—will they pay them to me straight away?"

"Of course. Every man has some debts to settle and purchases to make; this is to fix it all up, so that your mind will be easy on the way. But if you don't stay with the circus until winter, they take off seven marks—that's the bargain. You can drop in at the office for the money—those are the doors straight across from the secretary's. But now come and try on your rig. It may have to be altered a bit."

They walked along the corridor beside the ring. Kerholec greeted the horseman in some foreign tongue and the latter nodded his head, but without taking his eyes off the legs of the horse. The latter now moved in some strange, unnatural stride, as if it were slowly dancing. On the other side of the ring, between the tiers of seats, there was a gate, and above it a sort of balcony. Kerholec turned into the dimness of the corridor, which ran in an arc beneath the galleries. Here there were doors leading, as Kerholec explained, to the wardrobe rooms. They passed several of them, then Kerholec opened one.

A great, dark room appeared, full of all sorts of strange rubbish, above which hung masses of clothing. Out of the darkness at the back of the room there crawled a lame man with a thin face which was full of folds, as if nature had given him much more skin than his narrow face required. But his nose corresponded closely to the arrangement of his skin: it was long and hanging,

12

and the two eyes, set close to it, looked out so uncertainly and so sadly that without thinking you had to laugh.

"A new man in the gang, Harwey," Kerholec said to him. "Find him a uniform in that rubbish heap of yours."

"He's as thin as a hop pole," answered Harwey. "Are you an Irishman?"

Karas looked uncertainly at Kerholec. Evidently he didn't know what that meant.

"No, Harwey, he's a Czech," Kerholec answered for him.

"That's better, Karl, much better. I can't stand Irishmen. If an Irishman got into the outfit it would poison my whole life. But a Czech's a Czech. When they're Czechs you can always alter an outfit for them if it doesn't fit. Maybe that old one of Rudolf's would fit him now, though he was a little shorter and it may have to be taken in around the sleeves."

Harwey limped back into the darkness, rummaged around there, breathing heavily, and at last returned. In his arms he carried a magnificent scarlet uniform with a mass of gold lace on the chest, gold fringe on the shoulders, and red stripes on the trousers. Karas's eyes refused to believe it; in his whole life he had never seen anything so luxurious, unless possibly that time when the bishop had visited Budejovice, when the Schwarzenburgs, Bukvojs, and Cerníns assembled with their lackeys in full parade.

"Am I to put it on?"

"Of course, straight off, so that we can tell what kind of an impression you'll make on the international situation."

Karas threw off his coat and put on the scarlet and gold. They had to show him how to button it in front by its little gold knobs. Harwey pulled it down at the back by the belt, then took him by the lapels and jerked twice, then smoothed it out across the shoulders.

"Fits him like a glove. It sits beautifully. Only those sleeves are too short, but they can be let out. We won't have to try on the trousers."

"Man, it's wonderful." Kerholec looked Karas over, stepping back two paces. "You look like a Turkish general, at the least. When the old man sees you, he'll be as pleased as Punch. Harwey, give me the chit for the clothes; Anton can sign that he's drawn out two pieces. And then we'll get on."

Karas scratched his name on the receipt in a childish script and walked out just as he was, covered with gold, carrying his old coat and his new trousers over his arm, behind Kerholec.

"Now let's go to the cashier's office for those seven marks; that's the most important thing," said Kerholec as they walked along. "Pay attention to what I'm going to say. This woman cashier is some kind of relation of the director, Berwitz. She comes from our country, from Vienna, though the director's wife is from somewhere in Belgium. When you meet the director's wife, just say, 'Good day, madam,' or 'Good evening, madam,' nothing else, understand? But to this female at the ticket window you must say from the very beginning, 'I kiss your hand, madam,' 'I am your humbled servant, madam,' and she'll answer, 'Grüss Gott, Anton,' and to that you'll say, 'God bless you, gracious lady,' and you'll find she'll always come across when you need an advance.

"She, the cashier, has to sew and mend for us, too, but you have to pretend to do all that yourself, and go and borrow a needle and thread and the scissors from her. Then you'll start to poke about with the needle, and even if you know how to do it she'll jump up anyway, snatch it out of your hands, and do the sewing herself. That's the way you have to behave with her, you understand; she's a very fine woman, but she's got her peculiarities. She's the widow of some major or other, Frau von Hammerschmidt's her name, and she's got a lot of influence with the director. But look out for the director's wife—she's a sharp one. You'll come across her wearing an old, worn-out man's coat, a man's hat. You wouldn't give her a farthing—though she'd be willing to take it. Berwitz is a grand fellow, a great boss, but he likes all that kind of thing. All in all . . ."

Kerholec stopped and took Karas by the shoulder.

"Here's the door to the cashier's. Afterward you'll find me in the ring or in the stables. Only I just want to say that everything depends now on how you like your work here. The people, the animals, the material, the job—everything. There's a lot of work here and you have to do whatever comes along. But if you like the work it gets into your blood and for the rest of your life you won't want to do anything else. For we're one big gang here, from the director on down to the stable hands; we're all dependent, you understand, on each other, it all has to work in and fit together. But that's the joy of it, man."

A quarter of an hour later Antonín Karas, the mason from Horní Snezná, was sitting in front of Frau von Hammerschmidt, while she, with short, skillful stitches, let out the sleeves of his uniform. He had just told her his story: how he had buried Márinka, and how with Vasek he had been landed in Hamburg without any work.

"So you had a hard trial, Anton, a hard trial; I believe you." Frau von Hammerschmidt nodded her head, with its brown and gray hair gathered into a huge knot. "But now you can be easy in your mind; you're in a good job. The Berwitzes are fine people, sticklers for work and for discipline, of course, but you'll please them. Why, you're a countryman of mine, you're a Czech.

"Lord, how many Czechs I knew—I've always found it easy to get on with them. That last cadet of Major von Hammerschmidt's, my late husband, came from Vysoké Myto—that's somewhere there in your parts. He was an agile fellow; once he had observed a thing, he could do it right off. And don't worry your head about that boy of yours. We have a number of children in the show; the Berwitzes, too, have a girl named Helen—how old did you say yours was? Seven, well, that's the right age, then they don't give any trouble and they soon get used to it. He'll be the happiest boy, Anton, mark my words.

"There, your sleeves are fixed; you can take it now—and be careful with it, that's our property, you know, which we're entrusting to you. Mr. Berwitz likes everything to look good, only our people must have respect for it, and nothing must be needlessly destroyed. The animals tear up enough, goodness knows.

"Bring the boy to me this afternoon, so I can meet him and then keep an eye on him. Here are three tickets for you: one for him and two for your nice landlady and her daughter. Let them come and watch the show this afternoon. . . . Yes, that fits, it fits as if it were made in Vienna, where they really have tailors, though really most of them are Czechs. Vienna, my God, Vienna, that's a city, Anton, that's a city! . . ."

When Karas passed the ring the rider on the black horse had finished his practice. The horse was covered with foam and sweat and tossed its head high as soon as its bridle was released. The rider jumped down and caught sight of Karas's red livery.

"You're new here, aren't you?" he called to him in German.

"Yes, sir," nodded Karas.

"And where are you from—what country?"

"Bohemia, sir."

"Oh, you're a Czech. . . . Well, lead the horse off to the stable!"

Karas had already gathered that to these people to be a Czech meant that one could do everything. And since Kerholec's advice still sounded in his ears, he stepped into the ring and walked over to the horse as if he had grown up on a farm. Although he had had no experience with horses, he realized as soon as he caught sight of the noble head and fiery eyes that he had never seen such a beautiful animal before. To take it by the bridle would have been the natural thing for him, but as he reached for it, a memory from childhood came back to him from the hundreds of times when he had seen horses shown at the yearly fairs in Budejovice. They had always led a horse with its head held aloft. So now he took the bridle firmly in his right hand and raised it on high. The horse flicked its ears, reared up lightly, and then ran along at a short trot, sidling a bit as Karas led him to the opposite gate. They ran down the short corridor and the smell of the stable surrounded them.

"Hi, Santos! Over here with Santos!" someone there called to Karas, but the black horse itself knew where it ought to go and turned left into its stall. Karas let the bridle go.

"Well done, Tony," called Kerholec's voice from the other side. "You led him well. And now come with me—we'll go for the bricks!"

"For the bricks?" repeated Karas in amazement, and his fingers involuntarily stretched out to the width of those red, rough shapes which from youth he had been accustomed to throw, to catch, to weigh in his hands, to break in half, and to square off.

"For the bricks," confirmed Kerholec, but he gave his compatriot no hammer or trowel, but instead a wicker basket and a

16

huge shovel with a turned-up piece of tin on each side. He led him through the stable between the sixty horses, which munched their hay, snorted into their troughs, and clanked their harness, out to the adjoining room, which was considerably higher. It contained a low platform, and on this platform there stood an elephant, rocking from one foot to the other. Karas had never seen an elephant before and stood still, a bit frightened, when he caught sight of this mountain of dark flesh, with its two huge flapping ears.

"This is Bingo," Kerholec told him, "the pride of our enterprise. Good day, Bingo, how are you, old fellow?" The elephant stretched out his trunk toward Kerholec, who took it in his hand and gently blew on it several times. "You're a nice chap, Bingo. But now let us in behind you a bit."

He patted the trunk, from which a pleased snorting issued, and Bingo advanced the two steps which the chains on his feet would allow. Kerholec pointed something out to Karas.

"So those are your bricks"—Karas grinned in disappointment—"not even fired yet!"

"Do you think we're going to bake them for you?"

Kerholec showed Karas how to hold the shovel under his left arm and the basket on his right so as to gather up the tremendous brick production of the elephant as quickly as possible. When they were finished he led Karas off to the dressing room and pointed out a peg for him, on which Karas now hung his magnificent uniform.

"This is the midday break," Kerholec told him. "At three the performance begins—at half-past two you must be back here. Now let's go and drink that beer you promised me."

"Couldn't we wait till the evening? To drink beer before dinner . . . ?"

"Don't say it, don't say it! Of course you'll come for some beer —you're a Czech."

So it was that Antonín Karas, mason from Horní Snezná, entered the circus in the spring of 1862. And that very afternoon, completely entranced, his seven-year-old Vasek saw the circus too, for the first time.

CHAPTER TWO

THE UMBERTOS were a famous Italian family of showmen. Originally, so far as is known, they had been tightrope-walkers and acrobats. One of them, Carlo Umberto, had fallen once in Arros when a poorly tied cable had come loose beneath him. He had broken his legs, so that it was no longer safe for him to risk himself on the tightrope; he could still walk, but his big toes had lost their sensitiveness and his soles their elasticity, and without these two properties it was impossible to trust himself on a rope. So then he had bought a bear and a monkey and had trained a dog, and with these he accompanied the traveling show of his family.

At a fair in Lyon he had met Luisa Bolier, whose family owned a menagerie. It consisted of a poor open booth with half a dozen monkeys, two hyenas, a smelly fox, and a bald lion that was out of sorts because his teeth hurt him. Carlo Umberto was no longer happy with his own people; his brothers and sisters upbraided him with the fact that they did not need his bear and his monkeys for their success. Luisa Bolier was unhappy because her father was a great drinker and the animals went hungry. Actually her mother supported the family by telling fortunes with cards. Carlo Umberto then married Luisa Bolier, who brought him the menagerie as her dowry; in return the new son-in-law had to pay out of his savings enough to buy her parents a small booth in which Madame Bolier could appear as a fortuneteller and clairvoyant.

At first the two households traveled together, but this arrangement proved a failure; whenever Papa Bolier had one or two too many he would mix up his announcements, stand in front of his wife's booth and shout aloud that here were to be seen the most ferocious wild beasts in existence, or climb onto the platform in front of the menagerie and invite the ladies and gentlemen to come in and have their fortunes told. Because of this there were rows and arguments, and again Umberto preferred to reach down into his purse and buy his father-in-law a little wagon with a canvas top, and a withered old nag, while he himself, with his two wagons of cages and his green dwelling on wheels, turned back toward Italy.

In Grenoble he met a practiced healer, who made him an offer to pull out the lion's three diseased teeth. The beast then recovered enough to execute a few primitive tricks with him in the larger cage. These old Hassan, the lion, remembered from his youth, and he did them automatically so that after they were over he might be left in peace. Before this Umberto had bought an Indian python in the port at Marseille. On the way to the Alps he trained the draught horses which pulled his property, and as well as all this he collected five mongrels, which he trained to walk on their hind feet and do somersaults.

With all this, and with his old dancing and wrestling bear and the monkey Fiametta, he opened THE GREAT UMBERTO'S NATIONAL CIRCUS in Turin, in which Signora Umberto appeared as an English rider and as an Indian snake dancer, while Signor Umberto wrestled with the lion and the bear, and their two assistants acted as clowns and did tricks with the dogs and monkeys. In a few years Carlo Umberto had six pure-bred horses in his show, four draught horses, a pair of young lions in the menagerie, a crocodile, and twelve cages with various smaller animals; and he had a daughter, Antoinette, who danced charmingly on the backs of the horses and jumped through paper hoops.

In Münster he was joined by the young Bernhard Berwitz, who came from an old family of clowns from Saxony. He performed as a juggler and a knife-thrower, and besides this he brought with him a collection of animals: a trained donkey, a goat, and a young pig, which were joined by Umberto's traditional dogs in a great comedy number. In a few years Bernhard Berwitz married Antoinette Umberto and, with typical German persistence, he began to enlarge the family enterprise. When, after some years, there was born to them a son, Peter, they already

19

possessed a fine round tent with a ring ten yards wide, twenty-four horses, three lions, two tigers, and a menagerie which classes of schoolchildren used to come to see. Peter Berwitz grew up in the wagon of his Italian grandfather and his French grandmother; from his father he inherited his skill, courage, and persistence; from his grandparents, however, he got his love for all kinds of display.

Old Umberto was a famous barker; he could improvise fantastic cascades of eloquence in six languages. He filled all his speeches with a stupefying pathos. He loved beautiful, melodious, picturesque words; he loved lofty, heroic, court postures and polished gestures, he loved the glitter and brilliance of magnificent costumes. His wife had an amazing ability for making striking costumes for all the members of the circus from the odd bits of gaudy striped material which she bought for a song in the markets of the big cities, so that the troupe appeared before the crowds dressed like great heroes and heroines from the *Thousand and One Nights*.

Carlo Umberto had never been a soldier because of his injury, and hence felt a tremendous respect for uniforms. Wherever it was possible he purchased from old-clothes dealers or at estate auctions masses of old colorful military uniforms, soldiers' caps, helmets—anything, as long as it shone with gold, silver, or brass. In his circus everything was out of the ordinary. As he hadn't enough money for an identical livery for all of his equerries and grooms, his people would appear in a variety of brilliant uniforms, as colorful and variegated as a group of exotic military attachés. And in the course of time his horses received ever more perfect, more beautiful trappings of dyed leather, brilliant with glittering metal ornaments and topped with gigantic plumes of ostrich feathers or dyed horsehair.

All this was familiar to Peter Berwitz from childhood. He heard the astounding torrents of his grandfather's speech, and saw how the old man could never look his fill on that magnificence which he had created with his own hands. Best of all Carlo Umberto loved horses, for their care was the most noble and the most refined work in the circus. From childhood his grandson inherited this love, and when he was only six they furnished him with a small pony so that he could join in the parade of the caravans when Umberto's Circus rode into a new city. Peter spent three-quarters of his youth in stables and among horses; the finest riders his father hired taught him all the tricks of their riding, the most experienced horse-trainers initiated him into their secrets.

He was fifteen when their acrobatic rider, Miss Arabella, had a mishap while jumping over an obstacle, as those colored strips of cloth are called which are spread out over the ring in the form of a star for the rider to jump over. While jumping onto her angular saddle Miss Arabella slipped, fell, and sprained her ankle. Papa Berwitz declared that the program could not be without a woman as an acrobatic rider, and since they had no other at that time, the next morning they dressed up Peter in tricot and gauze skirts, laced him up at the waist, made up his face, and the boy rode, danced, and jumped for three weeks as Mlle. Arabella, earning tremendous applause, and with constantly increasing success.

At first it had irritated him when he had to ride sidesaddle like a woman, but later he learned to find his own private amusement in the way he mastered the art of imitating all female postures. Old Man Umberto snorted and sputtered with pleasure behind the green curtain over the entrance as he caught sight of Peter's whaleboned figure and laced-up waist as the equerry helped him to mount his horse. Then, one day, the boy threw his heart into the show to such an extent that, to the amazement of the public, he jumped over the last obstacle, at the same time making a somersault.

The first time he performed this unannounced feat he had almost fallen, for in his boyish eagerness he had not considered that he would alight a second later than he intended. In fact the saddle had actually passed by underneath him, but the boy was so skillful that with his soft shoes he had been able to hold onto the broad back of the spotted stallion. For his daring he received a box on the ear from his father, but it didn't hurt much, for he had still not taken off his wig. And he realized only a little later that his idea had been a success, when his father commanded a special rehearsal for the next morning to try out the possibility of slowing down the gait of the horse so that the boy could fall on his saddle.

Meanwhile Miss Arabella raved and even jumped out of bed, but all her envy and jealousy could not ease the pain in her left leg. For the time being she had to make peace with her counterfeit rival. In three weeks the boy had so perfected his jumping and executed it with such bravado that he could do somersaults over eight obstacles in a row. Old Umberto beamed, and at dinner banged his fist on the table and informed his son-in-law that a new act had definitely been born. Everyone admitted this, and when at last Miss Arabella mounted her stallion again in Ulm she could not prevent the appearance of a certain Miss Satanella, who, in the bravado of her jumping, far outshone the former's traditional act.

Peter kept this role of an acrobatic rider for a year and a half. At times it was extremely difficult to conceal his secret from the public, especially when the officers of various garrisons asked insistently to be presented to the daring rider. His career in disguise came to an end quite suddenly, however, in the Hungarian town of Szegedin; there the nineteen-year-old son of Count P. fell so madly in love with Miss Satanella that after all his vain requests to meet her, his invitations to dinner or to go riding, he made an onslaught backstage with a pistol in his hand. Two shots missed, the third lightly grazed the stallion as it was being led away; and so the certainty that sooner or later the Berwitzes might lose either a son or a horse after some such incident forced them to take Miss Satanella off the program.

Berwitz Senior gave the order immediately after the shooting, but Grandpa Umberto made himself heard above all the excitement and declared by his right of seniority that the act must remain. After which he put on his dress coat, fastened on all his orders, had his old top hat ironed, and drove off to see the old Count P., to explain to him, with many elegant and polished speeches, what a public scandal the young Count had caused, how much trouble it had been to keep the police from interfering, and what damages Umberto's Circus had suffered. Evidently Grandpa Umberto put up a magnificent performance, for he remained with Count P. until morning; they drank twelve bottles of Tokay and three bottles of brandy together, and Carlo Umberto returned to his family a bit fatigued, but with a box in which lay a hundred gold ducats, and followed by two white Lipican geldings with which Count P. had chivalrously settled for the final disappearance of Miss Satanella from the face of the earth.

Grandpa Umberto's diplomacy was all the more timely, since Peter had already begun to put forth a rather thick beard and his voice was changing, so that he no longer dared to cry his triumphant "Hussah-haloo!" whenever he surmounted an obstacle. In place of Miss Satanella a Signor Pietro now appeared on the program, but no matter how much terror and wonder his magnificent feats awoke in the hearts of the audience, he never reaped the same harvest of bouquets, boxes of bonbons, jewelry, and rarities from his admirers that he had during those eighteen months when for a few minutes every day he had disguised his sex.

This was the day when the popularity of equestrian circuses was at its height. The aristocracy still stood at the head of the class system of many states and peoples, and for the greater part was founded on English manners and English taste. The Renaissance type of nobleman who had played the role of a Maecenas toward the arts and sciences, a type which had been still vigorous during the baroque period, was now dying out in many cases; much greater interest was shown in the more sporting aspects of life, among which the passion for thoroughbred horses and for skill in riding occupied first place.

If a good circus came to a capital city the nobility would drive in from their country mansions and take a box for a number of days, to look their fill on picked, carefully bred stallions, geldings, and mares, to criticize the art of their riders and trainers and, during the intermission, to use the circus stables as a promenade where they could meet and exchange opinions. The magnificent gesture of the knightly tournament, that pathetic apotheosis of adventurous heroism, had long since disappeared; but it was reborn in this vagabond knightly order, in this poor band of wandering knights without estates and without coats of arms. As long as there still glimmered a sense of vanished chivalry in the fading memory of the aristocratic families, the golden circle of the circus ring still attracted them—a dim reflection of the tournament ground of their ancestors. They came to the circus like sleep-walkers under the moon of their past; they associated with people who, like themselves, had cut themselves off from the bourgeoisie, if in the opposite direction.

Dukes and marquises crowded round circus riders who risked their necks daily for a few groschen, and a golden rain of favors and honors was showered on those charming girl riders with wasp-like waists, on those fairies and sylphs who flew through the air above their proud beasts, and sought to preserve perfect grace on the very frontiers between life and death. Many of them ended the game with broken ribs, underneath the body of a fallen horse, but many were carried by their last graceful jump to the very highest rank of society, to crowns and titles, whose bearers believed to the depth of their souls that in the eyes of their conquering ancestors they were committing no mésalliance.

But even those less fortunate were always surrounded by a swarm of admirers; even in the little, Godforsaken towns there were mounted garrisons, and their officers waited for the coming of the circus as the greatest event of the year. Skill in riding was then considered to be the pride and backbone of the army; hussars, dragoons, light cavalrymen, cuirassiers, and lancers were commanded by aristocrats, and many a garrison cut off from the world provided such an enthusiastic welcome for the equestrians that a few days of such hospitality meant for some of them years of debt.

Rarely was the word "circus" uttered on these occasions. From the first huge expeditions of the English acrobatic riders to the Continent down to the enterprises of such a director as the Czech Beránek, all these equestrian circuses were called simply "The Riding Society," "The British Royal Riding Club," and so on. Few of them had their own tents; for the most part they performed in "permanents"—round wooden buildings already built for them in the large cities, or which were constructed for them when they remained in one place for several months. Their programs were made up of the traditional numbers of the royal art of free-style riding and of the High School; of Roman riding, imitations of English fox-hunt riding, of vaulting, of dancing by the horses and dancing and jumping by the riders. A few clowns filled out the intervals when they were smoothing out the sawdust in the ring. If the "club" had an especially well-trained horse, the climax of the evening would be a dramatic scene, such as "The Arab and his faithful steed," in which the clever stallion would play the leading part. And finally there would be performed a great pantomime, in which all of the "club's" horses would take part and in which the most splendid riding costumes were displayed.

The true circus, with its typically heterogeneous program, then existed only on a small scale, at carnivals and fairs, very often without a tent, under the open sky, where a hat would be passed round among the spectators for donations. Umberto's Circus soon distinguished itself from both these types in that it combined a greater and more varied artistic spectacle with a menagerie, and could use this menagerie to enrich its program. In Grandpa Umberto's time it still confined itself to the modest proportions of the average circus of that day. His ring was sixteen English yards in diameter, just big enough to hold six performing horses.

When Peter Berwitz took over Umberto's Circus he quickly increased and improved the family stable, so that his circus might be counted among the most important equestrian enterprises, and therefore he had to think of a more spacious tent, in which his increased stock of horses might be utilized. After much consideration and consultation with his riders and trainers, he decided on a ring with a diameter of twenty-four English yards. They found that in a ring of these dimensions a horse ran leaning toward the center at such an angle that the rider's balance would be steadiest, and if a rider should slip while performing acrobatics, he would always fall onto the sawdust, and never be thrown toward the outer side onto the track, as Mlle. Arabella had fallen, for example. And within these dimensions Peter Berwitz could show in free-style performance the impressive array of twenty-four horses.

Umberto's Circus now ranked among the foremost equestrian societies, but Peter Berwitz did not renounce his grandfather's program. In particular he remained faithful to his grandmother's love for lions and other big cats. He expanded his menagerie through purchases and barter and joined the ranks of the few great directors who fostered the training of wild beasts. Grandmother's old Hassan had died long ago and his skin lay in the traveling caravan between the beds, but in the cages of the menagerie five lions, two of them males, two tigers, and three bears ran back and forth behind bars, each animal trained for an appearance in the arena.

In those days they still had not mastered the art of quickly running up a grating round the ring and of showing larger groups of beasts in a big, open space. The old tamers themselves went into the cages with the beasts. These cages were crudely constructed boxes with bars on one side. There was no room in them for great jumps. The spectators sat in awe, watching the daring man or woman who risked his or her life with a whip and a pitchfork among the roaring and bristling lions.

The act itself was a short one: the lions had to stand up at the command, approach, sit or lie down; sometimes the tamer would wrestle with a reliable beast and then finally put his hand or his head into the animal's open jaws. Such performances might be repeated ten times in one afternoon, as often as the barker succeeded in drumming up spectators. The old side-show men had a revealing name for these exhausting continuous showings: they called them the "shambles—slaughterhouse work." Carlo Umberto, too, had to arrange such a "slaughterhouse" act, so that a number of performances might be held in one afternoon. In the days when he gave his show under an "umbrella," as a poor, small tent was called, he arranged his show in this "shambles" fashion, but later, with his son-in-law, he was so far away from that sort of thing that he gave only two performances an afternoon. There were no evening performances, for they had no light. In buildings they used candles for light and later gas, but in tents they still feared illumination; the danger of fire was too great.

Even more than for a big tent old Umberto longed for a "circular performance." He was a child of the open spaces, he was accustomed from his days on the road to have spectators round him on every side, and so he considered the "circular performance," as the circus staging was called in contrast to the single theater stage, to be the only art really in contact with its audience. To do tricks in a menagerie cage irritated him; everything was concentrated on the side where the bars were and three sides of the horizon were empty and dead.

So when Umberto's Circus was beginning to pay its way, he purchased a movable cage, a real cage with an iron grating on all four sides and mounted on low wheels, into which the beasts designed for the performance were driven, and which was then pulled into the ring by a splendid team of four horses. The cage was three yards square; with some crowding it was big enough for two animals, but Carlo Umberto was in the seventh heaven when he could, according to the fashion of the day, chase an animal from corner to corner, crack his whip, fire a round of blank cartridge, force the terrified animal to roar and bare its teeth, and finally induce it to lie down with its head on its paws while he, the great tamer Signor Carlo, would theatrically place his right foot on its mane, to the wild burst of applause which would descend on him from every side.

Once Umberto's Circus had been caught in northern Lombardy during the Easter season. On Maundy Thursday, Good Friday, and Holy Saturday it was impossible to play before the Italian people. These days were set aside for making major repairs and for seeing to the tents, the wagons and equipment, over which the grandparents, Umberto and Luisa, always kept a personal watch. This time they announced to Bernhard Berwitz that he ought to take over the supervision of repairs himself. They showed him the defects which they had observed, and then they made their departure.

While making up the beds Antoinette Berwitz discovered that her father had taken with him the old cigar box he always kept under his pillow at night. This was the box, tied with many cords, which Mother Bolier had given to him on her deathbed. The box had been almost full of the gold louis d'or which the clairvoyant had been able to save from her drunken tamer-husband. Antoinette knew that her father had long ago filled this box to overflowing. He had opened it only a few times in his life, when some serious calamity had struck the circus, or when he had had the chance to make an extraordinarily profitable purchase of some valuable animal; and afterward he had again saved and scraped until the Habaños box was full again.

The Berwitzes now realized that something important had happened to the old man. On Holy Saturday he returned with his wife as if nothing had happened. However, at the holiday dinner he suddenly began to look festive and, drinking a glass of red wine, announced to them in his sonorous Italian adorned with courtier-like phrases that with this year he had reached seventy; that to be sure he still felt vigorous and healthy and could, as the whole world knew, still present his productions in full force, but that God's wisdom enjoined man not to overstrain the cord of life needlessly; that therefore, following the example of all his ancestors, the jugglers and tightrope-walkers of the great name of Umberto, he had resolved on a well-deserved retirement, for which he and Mamma Louise had just bought a pleasant little cottage in the mountains of Savoy, covered with vines, with a garden and a yard. Here, in the fear of God, they intended to train dogs, cats, monkeys, parrots, and other small animals for Umberto's Circus.

And since the merit which he had earned as founder of the circus should not be passed over in silence, and since it was the unbreakable law of show people to make capital of everything they did, he desired, and at the same time, in his function of senior director, commanded, that in each town in which the circus appeared before his departure they should present one gala performance for the leave-taking of Signor Carlo Umberto, the first and greatest tamer of rapacious beasts, the famous artist of the tightrope, the worthy trainer of horses, and the great and meritorious founder of this, Umberto's Circus, which had earned the glory and favor of all the crowned heads of Europe. During his speech Grandpa Umberto had so worked himself up to his best barker's fire that his family involuntarily burst out in applause.

One other significant event occurred in the family annals that same year. The circus was in Antwerp when an elderly, venerable, and bewhiskered gentleman came from Brussels to see them, in the company of two young ladies. He asked to be led to the director's wagon, where he made a request to Berwitz Senior that the latter should organize a charity performance in Brussels, in which the circus artists should take part in company with ladies and gentlemen of the best Brussels society. The bewhiskered gentleman was the King's Second Chamberlain, Count d'Ascensons-Létardais; one of the ladies was his daughter, Marie Anna, the other her friend Anna Steenhouwer, the daughter of the State Commissioner in Turnhout. The Second Chamberlain guaranteed the director the usual revenue of a sold-out house and the presence of the King with his family and the whole Court. And, should His Majesty be pleased, no doubt there would be some order or other into the bargain.

Of course Bernhard Berwitz accepted this magnificent offer, and the following day the Countess Marie Anna and her friend began to visit the stables and the main tent every morning, and there practice jumping and riding on the circus's best stallions. Later they were joined by several other young men and ladies, who were to ride in a quadrille. Peter Berwitz was assigned to this whole circle of nobles and burghers as chief equerry and instructor.

After ten days Umberto's Circus left Antwerp and went on to Brussels, where tremendous publicity had already been given them. The opening performance for the benefit of the royal orphanage was a tremendous success. Count d'Ascensons-Létardais appeared in it as a great archer, a young marquis even took the part of a clown, while Miss Anna Steenhouwer distinguished herself not only by her riding, but also by the great beauty of her free-style performance with six white Lipicans. His Majesty was enthusiastic, Bernhard Berwitz received an exalted order with palm leaves and the title of Royal Court Equerry, Grandpa Umberto a gold watch, and Peter Berwitz a gold ring set with diamonds. And besides all this Peter had become the personal friend of many of the young nobles.

Umberto's Circus stayed five weeks in Brussels. Just before the end of their happy stay in the kingdom, where everything seemed to be part of an operatic aria, Peter Berwitz went to look for his mother, found her in the wagon peeling potatoes, and with much embarrassment confessed to her that he and Anna Steenhouwer were in love and wanted to marry; that the Countess Marie Anna approved, and was delighted, and that she had even promised to undertake to persuade Anna's parents. This was a matter which Mamma could scarcely handle by herself. It was even beyond Grandpa Umberto. He scratched himself behind the ear, and said something or other about the "morganatic" marriage of an artist with a burgher's daughter; but he did admit that the girl had shown the Lipicans in fine style and that when she jumped on horseback, she had stuck to the saddle as if nailed there.

"Well, with our Lady Mary's and holy Jesus' favor everything on earth is possible," he had added, then, crossing himself piously, "even that a girl of good family should become a free artist in a circus. State Commissioner is not a bit finer title than Court Equerry to His Majesty the King of all the Belgians. Only I think we should ask her family what kind of a dowry they intend to give. When I had only a bear and monkeys I married a whole menagerie."

After this favorable opinion of the old man's Father Berwitz could no longer raise any obstacles. He demanded a day to think it over, but this was only to take one more look at his son's fiancée as she rode in the ring that morning on the stallion Pompon. He decided that the girl was slender, had long legs and supple joints, that she held her head and spine correctly, had a commanding gait, and that she guided her horse with a firm hand. Only then did he embrace Peter and wish him good luck in the forthcoming interviews in Turnhout. There the matchmaking was more difficult. There were cries and sobs, but after the intervention of the family of Count d'Ascensons it ended in the quiet resignation of the parents and the ecstatic triumph of their only child. The final humiliation came for them at the signing of the marriage contract: it turned out that Signor Carlo Umberto could neither read nor write.

So, with the departure of Grandpa Umberto to his retreat in Savoy, the other wheels of the enterprise all began to turn. Papa Berwitz became senior director while Peter took over the actual management of the firm. Now he put an end to his career as

Signor Pietro, with its wild rides and somersaults. His father took over the act with the wild beasts and Peter inherited the horses. Under the name of Monsieur Alfred he rode at the head of huge groups of magnificent stallions, while his wife appeared as Madame Sylvia, rider of the High School, on that same black horse, Pompon, on which she had ridden out in front of her future father-in-law to win his approval.

To everyone's wonder it turned out that Peter was by no means mistaken in his choice. The young director's wife had had a wonderful training as a housewife. She could make their simple dinner into a banquet by adding a few trifles. She won Grandpa Umberto's heart before his departure; he would declare that "That girl has introduced into our family the manners proper to those personages whom kings come to visit." And besides, Anna was very economical. She had many generations of officialdom in her blood and this taught her how to count trifles and convert them into much. She did not shirk any work which awaited her; in the morning she was the first to rise, in order that breakfast might be prepared for the others; in the evening after the performance she would sit with a needle in her hand and mend costumes or make new ones.

And to complete all her virtues, she loved the animals. She could not pass a stable or a cage without stroking all the beasts within reach and giving each of them some titbit or other. If she went to town to shop she would always take an extra shopping bag with her and fill it with carrots, turnips, apples, nuts, rolls, sugar, and scraps of meat which she bought with the pocket money her parents sent her. Before long her return from market was greeted by a great crying, roaring, tramping, and pacing behind the bars of the menagerie and with a joyful neighing in the stables. From the monkey cage there protruded fifty or more shaggy little paws, the hairless fingers of which, spread out like rose-colored fans, begged for presents. Raccoons, foxes, a wolf, a badger, bears—all stood behind their bars or nets on their hind legs; the lions and tigers pressed against their cages so that they could see as far into the distance as possible; the parrots ruffled up their feathers and cried their own praises; the surging sheep pushed to the front of their stall; the trained geese honked; and the old goat Bluebeard, whose whiskers Grandpa Umberto had dyed a beautiful azure blue, almost knocked out the gate of his stockade.

Bluebeard and the four white nanny goats knew no tricks, and took part in the circus only in pantomimes, where they impersonated peasants fleeing before a foreign army. Then Bluebeard would race after the flying flock of geese and, to the delight of the children, would jump over the most neck-breaking obstacles. This performance was little enough to give in exchange for all he devoured, for his appetite was insatiable. For the rest he only got into mischief, but they took him with them all over the world, for they believed that goats chase infectious diseases away from menageries.

The circus is full of all sorts of superstitions, and Umberto's people esteemed it not a little that the new director's wife soon knew and respected them all. Shortly after the wedding Grandma Umberto had caught her by the arm as she was about to lay a mended costume on the bed.

"*Nom de Dieu, ma chère,*" cried the old side-show woman, "never do that, never do that! A costume on the bed—half a year without a performance."

Anna raised her eyebrows, nodded her head, and from that time onward she always hung costumes up without laying them down. It was clear to her that she was in a world which had its own strict and unbreakable rules.

Everything would now have promised a most happy future if it were not that the circus, in the nature of things, is always involved in a game with death. It began when the tigress Miuma was pregnant, for in that delicate period she caught a chill and, in spite of all the keepers' care, died. The tiger Pasha became lonely and evidently was grieving. Anna was the only one who went to his cage with caressing calls and tender words. The men thought that the only way to master wild beasts was by frightening and terrifying them. Pasha was full of distrust for people, and it took him quite a long time to become accustomed to the figure of the slender woman who brought him pieces of meat and fed him at unusual times, and who never harmed him. But the day came when he began to wait for her with impatience; when she appeared he would rub his ear and neck and then his entire side against the grating of his cage, uttering low whines with which he sought to gain caresses. Anna stretched out her hand and scratched him lightly at first, then more heavily in his bristling hair. His ears lay down, and he was evidently only too willing to endure this delicious play for hours on end.

When Miuma died his liking for Anna developed into a real passion. He paid attention to no one but her; when she came he would jump up against the bars as if mad; when she went away he would whine sadly and begin to pace back and forth behind the bars of the cage unappeasedly. He was a really beautiful Bengal tiger in the full vigor of a four-year-old male.

Anna kept urging her father-in-law to provide him with another tigress for a wife. Before one could be found old Berwitz sought to amuse him by training him for a joint appearance with the lion Sultan. It was work enough to get the two beasts in their adjoining cages accustomed to each other before they dared to put them into one common cage without risking a fight between them. When this had succeeded Berwitz began their training. After the first simple tricks he tried to teach them to sit for the end of the performance on two high pedestals, while the trainer bowed to the audience. It was then almost spring; the circus had turned aside toward Switzerland. When they were in Chur, warm winds suddenly sprang up; the varied scents of early spring were wafted over the peaks of the Alps.

"Pasha is uneasy for some reason," Anna told her father-in-law one evening. "Keep an eye on him, Father. Today he jabbed at me with his paw. It's the spring affecting him."

"Pasha's a bad one," answered her father-in-law. "I always keep a brace of pistols about me. But you go near him without anything. Don't trust him."

The next morning they repeated the rehearsals with the pedestals. For a long time Pasha refused to jump up. At last Berwitz forced him to do it and Pasha sat there, grunting and snarling, with an evil greenish gleam in his eyes. Meanwhile Sultan was running back and forth in the opposite corner of the cage. Now it came to his turn. The whip cracked. "Sultan, hop!"

Sultan backed away into the corner, crouched together, and with a great leap fell heavily on the pedestal. His jump was too quick; the pedestal turned over, and as he jumped aside he struck against Pasha's pedestal. Pasha's ears went down, he sniffed and crouched.

And then Bernhard Berwitz made a fatal mistake—he tried to raise the fallen pedestal. As he bent over, Pasha sprang. He landed with his paws on the trainer's right forearm, which he tore open with his claws. He buried his terrible fangs in Berwitz's thigh. The attendant who stood by the cage with a pitchfork uttered a cry and ran to the other end of the cage to chase Pasha away. But he could not reach him, for the terrified Sultan was running along the grating and Pasha had dragged his prey into the center of the cage.

Anna was tidying up in the wagon when she heard the cries of people and the roaring of the lion. She cleared the steps of the wagon with one jump and ran to the tent. As soon as she pulled back the curtain she saw what was happening. With a voice of command she cried:

"Pasha!" The tiger raised his head at her cry. "Pasha! Let go!"

Pasha bent forward to release the unfortunate Berwitz. At that moment a shot sounded. Pasha's back crumpled up; he bared his teeth but he was staggering. Peter Berwitz, who had run out from the stables in the meantime, loaded a second time. It was unnecessary; the tiger had fallen. With the attendants they chased the lion into the corner, dragged out the unconscious Berwitz, and drove him off to the hospital. There he awakened and smiled, seeing Antoinette and Anna over him.

The doctors assured the family that the wounds were not fatal, that their father would come back to them in a few weeks. Umberto's Circus went off to Zurich without its senior director. And it never saw him again. From Pasha's claws, tainted by putrid meat, Bernhard Berwitz contracted blood poisoning. Peter received a letter from his mother at Innsbruck in which she informed him that his father had died, that she would bury him in the cemetery at Chur and then would go back to her parents in Savoy.

CHAPTER THREE

So Monsieur Alfred and Madame Sylvia became sole owners of the firm of Umberto's Circus. The enterprise had an excellent foundation, laid by the work of three generations, and Peter was resolved to expand it in accordance with his personal desires, which differed significantly from the more moderate taste of his father. That winter, during which they were still wearing mourning, he dedicated to a painstaking renovation of all equipment and to the making of new, fantastic costumes. To the fairylike, ethereal costumes which had been kept from his grandmother's time they added new ones, dashing, bright-colored, exotically cut and full of gold, silver, and gleaming sequins. For the first time Peter dressed his grooms and servants in a uniform green livery; the equerries' and stable hands' were blue, the musicians' scarlet. And at the same time he began to enlarge the menagerie.

A few years before this a certain Herr Gottfried Hagenbeck of Hamburg had changed his business of dealing in salt-water fish to that of importing animals from all over the world. At first he had bought only at random, from whale-fishers and returning sailors, whatever they had happened to pick up: a pair of seals here, some polar bears there, a parrot or a monkey. He had begun to exhibit them as a specialty of his at the fair at Dom, but in the end he found that he did still better selling them to circus troupes on the road. And then they began to come to his store in search of all kinds of exotic animals, even wild ones, to make inquiries and purchases from him throughout the year.

Formerly this sort of merchandise had entered Europe only by way of London and Liverpool and was frightfully expensive in English pounds; now Herr Hagenbeck set up a new store on the old market place on St. Paul's, which was kept well stocked as soon as the captains and sailors of transoceanic vessels were assured that it was quite profitable to sell what they had once brought home only for their own amusement. Already Father Berwitz had begun to trade with Herr Hagenbeck and spoke highly of him as a good and inexpensive source of supply.

Now Peter too came to him, and in addition to his purchases secured two invaluable bits of experience. First of all he made the acquaintance there of a Frenchman, Henri Martin, a handsome, gray-haired old gentleman who had been a tamer and trainer of wild animals all his life. Peter and he spent the evening together and for the first time in his life he heard from Martin that all the mad, wild training of animals by shooting and whipping was stupid and cruel, and that he, Martin, had known for half a century how to tame big cats without using force or torture. Involuntarily Peter recalled the methods of his wife; truly she had accomplished more with her simple love than Grandpa Umberto and his late father ever did with their whips and pitchforks—why, Pasha had even let go of his father at her call, and if Peter had not fired at him at that moment they might have had the valuable animal still.

The second important thing Berwitz learned at Herr Hagenbeck's was the news that on the Reeperbahn stood a spacious circus building fitted out for winter occupation, which was now free, and that in the increasingly wealthy city of Hamburg it would be possible, with occasional changes of the program, to keep the circus there a number of months. On the next day he went to look over the building and at once leased it. From then on Umberto's Circus was assured of regular winter activity, and it was no longer necessary to resort to chance, nor to have long periods of inactivity.

The next year Umberto's Circus was to set out on that glorious expedition which Peter Berwitz had dreamed of for many years. Through Warsaw and Riga their wagons, carts, and caravans of horses and draught animals journeyed on to St. Petersburg. There they performed before the Tsar and the imperial court with tremendous success. The old Baltic nobility adored the circus and overwhelmed its artists with presents; the Tsar himself decorated

36

Berwitz with an order and presented him with a Circassian saber. Then there were weeks and weeks of sold-out houses in Moscow. Peter Berwitz had the inspiration to add some of the *balaganshchiki*, the Russian popular comedians, to his program, and these folk were delighted to be allowed to perform their tricks and pranks in such distinguished company.

Round the ring there gathered the public, with its joyful, happy, childlike spirit, adoringly following each feat of courage and thunderously guffawing at every joke. Even the wealthy Moscow merchants with their plump wives and their children brought up like the children of noblemen, even the high state officials with gold on their collars and with their beautiful wives (who themselves staged a magnificent performance in their own loges)—all of them managed to come time after time to the same program, and loudly proclaimed their delight and their enthusiasm.

Starting with Kharkov, Peter Berwitz began, in addition to the *balaganshchiki*, to add to the program races between his own riders and the local Cossack elite. More than once his best equestrians were overshadowed and defeated by the wild bravado of the frontiersmen of the Ukraine, but all the greater was the flood of money which poured through the cashier's window, all the more enthusiastic were the crowds of people who rushed from far and wide to Peter's tent.

Along the Donetz and the Don there flew the glorious news of how a first-rate circus had arrived in the empire, of the magnificent crowd of horsemen who were here, of the great beauty of every one of their animals, of the challenge they had presented to the fighting Cossack brotherhood. By the time they had reached Ekaterinoslav it already seemed as if the glorious old days of Cossackdom had come to life again, as if the whole brotherhood had arisen under the leadership of its *ataman* to strike at its foes, the infidels—so deeply was the tent surrounded by the horses on which these visitors had come to see picked, bearded Zaporozhe Cossacks riding into the arena to the song which sounded in their mighty breasts like a great organ. And on to the Don, and on to the Kuban, where all the towns, villages, hamlets, and farms were out to see Umberto's Circus and the triumph of its riders over the cavalry of the West.

And then, after Georgievsk and Pyatigorsk, came the forked Caucasus with all its perfumes. The tiers of seats round the ring were filled to overflowing by the different tribes of these marvelously beautiful people, with their burning eyes and passionate temperaments. Peter Berwitz led his expedition on, over the precipitous green mountains to Tiflis and to the River Kura, and to the pale waters of the Caspian Sea and again over mountains into mysterious lands, where tanned people appeared on camels and where all intercommunication ceased, and three dragomans had to act as the company's Persian interpreters. Through the dust of the desert and the waste of the cliffs the caravan crawled on to Teheran.

Peter's romantic dream was fulfilled. But no rose and gold capital of Oriental splendor appeared to him. Teheran was an endless heap of crudely plastered, mean little buildings and dirty streets. Here dwelt the man whom Peter Berwitz, in his surpassing craving for adventure, had yearned to see. Here dwelt the Shah of Persia. As in the fairy tale, he was named Nasreddin; in the morning he judged trespassers in the sixth courtyard among the fountains, condemned them to the bastinado or to the loss of an ear—and then composed love poems, though he also had his own royal poet at Court. And Shah Nasreddin visited Umberto's Circus with his counselors and generals and watched the whole performance with an emotionless expression, with pensive eyes which looked out from under half-closed lids. Was he pleased? Not even the experienced Anna could guess the secrets of that melancholy face.

But the next day they brought to Peter an officer who announced to him in French that His Majesty the Shah of All Kings had been pleased, and intended to return that evening. And the Shah came day after day, always with the same lifeless face which did not alter during the leap of death any more than it did during the tumblings of the clowns—a motionless apparition which bent its head with its high fez only when, during the grand finale, the Persian flag was unfurled before his loge.

Thereafter Peter received daily from strange old men all sorts of little parchment rolls, filled with arcs, strokes, and dots; at the embassy they told him that these were Persian poems which sang the magnificent art of the honored foreigners. Only when Umberto's Circus announced the end of its performances was there obtained what Peter had so eagerly waited for and what he had in fact come for: the Shah sent him a letter signed by his own hand in which he thanked him for the enjoyment Peter had given him. To the letter there was attached a document in which Peter was named Emir of White Horses and given the honorary rank of colonel in the Persian cavalry. The deputation which delivered these papers also brought a magnificent colonel's uniform which His Exalted Highness presented to Peter as a keepsake. From this time on Peter Berwitz always appeared during his performance in the Persian colonel's uniform, with the Circassian saber at his side.

Originally Peter had wanted to go on past Teheran; in his mind he had fashioned the fable of a triumphal journey through India. But Anna said no to this. Her watchful common sense apprehended all the incompleteness of their preparations for such a trip through inhospitable lands: the defects of their wagons, the hardships that would befall their people and animals, many of whom were even then near death. Moreover, the financial success of such an undertaking was far from certain, for each station on the way would be achieved only by surmounting distances and expending efforts which were far too great.

Peter was half-convinced, but he only gave up his idea when in Teheran he ascertained that they were on the threshold of a world where there flourished quite different feats of magic than those which Umberto's Circus knew. Even in the little market towns he met with half-naked jugglers, charmers, acrobats, and fakirs who did feats which were completely unknown in Europe, or who performed in the most effortless manner tricks which were considered the height of difficulty in the West.

He saw Arabian tumblers who executed a double leap with a gracious smile on their faces, he saw young boys do handsprings on one spot with helter-skelter rapidity, so that their bodies resembled wheels circling in the air. In one little town he discovered a band of cross-eyed, yellowed, ugly men who balanced revolving plates on their long poles with a perfection he had never seen in Europe; and it was quite common to come upon fakirs who owned dancing snakes, or others who had pierced their bodies and tongues with sharp instruments and who walked on hot coals. Here were magicians who could make bouquets of blossoming flowers grow out of empty metal plates, here were fellows who had nothing more than a dirty rag round their loins, a plate for coins, and a pole they would place in the ground and then climb up as if it were the most solid of masts.

He saw camel-drivers who could perform the most extraordinary tricks with their favorite camel, though everyone knows that the camel is the most stubborn of all beasts. He saw trainers of great shaggy cats who could enact a whole theatrical sequence with them. He saw male dancers in women's clothing and puppet theaters and magic silhouettes, and outside the city he discovered a vast open-air theater where they performed a sort of passion play about Ali, the holy martyr, during which there appeared on the stage hundreds of riders on Arabian and Persian horses.

In one town he encountered a tame tigress which her owner led on a chain along the street. He would come back from these reconnoiterings with a heavy heart and sigh to Anna during supper. "What a country, O Lord, what a country!—If we could pack it all up and take it back to Europe, then, only then, would we have a circus worthy of the name!" In saying this, Peter Berwitz anticipated great new ideas. Not long after this the first Arabian acrobats arrived in France, then came Chinese jugglers and Japanese equilibrists, and Europe began to marvel over the perfection of the ancient acrobatic traditions.

One day, however, Peter Berwitz rushed to find his wife in special excitement. In a southern suburb of Teheran he had discovered a trained Indian elephant. Its image still burned bright before his eyes and his mouth and hands did not suffice to give any conception of what a colossus it was and all it could do. He had still not finished when Anna was already fastening on her hat. She saw what had got into him; he wanted to buy the elephant. One of the symptoms she recognized in her Peter was his Umbertian obstinacy, with which he would carry out whatever he had taken into his head to do, no matter what it cost. But her careful deliberateness put up a resistance to this "no matter what it cost." She determined to look at the elephant herself and to introduce her own economical cast of mind into the whole purchase. These tactics succeeded best with Peter when he had lost his head over something. She would go along with him only so far, and then suddenly she would apply the brakes until the matter was back on a more sensible basis.

This time, before they rushed off to the suburb, she forced Peter to admit that they could not appear at once as buyers, and that they ought first to go elsewhere and ask how much such an animal was worth. Against the elephant itself she had no objection; she fell in love with it at first sight and herself could appraise the value it would have for many years as an attraction. Moreover, there were large savings in the heavy bound coffer from the profitable journey, and possibly it was more sensible to spend their exotic currency on a suitable purchase than to exchange it at the banks at a loss. But they must do it cautiously. The elephant belonged to a small band of traveling show people, evidently a family, and constituted their collective fortune.

That same afternoon the Berwitzes went around the European colony and took counsel with friendly merchants. The outcome, according to the advice of the most experienced dealers, was to hire a native negotiator, preferably a Mullah, a sort of priest-scribe, and to make the elephant-owners an offer to exchange some of the animals in the menagerie for the elephant. The main thing was not to hurry. A week or ten days was nothing for such a business deal here. In fact, the negotiations with Arr-Shehir, the elephant's owner, lasted a full seventeen days, and the purchase would never have been consummated if at the critical moment Anna had not arrived at the happy idea of taking Arr-Shehir and his family with the elephant.

It then appeared that it was a question of a rather extensive relationship and that the intentions of the various members were different. Arr-Shehir himself and his wife had evidently been taken by the idea of traveling over the wide world with the white sahibs; the others, however, wanted to turn back toward India. It finished by Peter Berwitz's giving the mutinous relatives an entire little menagerie, paying off Arr-Shehir with a great pile of

Persian and Russian money, and hiring him for five years as trainer, leader, and keeper of the elephant, with a salary which was princely by Indian standards. His wife was to accompany him. So the elephant Bingo was added to Umberto's Circus, and the director's wife had one pet the more.

After this acquisition Peter Berwitz no longer opposed their return to Europe. For it he chose the caravan route of the European couriers through Tabriz and Erzerum, a route which was under the supervision of three embassies, the British, French, and Turkish, and on which, he was told, there were comparatively more caravanserais. But it was a far worse trip than the one they had made on their way out. The alleged road was almost impassable for the wagons; there were no bridges; it was a perfect example of the Persian view that good roads would bring enemies into the land. In places they trailed through the desert, in places they had to defend themselves against the Kurds.

Of food there was little or none, and the weather was against them. The wagon wheels turned uselessly, sometimes in dust, sometimes in mud, sometimes in fissures in the soil; people fell sick, the animals were often half-dead with hunger and thirst. On the Turkish side it was somewhat better, mainly because they would more often come on a town where they could remain a few days and recover their strength. But this exhausting journey across Asia Minor seemed to have no end, and in some of the wagons they began to grumble that they would all perish on the way, "and all just because the director had wanted his Persian colonel's uniform."

During these days it was Anna and the elephant Bingo who had the most energy. Anna, wasted from the heat and exertion, rode back and forth on her Pompon along the whole caravan, helped at each bogged-down wagon, led the mounted expeditions in search of forage, roused the sluggards, visited the sick, and even managed to find some titbit or other for her beasts in the poor, broken-down villages. The elephant Bingo walked with his steady, peaceful gait in the middle of the caravan; neither the heat of the sun nor the downpours of rain could disturb him. Wherever a wagon got stuck and the horses and people vainly toiled to pull it out, Bingo would lean against it with his forehead and push it out onto firmer ground. But whenever they came to any kind of stream of water he would not allow himself to be held back; he would raise his trunk and with a joyous trumpeting run off into the river, where he swam and rolled in the mud, sluiced and splashed himself, to the accompaniment of continual trumpetings of satisfaction.

So little by little, in their saddles and wagons, they put the unkind, inhospitable land behind them, stopping once every day, even at poor, tiny villages, to give a "performance." It was for them a rehearsal, without any tent, under the open sky, so that they might not get out of practice, a mere repetition of the movements of the performers and the animals. The populace who gathered to watch brought them bread or sheep's milk and cheese.

Peter Berwitz came from an old family of acrobats and knew well why he stuck to daily training and practice so insistently. He remembered one incident when a month of idleness had been enough to destroy the perfection of an artist's performance for a whole year. And all the others felt a passionate need for the daily work to which their hard life had accustomed them. So even the sick crawled out of their wagons at these stops and helped to give these remarkable performances, for which the workers had smoothed out a ring in the form of a round enclosure precisely twenty-four yards in diameter.

And so somewhere above the dried-up river Kizil Uzen or on the shores of Lake Urmia or on the threshold of the Kara Dağ Range the sound of brass music would suddenly burst forth and two riders would dash into the ring, each standing on two horses, the opening number of the Roman riding act. And then, cracking his whip, Monsieur Alfred would parade the horses, minus their usual plumes and spangles, Madame Sylvia would ride in the High School, the other riders would vault, the acrobats would jump, the clowns would stagger and fall, Léon Gambier would wrestle with the bear and force the lion to walk on a ball, the clown Hamilton would ride on a wild ass, and finally, the giant Bingo would tread in with deliberate steps and dance on the rows of bottles on the ground.

Whenever it didn't go well it was all repeated again and again, under the high blue vault of Asia, before a background of un-

43

paralleled scenery. Once they rehearsed among the ruins of an ancient city; on the horizon before them stood the giant peak of Koh-i-nuh, which people told them had destroyed many settlements on its slopes in a volcanic eruption many years before. The circus people nodded and went on with their practice, knowing nothing of the fact that Koh-i-nuh was the Persian Mt. Noem and that this volcano was Mt. Ararat, and that the ruin all round them was the ancient Armenian city of Artaxata. A week they remained in the Turkish fortress of Erzerum and took not the slightest interest in the battle which the Russian General Paskevich had fought when he took the city. They straggled along the little river Kara-gu and had no idea that this was the mountain source of the Euphrates on which, after a thousand miles of passage, lay the Babylon of the Bible. They played in Qisarya amid Roman ruins, and were not the least concerned that these were the remains of proud Caesarea, the capital city of old Cappadocia, the birthplace of St. Basil.

They journeyed along the banks of Kizil Irmak and did not know that this was the memorable Halys, which had once formed the frontier of Persia. When it led them to the city of Angora they admired the fluffy splendor of the white cats, the rabbits and goats which were bred there, but they knew nothing of the fact that they were entering ancient Ancyra, founded by King Midas, and that the immense broken columns among which Berwitz ordered them to stop the wagons were the ruins of the mighty temple of Augustus. In Eskişehir they took an interest in the graves of some Mohammedan saints, by the sides of which devotions were constantly being performed, but how could they know that here had been the bastion of the knight Godfrey de Bouillon?

They were simple people, who for the most part could not read or write, and who knew nothing more important than how to maintain or to increase their skill. They all threw themselves into their work with the passion of people in love with their calling, forgetting pain and hardship and feeling that their mission in life was to achieve that perfection they must demonstrate regardless of whether they appeared before the Emperor of the French or the ragamuffin Kurds, Armenians, and Turks; that in truth by this perfection for perfection's sake they created an exceptional artistic unity which could not perish and which could not be broken down and in which the individual was lost in the united and indivisible Umberto's Circus.

At last there came the day when they realized from the greater traffic on the road and the denser population of the country that they were approaching a great city. Peter and Anna slowly left the trailing wagons and trotted on ahead, up the steadily rising hills on the crest of which the countless cypress trees stood like black candles, heralding the presence of a cemetery. The couple impatiently rode on and both checked their horses at the same spot, for below them there gleamed the green of the Bosporus.

White foam outlined both banks, which narrowed together to the right, and twisting, were lost in the misty distance. A thousand white and colored dots gleamed on the silken plain; these were the ships and boats which plowed over the motionless surface of the water. And on the left, opposite them, there swelled another sea, less calm and more broken, a shining white sea of stone walls, bell towers, and bristling minarets, gathered together in the distance by veiled, toothed ramparts, the black towers of which rose and fell with the hills and the valleys until they disappeared—this was Istanbul, Constantinople, the city of the Sultan. Anna could not look her fill at the miraculous beauties which opened out beneath them. Peter came back much sooner to his everyday concerns.

"Wonderful decoration," he said after a while. "And most important—it's Europe at last. Where do you think the Sultan lives? We must stop the wagons as close to the palace as possible. But we should arrange the cavalcade from the other side, from the walls; an entry from the port and the boats would be hard to stage. And in Constantinople we need to do as much business as possible."

While they were still standing there the idea ripened in his mind to take the whole caravanserai across the city secretly, without being observed, to the ramparts, and there to prepare the triumphal entry into Constantinople. For two days his wagons waited in Scutari while he arranged the whole thing. On the third day toward evening they began to load onto the boats he

45

had hired, and it was already dusk when they landed, load after load, at the Golden Horn. It was a bit cumbersome to have to move with the wagons and horses over the piers by the light of lamps and torches, but they managed it without a mishap. Through the dark, unlighted streets carriage after carriage now crawled through the unknown city, accompanied by a few dozen Turkish porters, until a black gate opened before them and after a few steps they found themselves in the open country. They turned to the right and slowly descended into a hollow under the ramparts. After a bit lights shone among the hedge of wagons and again the camp life began.

They remained in this deserted hollow for five days while everything which had been damaged by the hardships of Asia was completely repaired. Meanwhile Berwitz had rented a vast empty lot near the great mosque of Achmed and had prepared Turkish and French throwaways, as they always call the long, narrow circus handbills. On the sixth day the glorious entry was finally made. All the members of the circus had to wear their most festive dress, and in addition Berwitz made arrangements with the authorities to borrow a hundred and fifty soldiers, whom he dressed in pantomime costumes. At last a procession started such as Constantinople had never seen.

In front, behind the squadron of porters, there went two medieval heralds carrying long silver trumpets with which they sounded a fanfare whenever the music behind them came to a halt. Then three Roman riders appeared, with metal guards on their bare calves and with helmets above their beardless faces. The center one carried the standard of Umberto's Circus. Behind the Romans came a flat wagon on which the musicians sat in their red-and-gold liveries, their backs to one another, and played march after march. Then, following a whole troop of ancient riders, there appeared the golden racing chariots of the Roman circuses, drawn by four horses abreast, and on one chariot stood Peter Berwitz with a purple mantle, in the pose of Caesar.

After this scene from antiquity came the chief equerry and Madame Sylvia, both in English hunting pink coats and black caps, as if they had ridden out of the most fashionable London engraving. Behind them were three girl riders in rose, cream, and azure skirts, then two Spanish hidalgos covered with silver sequins, with black, flat Seville hats which they waved at all the pierced-fretted windows in grandiose style. Then came a troop of soldiers dressed like Arabs, in long, flowing capes, and then a troop of Russian Cossacks. At first these soldiers had refused to put on the dog's uniform of an enemy of Islam, until Peter Berwitz persuaded them that it was a prize of war. Only then did they take great delight in putting on the Russian caps at a rakish angle and riding through the city with their left hand on their hip. Behind them the blue-liveried master of horse led the pride of Umberto's stable, six white horses with pink nostrils.

Then came a group of soldiers dressed like Persian falconers—this was a new idea of Berwitz's which he had got in Teheran—they carried many-colored, screaming parrots on their leather gloves. Then there was a cage of tigers drawn by two zebu bulls, and a cage of lions pulled by a team of four horses. Behind these marched soldiers dressed in blue, red, and gold costumes, called "Moroccan" in the circus. In their arms they carried gilded cages with little monkeys. Eight hired hamals with blackened faces and arms, giant feathered turbans on their heads and in fantastic yellow and red attire, carried an ornamented Chinese sedan chair in which sat two women performers in the guise of fairies.

And then there appeared before the awed spectators the majestic Bingo, covered with red trappings with gold tassels; on his head sat the worthy Arr-Shehir in white costume with gold turban; on the elephant's back a palanquin swayed, in which there were four houris, their faces covered by veils. These were wives of the servants and grooms, washerwomen and scrubwomen who, with their eyes painted, looked like the most seductive of visions.

But this was by no means the end of the procession. Still to appear were the clowns with their trained dogs, at their head Hamilton on his wild ass, this time miraculously obedient. Amidst the jumping and somersaulting clowns the servants led the goat Bluebeard with his white retinue garlanded today, a pair of mouflons, the flock of sheep, the badger and the bear. This was the most variegated collection, for the servants wore all the old glittering uniforms which Grandpa Carlo had collected in

47

his day. And then came several more medieval armor-bearers, again with the standard of Umberto's Circus, and it was over.

Peter Berwitz was amply rewarded for the care and expense he had devoted to the arrangement of his entry into Constantinople. Performance after performance was played to packed houses; the European colony and the Sultan's subjects came again and again. The Sultan did not appear, but he sent a message to Berwitz to ask if it might not be possible to arrange a special performance for him and his Court in the imperial gardens. Of course Berwitz eagerly consented, and played three times in the presence of His Majesty and of a tribune covered with a veil behind which the whole imperial harem was seated. Abdul Mejid was so well pleased that he allowed Berwitz to be presented and invited him to an inspection of his stables.

Peter was a connoisseur of horses and was proud of the noble animals in his enterprise. But in the Sultan's stables he could not conceal his surprise and delight. Here in long rows were the most beautiful descendants of the five sacred mares of Mohammed: Julfa, Hoheila, Manet, Saklav, and Tusie, all with magnificent deep chests, fine muscles, long shoulder bones and short forelegs, short in the ribs and strong in their slender legs, as if made for constant, swift gait, true inebriates of the winds. Here were stallions from the Nejd, the best-bred steeds of the glorious horse-breeding clans of Beni Sacher, Hadjerad, Muali, El Ruola, El Sbaa; here were even white mares of the more tenacious breed of Txaifa and long-necked Manakui, bred by the clan of Vuold Ali. These Peter could well appreciate, for he knew the tradition that mares of this breed were considered priceless by the Arabs and were never sold.

All these immense stables housed only white horses. They were of all shades of white: velvet, silver, steel-gray, ashen, milky, reddish, bluish. Here were horses with large spots and small ones, and as the greatest rarity, here were two satin steeds with rosy hide and silken, shining hair. Behind the Arabs there ranged magnificent Berber stallions with arched noses and stag's necks, sturdy white steeds of the race of Ben Chareb, brown ones with high gait from the breeds of the Haymur, and small indefatigable pacers of the Meziris breed.

And here were Persians: straight-legged horses from Iraq Ajemi; Spanish, proud Andalusians with fiery eyes and knees which lifted high into the air. Peter Berwitz could not believe his eyes; but they still had to visit the English stable, where he found descendants of the most priceless racing thoroughbreds, members of the famous breeds of Herod of Byerley Turk and Matchem of Godolphin. There remained only the domestic Turkish horses now, the Caucasians, Armenians, and others, unknown breeds of utility horses. In the stables Abdul Mejid warmed up and began a conversation, and Peter was amazed at his vast knowledge of horses.

When they returned to the Sultan's salon and sat down with his favorite son to little cups of black coffee, the Sultan questioned him for more than an hour about all the practices of Western breeding, the care of sired mares, and the use of various remedies for horses. Evidently Peter passed the examination, for after a lapse in the conversation Abdul Mejid invited him to come to his own chambers. Salon after salon presented collections of imperial treasures, a staggering multitude of ornaments in gold and silver, and in one room there were only heaps and heaps of the most precious stones.

Amid all this lifeless wealth the Sultan again fell into silence. Only in the hall with the snuff-boxes did he stop, walk round the tables, pick up a single, heavy gold box with carved arabesques, and without a word offer it to Peter, who bowed deeply. In the chamber with the precious stones the Sultan turned over a pile of green stones on an agate platter, and picking out one of the largest sapphires, gave it to Peter with the two words "For Madame." And then he and his host parted.

All this was more than enough to bring Peter Berwitz to the height of personal exaltation. But yet one more thing was added. Before the departure from Constantinople he was named Inspector of the Imperial Ottoman Stables, with the title of Liva Pasha, and received the Order of the Crescent of the second class with a cloak of honor. Without delay Berwitz pinned the order onto his Persian colonel's uniform. And Constantinople had been fruitful for him financially; he had again filled up the coffers which had been exhausted by the journey over Asia. And so

Umberto's Circus returned in glory and happiness across the small dependent Balkan principalities to Budapest and Vienna.

There Berwitz found his cousin Elisa in deep mourning for the death of her husband, Major von Hammerschmidt, and not a little concerned over her own future. He solved her troubles by engaging her as his cashier. He could not forget how advantageous it had been in the time when, some years before, Umberto's Circus had been managed and guarded by six members of the family. To be sure, he knew that he had good and reliable fellow workers, but somehow the notion had got into his blood that the circus should be more than a mere business enterprise, that its basic foundation must always be the family.

Anna fully approved this, though she did not feel the weight of tradition in it. And when she learned from home that her cousin Frans Steenhouwer, a Dutchman, had completed his high-school studies and, instead of continuing them, wanted, at any price, to enter a business firm in the colonies, she wrote to him after talking it over with Peter. Frans Steenhouwer gladly exchanged his craving for exotic and distant lands for the no less adventurous career of journeying with the circus.

So it was that Umberto's Circus had formed and crystallized up to the time when our Czech mason, Antonín Karas, found it as its winter stay in Hamburg was coming to an end, and everything was undergoing final preparations for the spring journey on the road.

CHAPTER FOUR

DURING THIS MIDDAY visit to the Sailor's Bride to which Kerholec had challenged him the sun began to shine more brightly over Antonín Karas. He felt that he had acted rightly and that it would have been ridiculous to throw away this magnificent opportunity. As if all his cares had fallen from his shoulders, he shoved his hat back on his head and drank a toast with Kerholec.

"You old rascal, here's to you, you sly devil, you really know your stuff!" And Kerholec responded:

"Here's to you, you sheepherder, you wooden bricklayer! I'll be damned if you won't make a foreman for Berwitz after all!"

And Hein Moesecke rasped in his weedy voice: "Here's luck; let's pour out another one, no? I told you, didn't I, that Hamburg has a place for everyone? Karlchen, I'll draw one for myself, no? Drinks are best when they're clinked by threes, gentlemen. *Zum Wohlsein!*"

Karas returned home a bit lit up, and even felt like singing. But when he found himself on the dark, narrow staircase which mounted to Frau Langermann's apartment on the fourth floor his good spirits departed. "Lit up, of course you're lit up, man. That bloated old rasper, that Moesecke, poured five of them into you that morning, and all on an empty stomach; sure you felt like singing. But now, Anton, the Sailor's Bride's behind you, there's your boy, there's Vasek up there, and he's waiting desperately for his old man to come home with something. And the old man's coming, coming straight from his beer, the villain, and he'll say, 'Well, Vasek, we're going off with a circus.' And Vasek, what'll Vasek say? These damn steps—there's no end to them. Vasek will say nothing. Vasek will only look. And that's the real trouble—he will look. The very way she, Márinka, would look. The same eyes, exactly, the same blue-green—a man couldn't really tell what color they were—but her eyes they are, the eyes of the poor woman who lies under the larch tree." Her eyes are here and watch him to see what he does with the boy and the way he takes care of him. What a fine woman she had been all the same! And the boy was like her; how could he tell him that they had joined the circus?

Heavily and unwillingly Karas turned the doorknob and slowly hung his hat on a hook beside the door. Frau Langermann opened the door from the kitchen. The boy stood by her and close beside him squeezed the widow's six-year-old Rosa.

"Father!" Vasek cried joyously.

"Well, did you find work?" asked Frau Langermann.

51

"I found it. But it's something queer—I don't like it," answered Karas, and slowly walked into the kitchen, which was filled with the scent of marjoram.

"How is that? Sit down, we've been waiting dinner for you; then you must tell us all about it."

"Father—have you got a job?" asked the boy.

"Yes, Vasek, but I don't know what you'll say to it. I . . . we're going to be together in a circus."

Now he waited for the angry silence. But Vasek, who was quite satisfied when he heard that a job had been found and that they would stay together, turned his great, trusting eyes to him and asked calmly:

"But what is a circus, Father?"

Karas was relieved. He had not realized that the boy had still never seen a circus or traveling players, and that he had never heard the word even, in all probability, in their backwoods village. He felt as if a load had fallen from his heart, and he livened up and sat closer to the boy.

"It's a kind of theater, you see. There are gentlemen and ladies there and they show people beautiful horses and all kinds of animals, and each animal can do some kind of trick, maybe dance or play the hand organ, and that amuses the people. And when it's over they take the theater down and pack it onto wagons and go off somewhere else. And Father is going with them and will put up the theater and take it down, and you shall come with him in the wagon and see the whole world."

"And what kinds of animals are there? Horses?"

"Horses and lions and tigers and a donkey and a goat and bears and an elephant . . ."

"Elephant? A real elephant? One with a trunk?"

"Yes. A really wonderful animal. This one couldn't get into the kitchen here."

"Well . . . I'll go and see him and climb up on him and ride on him. They really do ride on elephants, don't they? Frau Langermann, Frau Langermann, *ich werde reiten* elephant!"

"Of course you will, son," laughed the widow, pouring out the soup. "What is it you've got, and what's this about an elephant?"

Karas now explained everything in more detail to her, including the fact that he was uncertain whether he had acted for the best.

"But Lord, man!" The landlady clasped her hands. "Thank God that it all turned out so well for you. And don't worry any more about your dead wife. You used to go out into the world for work, anyway—and how can she know how you live? How about those thousands of women whose husbands go on a ship and disappear for a couple of years and never even send any word of themselves; and when at last you get word about them, it is that . . . the fellow . . . that the water took him, so they told her . . ."

Frau Langermann's eyes were moist. As if in a mist she saw that dark, evil day when two officials from the steamship company stood in this same kitchen and with embarrassment informed her that the harbor boat *Rosamunda* had struck a coal boat in the fog, and that the helmsman Felix Langermann had fallen into the Elbe, and that, as the river was full of ice, it had been impossible to lower a boat to save him. She overcame her agitation and added:

"A circus is a thousand times better than that, in my opinion; you always have solid ground under you, at least. And Vasek will have experiences, he'll see the world, get to know people—that's very important for a boy, Mr. Karas."

Antonín Karas could not but cheer up during dinner. Again and again he had to explain to Vasek everything about the circus which he had already grasped himself. But the great event was of course when he came out with the tickets for the afternoon performance.

Karas did not see the effect on Vasek of his first visit to the circus. He went back about an hour earlier, his trumpet under his arm, and had hardly appeared in the main building when Kerholec called him, thrust a rake into his hand, and ordered him to smooth out the sawdust in the ring nicely. Then they put him behind the gate, so that he could help pull away a cage —they told him it was for the lion or something. And then some fellow ran up calling for Mr. Karas and told him that the conductor was looking for him.

Leopold Selnicki, Berwitz's conductor, was a Viennese, a former Austrian military band leader, a man like a mountain, with huge mustaches reinforced with side whiskers. His shaggy eyebrows were just as terrifying, but his eyelids were wrinkled and the skin around his eyes was loose for some reason, probably from drink. Selnicki's whole expression reminded you of a good-natured St. Bernard. He was perhaps the only man in the whole circus who was not subject to Berwitz's precise discipline. He did nothing except conduct the music: any kind of help for the others in the circus he refused as unsuitable to his artistic personality.

He occupied himself for whole days and nights with the terribly important problem of what delicacies he should eat and drink. He was not a gourmet in the true sense of the word; he never sat down to a rich feast or a magnificent supper. But when he awoke in the morning he would lick his chops and remark that some ham and eggs and a couple of Pilsens would "just hit the spot." If there were no Pilsen anywhere he would drink ordinary beer, but since it was weaker, he would take a seidel more. For this he had the ratio of two to three; he said that this "kept the temperature even in his body."

Then he would drop in at rehearsals, to see if they might want anything new in the music, would chat a bit with one person or another, drink three or four glasses of rum, and announce that it was time for a snack. Upon which he would majestically quit the circus and hunt out one of his favorite little restaurants where he would eat goulash or paprika, light a long thin cigar, and patiently wait, to the accompaniment of glasses of Austrian wine, for the time when hunger should again seize him. When he had satisfied it with a portion of Hungarian salami he would go to dinner, nibble at his food, and complain to his neighbors that "as far as he was concerned he could do without dinner entirely," that he never "made much of dinner," and only took it "as a foundation" for two or three glasses of beer.

And then he would go out somewhere else for dark beer and brandy; if there was an opportunity he would play a game of billiards, then go somewhere else to stimulate his appetite with a small glass of vermouth, after which he would show up at the circus just before the performance, put on his red coat with its gold collar and gold epaulettes, at the same time pouring down his throat a jigger or two of rum from the bottle he always carefully kept in his dressing room. And then he conducted—without stopping, so to speak, for the most part with his back to the orchestra—the whole musical accompaniment to the performance; and then threw off his uniform and took himself off for some kind of refreshment before supper and something to drink after it.

But Berwitz knew why he kept Selnicki: in no other circus did the music sound so brisk, nowhere else did they play such stirring marches, nowhere did they have such fanfares and flourishes, and if it were a matter of a sentimental interlude in the pantomimes, no one could boast of such fine harmony as could Umberto's Circus.

But his chief merit showed itself at rehearsals. If the horses were being taught some number or other Selnicki would look down on them with his sad eyes, gulp down some rum, and say, "That's Lanner's *Waltz of the Daisies,*" or "That's Strauss's *Cavalier March,*" or "For that we'll use the *Polka Bohémienne et Trio* from the *Gavotte Bleue* with eight bars added from Schubert's *Intermezzo* and a flourish." And that was the way they did it. For him every new act converted itself into music, into individual compositions which sounded in his ears in a flash, as perfectly designed as if he were reading them in the score; each of them corresponded perfectly to the tempo of the production and improved tremendously the manner in which the horses took to the rhythm.

Selnicki had learned a bit of broken Czech in Vienna and now greeted Karas in that language when the latter appeared on the bandstand, before he passed into his nonchalant Viennese German.

"You are the new Czech man, yes? God greet you. You know some German, yes? Well so, Pane Karas, how goes it with your trumpeting? You read music?"

"No, I don't, Mr. Conductor."

"Well, that doesn't matter, you'll learn with time. But you can play the trumpet?"

"As much as they needed it in our little band. We all knew the main melody, and when a man already knew that part he would pass into a different part or take over the melody on the repeats."

"Of course. I know how it is with a band like that. Play something for me now before the people come, so that I can see how you do."

Karas was on tenterhooks—nothing would come into his mind now he was alone, without the support of his old gang. But he felt that there was no other way out. He pulled out his trumpet, set it to his lips, half-closed his eyes, played the opening bars of a *Laendler* four times in order to get into the mood, and then, just as at home when he used to practice in the evening in the meadows, he came out in full volume with his own favorite piece, *The Maidens Come from the Forest; Only Mine Doesn't Come. . . .*

In the empty round building it sounded with such tremendous force that he frightened himself with the noise, and during the repeat switched to a *pianissimo*. And already his heart was touched, he played this lovely melody as if he were caressing it, gently, fully, as if he were telling the blackbird, the little black fellow, how the blood of his beloved had flowed from her body.

Then he opened his eyes and caught sight of the conductor as the latter was pouring himself some rum. For a second the glass almost disappeared under the thick mustaches. Then he poured a second glass.

"Here, take one, Pane Karas," he said in Czech, "one little swig for your health."

And as Karas respectfully bowed and drank down the rum in two gulps, Selnicki went on in German:

"That's it, all right. Real Czech trumpet-playing. It's not a matter of playing from music. What we play here you can learn in a week. And if we try anything harder, come to me and I'll whistle it for you. Sit down here by this music stand and play a few openings. It'll come out all right. It's the sort of thing a man can't help, it's a gift, a God-given gift."

Selnicki took another drink, bent over to Karas, took him by the shoulder, and spoke more quietly, in Czech, with an air of tremendous importance:

"Music . . . you know . . . music, of course, isn't intended

56

for any circus. But remember that song . . . that would go good with one of the dancing numbers. Here's to you!"

Meanwhile people had been gathering from afar, taking off their working uniforms, putting on their bright-red liveries and taking their places with their instruments in the orchestra. All shook hands heartily with Karas as a newcomer, even telling him their names, but Karas heard none of it in his agitation. He was more interested in the fact that he had caught the sound of Czech conversation coming from the far corner of the bandstand. He was just on the point of going over there when suddenly a clapping sounded from down below.

"Hello, music, begin!"

It was Kerholec giving this command from the main entrance. The circus was still empty, but outside people were crowding, and the music from inside was meant to arouse in them the desire to come up to the ticket window. Selnicki had still not appeared. On the right a man with a trumpet looked round and said:

"Well, men, let's begin."

They raised their instruments, the one on the right sounded the tempo twice with his trumpet, then nodded and with that they broke into a march. Karas joined in. He felt that it must be a well-known march, of the sort which he and Milner had played by the hundreds, often straight off without rehearsals, just as he was playing now. But he did look at the man on his right, for he could see in the other's eyes where to pause and where to play more softly. And this man also squinted over at Karas to see how he was getting on.

The first time everything went off quite decently. Then they played something slow, and now Karas had to pay more attention, and more than once he preferred to sit back and listen to the turns of the unknown melody. Immediately after this came a waltz and again it went off easily! Tralala, tralala. But the boys kept at it without a breather; they hardly even took time to blow out their instruments. It all went on and on, just the same, without music, piece after piece. Karas had to admit that this was a wonderfully unified band.

Then Selnicki arrived. For a while they took a rest and Karas of course stretched his neck to see what was going on down below. From there a great uproar and din arose. Wherever he looked there were crowds of people, row after row of them, and newcomers kept streaming in and climbing aloft along the numerous aisles. Some boys below were yelling noisily. "Somewhere there Vasek is sitting," Karas said to himself, but he gave up all hope of finding him in that flood of humanity, nor did he have time to, for already Selnicki had stood up in front, saluted, twisted his mustaches, taken up his baton, looked around, and begun. Lord, now it really was something, a never-ending tune; they scarcely took their instruments away from their lips.

Even when Selnicki signaled a halt and applause rose up from below they still had no rest, the baton waved again in the air, suddenly flashed, and now they trumpeted forth flourishes, long, noisy flourishes which mixed with the applause and the cries—flourishes in which they modulated up and down over the main chords until the baton finally dropped again. Then at once a new piece began, and so three-quarters of an hour flew by without Karas's even having time to collect himself. This was quite a different thing from his quiet playing with Milner at village festivals!

Suddenly Selnicki stopped and put down his baton. Everybody stretched out on their chairs and rested. Karas was curious to see what was going on below. So far he had seen nothing more than Selnicki's back, his baton, and a few of the top rows of people. Anything below that he could not see from his chair. Now he half stood up as everybody else moved and caught sight of Kerholec, who was hurriedly rolling up some sort of carpet.

At some distance from him in the ring stood a gentleman in a dress coat and top hat, with a big whip in his hand. Beside him stood a strange fellow dressed in terribly wide trousers which flopped all around him and in a great white waistcoat going down almost to his knees and from out of which stuck a dirty shirt front. He had a nose like a red tomato, a white mouth, red whiskers under his chin, and on his head a small cap with a feather.

"So you think, August, that only stupid people live in Hamburg?" asked the elegant gentleman.

"Hoho," spoke the booby, and answered something which

58

Karas didn't understand, but at which the audience roared and thundered with laughter.

"That's the intermission number with August," his neighbor explained to him. "It's to give them time to get ready for the next act."

Karas did not want to seem curious and therefore sat down again, and heard, between bursts of laughter, how August again and again asked of the other, "Herr Stallmeister, do you know the difference between a carriage and a casserole?"

Karas knew this old joke; if you didn't know you were told never to sit down in a carriage, for you might be mistaken and sit in a casserole. All the side-show men at the country fairs asked this riddle, but all the same Karas could not help laughing in advance, and when the answer came the people too laughed at the way the little fellow had put the elegant gentleman in his place.

"It's too bad," said Karas, to himself, "that Vasek won't understand that sort of thing, he doesn't know that much German. But he'll laugh; any kind of fun always amuses him."

But now Selnicki rapped and the musicians raised their instruments; the intermission was over and the music must start again. Throughout they played from memory, which by now did not surprise Karas in the least. However, sometimes he observed something rather unusual to which he was unaccustomed: at times Selnicki would quietly call "Attention!" and look fixedly down, conducting rather more emphatically and even a bit ad lib. The eyes of all the players were fixed on his ivory stick that they might keep together with him.

Karas had the impression that in those moments the music was not simply playing an air, but was being adjusted to something which went on down below. There were evidently horses there, for at times he caught sight of high red or white plumes as they waved aloft in a row. Only twice during the whole production did the band have any more rest: once during a talking number below, and once when Selnicki quickly cut short the music, and it was as quiet as in a church in the whole building.

"The leap of death," Karas's neighbor whispered. Below something crackled noisily, like the fire of rifles. Karas did not dare to stand up, for everyone was ready to play and Selnicki had his baton raised. Suddenly, down below, someone cried, "Halla ho!" and a salvo of shots cracked through the air. Already the conductor had waved his arm, and they let out a thunderous fanfare which mixed with the gigantic applause and shouting that arose on all sides.

Karas made up his mind that as soon as they had finished he must ask what this incident had actually been, but when they were done at last and Selnicki had gone off, the musicians at once rushed one after the other to the stairs and down below. Karas did not know the reason for this, but he went after them, and below Kerholec caught him and threw into his arms a great pile of gray canvas.

"Stretch that over the railing!" he cried to Karas. "Turn right at the gate and do the same as the man on your left."

Karas had to make his way through the ring with his bundle, for everywhere there were streams of departing people. The whole house resounded with the voices, cries, and shouts of the crowds. He came to a halt at the left side of the gate and saw what he had to do. The front wall of the ground boxes had a plush edge as a rail, and in his arms he carried their protecting covers. Piece by piece he dragged them out and pulled them onto the red plush. At first he did it slowly and he finished his half considerably later than did his opposite number. All the people were gone by now, and the circus seemed suddenly dead. However, Kerholec was at his side again, minus his coat and waistcoat, and with his sleeves rolled up.

"To the stables, Anton, to feed the animals—and hurry! But first take your uniform off!"

Karas was completely confused by it all, but he felt that the people around him somehow burned with enthusiasm, and he ran out now to the dressing room, threw off his resplendent uniform, and ran like Kerholec in his shirt and trousers to the stables. The stable hands were carrying out full armloads of beautiful trappings and harnesses, others ran along with buckets of water, with measures of oats or armfuls of hay. Kerholec stood supervising the distribution of the hay, and at once put Karas to work. Karas recognized the man who ran in front of him with a pile of hay;

60

he had blown the bass saxhorn with him the whole afternoon. When Karas came back for the third time, Kerholec nudged him.

"Greet that woman there, that's the director's wife."

At first Karas did not see any woman, only a beardless man in riding trousers who was examining the hoof of one of the horses. Only when he came closer did he tell himself that this really was a woman.

"Good evening, madam," he now said, as Kerholec had instructed him that morning.

"Good evening." She nodded her head, then looked at him more closely and released the leg of the horse. "You're new here?"

"Yes, please, I am," answered Karas and involuntarily clicked his heels together, stuck out his chest, and stood as if at attention. "A new carpenter and musician, Anton Karas."

"Anton, Anton . . . I don't believe we have any Antons here now," said Anna Berwitz, studying him, "so we won't get you confused with anyone. Good. Later on we'll have time to get to know each other. Now run along, Anton, the horses can't wait."

She nodded and turned back to the horse's hoof. And Karas understood the reason for this general rush: here dumb animals must be cared for first, and only then did people have time for themselves. A little later, when he stood with the others before Kerholec with the announcement that everything had been finished, he again felt as if he were standing at attention. This devil Kerholec seemed no longer to be the faithful countryman of the Sailor's Bride. He stood now with his legs apart and with a paper in his hand, and spoke in a voice of command.

"Who is on night duty?"

Three men spoke up; Kerholec looked at the paper and nodded his head.

"The others are free for today. But pay attention, the director's order applies to everyone: tomorrow after dinner you will move into the wagons. The new man, Anton Karas, will sleep in Number Eight. Look over every bunk and all the equipment and tell me tomorrow if there's anything wrong. And now you can go. Good night!"

"Good night!" called the men, and ran off one after the other to the dressing rooms to change their clothes and head for home.

Karas stayed to ask Kerholec what he meant.

"We're moving soon, Anton, and it's necessary that people get used to living in wagons again after the winter break, and then they won't give us any trouble on the road. You'll sleep with me, in Number Eight. It isn't comfortable, but you'll get used to it."

"And the boy?"

"He'll come with us in our wagon. I've thought it over."

"One more thing, Karel. What time shall I get here in the morning?"

"Six o'clock, Anton. For the morning feeding and for the cleaning of stables. Ask for me—I'll be here already."

"Thanks. Good night!"

And Karas walked off, suddenly feeling vastly more respect for this fellow than he had up till now. While he was putting on his coat a thought occurred to him which he had forgotten for the time being: how about Vasek? Had he liked the circus? Karas hurried home, to find out something about what he himself had taken part in but which he had not seen.

If Antonín Karas had been more cultured he might have explained quite differently the concern he felt for his son during these days. True, he actually knew Vasek very little. They had only been together for a few winter months each year when their hut was covered with snow and their whole life was played out in their little rooms, on a subdued scale. When the father of the family returned home late in the autumn, he usually rushed straight to his woodpile and split up the logs in the woodshed for as long as the frosts would permit. In his moments of rest he would examine the hut, the stables, and all the property, and would carry out minor repairs here and there. Then he would stuff all the window frames with moss, fill up the cracks between the logs—the hut was made of wood—and sometimes he would go off to the woods for brushwood. This was the time when Vasek could still run about with the kids in the village, and showed up at home only when hunger drove him to his mother's kitchen.

When the first snow fell, they huddled inside. Karas had plenty of time then to catch up on his sleep, to rest and stretch

62

his tired limbs. But he didn't loaf for long, he soon dragged out a good piece of hardwood and his knife, and began to carve something for the household or some figure for the Christmas manger scene. On Saturday Milner would usually knock at their door, and then they would go off together to some village for a drinking party, to return only on Monday.

Even now Karas did not spend too much time with Vasek. He was himself rather quiet, and preferred to bury himself in work rather than in any of the simple pleasures of life, and the boy regulated his own life accordingly. Vasek was used to their rough life; he saw about him only hard, exhausting toil, and ever since he could walk he had had to help wherever he could. He was an unusually sensitive and attentive boy. He realized by himself that his mother was ailing, that she wasn't well, and that his father came home tired out. He made himself useful to them at home, did not play pranks, and sought to replace his mother wherever he could. It seemed obvious to him that on some days he should go from one task to another, now helping in the kitchen, now cleaning up in the barn, now going to the woods for branches, for cones, for mushrooms, for huckleberries, for grass.

He did everything deftly, a trait he had inherited from his father. With the first jackknife he got he not only whittled wood into whips and whistles, but already began to try to carve all the things he saw his father making during the winter. When his mother took to her bed, the six-year-old Vasek would take over the whole care of the household in the summer, taking care of the goat and preparing the dinner, and with it all he was quite pleased that he could manage the work like a grownup. But when he had a little time, when his mother was better and told him to run off outside, he would shoot out of the hut like an arrow.

And then his temperament displayed itself. Among the other boys of his age he was soon the chief; he could beat them all and was the leader in all their games. It was as if something drove him to be the first among them in everything, to make sure that no one should be able to run and jump, to climb trees and throw stones, better than he. The spring games in the hollows always brought him the biggest stock of beans and marbles. He first knew of the young magpies in the thornbushes, and of the wasps' nests in the fields. It was Vasek who, among all the others, discovered how they could climb up on each other's shoulders and get into the priest's garden to pick the first cherries and pears. If the boys wanted to go for crawfish they would always elect Vasek as the real leader of the gang.

In all that belonged to the world of childhood, from somersaults to singing in church, in all of it Vasek took part, and for all of it he developed such a zeal that before long he was at the head of all the others. Some things he mastered with his strength, but still more he achieved by his cleverness and wit. Nothing which had any value in a boy's world missed his eyes. He ran out for a bit of fodder for the goat and at once noticed where a patch of green peas was ripening and where the blackbirds were flying about the nest of their young.

Every new type of work fascinated him like a strange mystery; he could run off from the wildest chase to stand motionless in front of the smithy and watch how old Barucha fired the iron in the forge and how he then held it over the anvil with his tongs. He was equally interested in the preparation of the stove for the baking of bread, and by the mixing of the malt, or when his father or some other worker made some trifling repair in the village. On the Sunday before Easter he could invariably be found in the bell tower, watching the motions of the bell-ringers, and for him a mere funeral was converted into a great spectacle, in which he watched avidly every gesture of the priest or the choirmaster. If he envied anyone, it was the boys on the big estates where there were many cattle and horses; it was his great longing to go there and be able to yell at the horses and pull the reins and crack the whip and swear like a farm hand.

But what was denied him there, he acted for himself in the woods. The woods of Horní Snezná—O Lord, what a green enchantment they were! In the village or the fields there was bright light, positive, hard, unyielding, but once in the forest and there was only half-light, dusk and dim glow, as if one walked among nothing but veils; and behind each curtain some great mystery lay hidden. The veils of the pines, the green ribbonings of the larches, the pillars of the beeches and the old forked oak, the moss, like a pillow, a pile of rocks like a giants'

64

altar—one called them woods, but they were really the forest kingdom of ballads and tales.

Vasek preferred to come here alone. In the woods one had to
move quietly, softly, so that not even a twig should crack. Only
thus was it possible to unveil its wonders, the chase of the
pheasant cock after the hen, the bluejay playing its tricks, the doe
with her fawns in the glade, the play of the badgers in front of
their trampled holes. Only by walking carefully could you come
upon the woodpecker's nest, the lairs of the rabbits, and the
hide-outs of the squirrels.

And how many tragic things could one find here! A tuft of
feathers with drops of blackening blood on them, the dead young
of rabbits, some little whitened bones. The woods are still, yet
everything in them has its own life; the woodpeckers circle around
the trunks of trees, the stag makes his way heavily through the
undergrowth; the cuckoo looks out for a nest and the oriole gives
its sad and haunting cry; adders lie coiled in the raspberry bushes
and the black snake shines along the banks of a stream.

To know all the secrets of the woods, to be acquainted with
all its hidden lore! When the forester, Mazur, appeared, the boys
usually ran away. But Vasek was not afraid, Vasek would run
up to him and question him with the eager curiosity of a child.
The tough Mazur could not resist the little boy; no one could
resist that broad, sun-tanned face, full to overflowing with insistent questions and ready, a moment later, to laugh at some
sudden prank or other. In this Vasek was different from his
father: he could reach an understanding with people in no time,
and they took to him at once.

But there was more in Vasek's early life than his native
village and the forests; ten minutes' journey from Horní Snezná
was the first German village over the frontier. It was larger than
Horní Snezná; they went there for their mail. A rich merchant
lived here, there were several artisans, and a mill. The Czech
village of Snezná was forced into regular contact with these
German neighbors.

From here the German villages stretched on without a break
down to Sumava; there were various German estates scattered
here and there among the Czech ones; German people walked

daily through the Czech village; the boys in the adjacent areas knew each other and met during their games, expeditions, and battles, and every Horní Sneznák was trained from childhood to make himself understood in German. For Vasek this only meant a source of new interests, for only a little way over the fields he found people who lived, farmed, dressed, and worked differently; and he wanted, of course, to get to the bottom of everything.

For Father Karas, coming back to the deserted little village after eight or nine months in the big city, Horní Snezná was only a tiny, poor nest where people were born, married, and died and where nothing unusual happened. But for his son this little piece of the world teemed with events, discoveries, and experiences, and such foreign contacts as he made only served to show him that the world was bigger than his native village, and that in it there was an infinite multitude of things which would be worth knowing.

His father still knew little of Vasek's passion for knowledge and his burning desire to be first, and had paid little attention to it. So in Hamburg he was uncertain what Vasek would say to all the unheard-of things which had happened to them.

From the hall he heard Vasek's cry and the cracking of a whip. He entered the kitchen, where Frau Langermann was just emptying a saucepan of potatoes onto plates. Vasek was standing on a chair on one leg and yelling, "Holla hop, oo! Ella, ella!" Rosa was running around the chair and tossing her head. When Vasek caught sight of his father, he cracked his whip, which he had made out of a stick and a piece of string, and cried:

"Look, Father, I'm riding my horse on one leg! And Rosa is the striped horse that runs around me!" Then he jumped down and rushed toward his father. "Father, you'll take me with you tomorrow, won't you? I'll come out into the middle like that man with the whip and the horses will run up and kneel down the way they did and get up again on their back legs, or I'll go and jump, this way, hop, through a hoop, and I'll lead the elephant and the lions . . ."

The boy choked with excitement as the different images flitted before his eyes in which he always imagined himself the hero.

66

Karas smiled with satisfaction at this helter-skelter agitation.

"So you liked it, then?"

"Yes, I did."

"And what was it they were shooting at, that time?"

"That was that man who kept trying to run away and kept falling. We laughed at him an awful lot, Frau Langermann and I and all of us; every time he fell down flat, and then the soldiers came with guns and stood in two lines and aimed up high and then the man took a run and jumped over all of them and twisted himself in the air and they all shot at him, but they couldn't hit him. We all clapped because they didn't hit him."

"And how about the elephant? Isn't he a big fellow?"

"Hmm!"

"And what did he do?"

"He ate dinner."

"How's that—he ate dinner?"

"Why, yes, he had a table there with dinner on it. A gentleman invited the elephant to sit down and the elephant sat down and they gave him a bib and then he took a spoon in his trunk and ate soup and something else and bread and then ordered some beer."

"He ordered beer?"

"Of course, Father. But that's right, you didn't see anything. He knocked on his glass and they brought him beer and he drank it and then another one and then another and then he got rather drunk and staggered till he fell over."

"How did it end up?"

"He was just like dead. The man climbed on his head and he didn't even move. So the man bowed and we clapped for him and then the elephant woke up and didn't know he had a man on his head. He was so ashamed that he went home to sleep, and carried the man along with him."

Anton Karas saw that there had been a great deal he had not seen and which he would have to go and look at one day. Far into the evening Vasek kept recounting the wonders he had seen, and when they had gone to bed and Vasek had said his prayers, and everything was quiet, suddenly a little voice sounded in the darkness:

"Father . . ."

"Why aren't you asleep?"

"Father, you know, I'm going to be a rider one day."

"All right, you can be someday, but now go to sleep!"

CHAPTER FIVE

KARAS CRAWLED out of bed while it was still dawn. Quietly he washed and dressed. In the kitchen he took the pot of almost cold coffee out of the oven, poured out a good-sized cup, cut off a slice of bread, and had breakfast. Then he put another piece of bread in his pocket and walked on tiptoe out of the flat. It was still not six o'clock when he entered the main building of the circus. Kerholec was already there, and at once told him what had happened during the night. The lioness Natasha had had cubs, three little cubs; luckily a new cage had already been got ready, the very one Karas had helped to pull out the day before. The lion Mahum, who up till then had been with Natasha, had been transferred to this cage. In the third cage the old lion Sultan remained with the lionesses, Bessie and Corina.

The blessed event had come earlier than had been anticipated, and this was the reason Natasha had been allowed to stay with Mahum until so recently. However, the director's wife had been uneasy; just before supper she had gone to the menagerie and discovered what was happening. At once they sent for Gambier, who was in charge of the great cats. Berwitz, too, left his supper, and with Kerholec and a few others he arranged for the transfer of Mahum.

The director's wife stayed with Natasha all night so that nothing might happen to the cubs. But Natasha was weak and hardly able to move. That morning the director's wife said that they would have to take the lion cubs away from her and nurse them, that Natasha was a bad mother. Karas went over to look at them. Natasha lay apathetically stretched out on her side in the old cage while something tiny stirred in the straw under her belly.

But there was no time for dawdling. All round him the animals were impatient for their breakfast. Karas turned back to the stables; it was the horses, after all, that were nearest and dearest to him. He helped to feed them and carried away manure. Then someone named Hans taught him how to curry a horse correctly and clean its hoofs. Only then did he have a little free time to walk round the whole outfit and get a little acclimatized.

The circus had a circular main corridor from which all its rooms were approached. The storage and stock rooms of all sorts and the dressing rooms of the personnel were on the inner side, under the gallery tiers of seats. The director's rooms, offices, and the dressing rooms of the more highly paid artists were on the outer side and had windows, or at least slits in the wall. Between the main entrance for the public and the side entrance for the personnel there was a little room and a kitchen; it was here the lame John Harwey lived, a widower and a veteran in the circus, with his daughter Alice, a plain girl with beautiful red hair.

On the far side of the ring from the main entrance stood the gate to the circus ring, now covered with a dark-red curtain; over it was the bandstand; beyond it were the doors to the stables and menagerie. These were spacious wooden buildings Berwitz had erected when he signed the many-years contract for the lease of the main building. In the building on the right stood the long rows of horses which were used in the performance. Berwitz kept the circus's draught horses in a number of rented stables. In the building on the left were the cages of animals. At the far end one could enter from either building into the latest addition, a high room in which, on a low platform, the elephant Bingo swayed from one foot to the other.

On this side Umberto's Circus extended out into the deserted open space along the Reeperbahn, and all around stood Berwitz's wagons, the living quarters of the circus people, some quite luxurious, others poorer, and almost every one different, depending for their character on what corner of Europe Umberto's Circus had acquired them in. Even now, during the winter when the circus remained in Hamburg, some of them were occupied by Berwitz's people, who preferred to remain faithful to their little homes on wheels rather than to move into the city.

In warm weather the open space among the wagons was a favorite practice ground for many of the artists; it was marked out and smoothed over like a ring so that those who were practicing should have an idea of the right dimensions. The whole field was a favorite place of rest for all employees, who sat about on logs or on the steps of the wagons. Often washing hung between the wagons, and in the spring a few hens scratched among the sparse grass, while the five or six children of the circus frolicked about at liberty.

"This will be a good place for Vasek to play in before we take to the road," Karas said to himself while coming back from his inspection. He was impatient for the boy to arrive; the landlady and he had made arrangements for her to bring him along when she went to market that morning to do her shopping. However it was already half-past nine when Alice Harwey appeared at the entrance to the ring and called, "A visitor for Mr. Karas!"

The first person to whom Karas presented the boy was of course Kerholec.

"So, you're the famous Vasek Karas from Horní Sneznà?" said Kerholec with a knowing wink, taking in the country boy's tanned face, with its great shining, alert eyes.

"Yes."

"And you've seen the circus?"

"I saw it yesterday."

"How did you like it?"

"It was wonderful!"

"And what did you like best?"

"The horses."

"You have a good eye. And you're coming with us?"

"Yes, I am."

"And you're not scared of the horses' kicking you or biting you?"

"No. I'll yell at them and crack my whip and they'll soon get back into line!"

"So you're going to be a horse-trainer, then?"

"Yes, and I'll ride up and down and I'll jump on the horses. Father promised me I could."

"Oh, if your father promised you, then of course you can. But you will have a lot to learn and it will be hard work."

"Let it."

"And you must never cry."

"I never do cry. When I had fights with the boys at home they all cried when they got hit by a stone, but I didn't; I ran after the kid who threw it and gave him a licking."

"But what if he got away from you?"

"He didn't. I always caught them up. But if they did get away, I always caught them the day after."

"So you were the best fighter in the village?"

"I don't know. But I always got the best of the others."

"Well, that's a good beginning for the circus. If you can stick it out, one day you'll be director."

"Well, maybe, but mostly I'm going to ride and jump."

Kerholec stroked the boy's head and spoke to Karas. "The boy's clever. He may amount to something, but you should start training him right away. Now take him to the cashier's and let him thank her for the ticket. That will please her, and make a good impression on her, and the boy will start off on the right foot."

Karas took the boy and led him off to the cashier's office. On the way he coached him with the necessary "I am very pleased to meet you, madam." Frau von Hammerschmidt greeted the motherless boy with great emotion. She didn't discuss boys or fighting, but she did speak very touchingly of his mother in Heaven, and of how a good boy here on earth would try to make her happy, so that she wouldn't seem sad in the presence of the Lord God.

And when she heard that Vasek wanted to learn to ride on horseback, she commended him and said it was an excellent decision, for the late Major von Hammerschmidt had also learned to ride when still a boy, and what a famous steeplechase rider he had been! At the Prince's fox hunts his arrival had always been a keenly anticipated event. And she promised to ask Director Berwitz and Mr. Perreira to notice the boy.

Finally she unfastened the drawstrings of her crocheted bag and

71

drew out half a roll, gave it to the boy with a big, smacking kiss, gave her hand to Karas, and turned back to her ticket window and her tickets.

When he re-entered the circus ring, the boy stood still as though bewitched—six snorting white horses were running round the ring. Behind the horses they could see a lady with a whip in her hand. At her call the horses turned round on their hind legs and ran back; at a second call they turned back again and crossed in front of each other until again they were in one column. Finally they suddenly turned their heads to her, reared up on their hind legs, and walked in to the center toward her, standing there erect until she lowered her arm with the whip.

Vasek squeezed his father's hand spasmodically and stared at the white horses as if they were a vision from Heaven. The circus building was empty; only Mr. Selnicki was there. Standing under a loge, his eyes a bit watery, he leaned against the barrier, from behind which he hauled a bottle of rum from time to time.

Karas thought that he might be in the way in this deserted place; perhaps it wasn't permitted to watch rehearsals. He drew the boy back into the passage, walked around the building, and led him over to the stables. On the way they met at least ten people whom Karas already knew by sight, and who, if they were not in too much of a hurry, now stopped and showed an interest in the boy, wanting to know if he was going to join the circus. Karas was pleased that everyone accepted the boy so heartily.

In the stable he took Vasek over to the same Hans who that morning had taught him to groom a horse, and announced that he had brought him a stable boy. Hans wiped his broad palm on his blue apron and shook Vasek's hand as if the boy were a grownup. Vasek didn't understand much of what this fellow Hans had to say—he spoke a different German from that which they talked in Sumava—but his child's instinct told him that this was a good man. And then he really belonged to these horses—he knew each one of them by name. Whenever he called one of them it would turn its head and look with its great soft eyes in Hans's direction.

But a still greater treat was in store for him: Hans took him by the sleeve and led him over to the end of the stable where, in

72

a special enclosure, there stood four dappled ponies, just made for a boy like Vasek. Overwhelmed, Vasek threw up both hands and cried:

"Oh, look! Pygmies!"

They bred just such pretty midgets at Hluboká and the ponies were well known in the region. The people there had found an expressive nickname for them: pygmies. Now Vasek had four pygmies in front of him, and when Hans called them by name they ran together and each one stretched its neck across the other. Suddenly Hans caught Vasek by the shoulders and before the boy could realize what was happening, had seated him on the nearest one of them. Vasek gasped a bit with amazement, but immediately pressed his legs together and grasped the pony's mane with his hands to keep from falling. At first Hans steadied him a bit, but then he let go, opened the gate, and gave a command.

"Go now, Mary!"

The filly tossed her head, walked out with Vasek into the corridor, and ran with short steps down the passage at Hans's side. Hans shouted something, Mary turned round and, heading toward the enclosure, broke into a trot, so that Vasek had to be careful not to fall. But he held on, and several grooms with brushes in their hands shouted "Bravo!" at him. In the enclosure Vasek climbed down off the pygmy and patted her. He didn't want to leave, but his father called to him to come, for he himself had to begin work. He led the boy out onto the open space to the rear. Here again people were rehearsing.

"You must wait for me here, Vasek, till it's time to go to dinner. Don't get into mischief, and don't go far away. Look, over there —there are two pretty children sitting on the steps; maybe you can play with them. Go over and talk to them. But don't go into the ring where the lady is rehearsing. You're not allowed there, and you'd only get in the way."

Anton went back to the horses and Vasek was left alone. At the moment all thought of his father or of the horses was crowded out of his mind, for he had before him a wonderful view of two men who were walking in a circle on their hands. This pleased him so much that he gave a jump and ran up closer, squatting on the grass so that he could get a perfect view of the show. Meanwhile the men were doing all kinds of tricks with their legs. They came to a standstill, spread out their legs in the air, slowly lowered them to the ground and then raised them up again.

Then all of a sudden they flipped over, stood up straight and shook their arms, rolling up their fallen shirt sleeves; then one of them yelled something to the other, the second one ran back, the first one squatted down on the ground and put his arms in his lap, the running one jumped up on them, and all of a sudden the squatter rose to his feet and threw the other one as far as he could, so that he did a somersault in the air. This was so amazing that Vasek called out "Whooo!" jumped up, and did a full spin on one heel.

But immediately he sat down again, for the two men were doing it again. They repeated it perhaps ten times. Vasek reflected that this was actually much nicer than riding on horseback. In his village there were boys who could ride. Franta Sember, whose family had a big estate, even rode with his brother to water the horses in the pond. He would sit on his glistening mare in soaked-through trousers and call to the horse with huge enjoyment, "Hihyo, old girl!" "Prr, old girl!" and "Move over, you cursed old nag!" But no one could jump like this; they would really gape at this, all of them. Franta and Pepík and Honza Bláha and Jirka Cikhard and Tonda Cerha. And to be able to walk on your hands like that to Grandma's hut and knock on her door with your feet—my, wouldn't she be surprised!

People were walking past, but they paid not the slightest attention to the rehearsal. This offended Vasek; he looked at each passer-by, expecting at the least some sort of surprise or sign of recognition, but they all went by in complete indifference. He felt it wasn't polite to the men who were trying so hard to give a good show. Just now, for instance, they had chosen a plot of ground and were clearing it by kicking the stones away. And then one jumped straight up on the other one's neck with both feet, and the bottom one—O Jiminy! he spun round and they both seemed to fall, but they didn't really fall down: the top one stretched out his legs and landed on them, pulled the bottom one through them and raised him up in the air on his hands till

74

he stood straight above him. And finally the top one jumped down.

O my, if he could only do that with Tonda Cerha, how Nanynka Cerha would have stared at him, and what a strong man and how clever Vasek would be! At once he felt the need to test himself and to show that he too could do a thing or two. Where were those kids his father had told him about?

Sure enough, they were still standing there on the steps. But they must be terribly well-behaved children; the boy had on a white collar and a tie, and the girl was wearing a hat and held a parasol. This displeased Vasek, but they were as big as he was, so he edged over toward them slowly, choosing a roundabout way, whistling and turning to look at this and that on the way, so that it wouldn't appear as if he were going right up to them.

But when he arrived at the steps, he felt the necessity of attracting their attention somehow, so he yelled, "Look at me!" and stood on his hands in front of the opposite wagon. Then he jumped down and did a somersault. Then he got up and looked to see what their reaction was. The girl burst out laughing and nudged the boy, who only scowled. Vasek took up a position in front of them, spread his legs and yelled:

"Are you in the circus like me? I'm going to be a jumper!"

The boy looked still more gloomy. Vasek put his fingers in his mouth and whistled. Then he blew out his cheeks and cried:

"I'm going to jump and walk on my hands and do somersaults in the air! What can you do?"

And then something happened which for the moment completely dumfounded Vasek. The well-behaved boy reached behind his back, drew out a top hat and an ivory-headed walking stick, climbed to the top of the stairs, and said angrily in a thin, irritated voice:

"Young man, you are deceived if you take us for children like yourself. We are adults, who perform our appointed tasks in the circus as dwarfs. If you wish to play, find someone of your own age. Good day. Come, Emilie!"

The midget jammed on his top hat, climbed down the stairs, and gave his arm to the girl, who had been laughing up to this point but now suddenly became serious. She descended the

75

stairs, gathered up the train of her skirt, put her left arm in her husband's, and they both walked off with their noses in the air.

Vasek stood as if thunderstruck. He had heard about dwarfs, but as far back as he could remember they had always been little old men with white beards, and it had never occurred to him that there must be young dwarfs too. But at the same time he still could not get rid of the impression that he had seen a boy and a girl, that he had undergone a defeat, and that now he would have to give that kid a thrashing, so that the girl would know what he could do.

Nonetheless he remained dumfounded by what had happened, and only after some time had passed did he recollect himself and, to save his *amour-propre,* jump up on the stairs of the wagon, and cry:

> Two little dwarfs
> Were smaller than small;
> Whatever they ate,
> They never grew tall.

He repeated this verse several times, but the little couple, engaged for the coming yearly tour as Admiral Tom Thumb and Princess Peasblossom, did not understand his jeering cries and went off into a building without even looking back.

Vasek liked it on the wagon stairs, from which he had a fine view of all his surroundings. For a while he kept up his taunts at the dwarfs, but then, through some mysterious association of ideas, his thoughts of fairy tales and of home carried him back to something he had missed ever since leaving the village— back to a song. He spread his legs, thrust his hands into his pockets, opened his mouth, and began to sing. But he didn't sing long.

"Sacré nom d'un chien, qui est-ce qui fait ce sal bruit?"

A frightful voice thundered in an unknown language directly behind Vasek's back. Vasek started up in terror and went down the stairs as though he had been shot from a gun. He looked back, and for the first time in his life he was so terrified that he stumbled, fell, and rolled over on his back.

The door of the wagon by which he had been singing was now

open, and in it there stood an immense giant with shaggy black beard and hair and savage popping eyes; he was half-naked and his whole body and arms were covered with some kind of blue pictures. On the giant's shoulders there sat a monkey; it held on with all four feet and its piercing yelps mixed with the deep roars of the giant. Lying on the ground, Vasek had but one thought in his terror: he had offended the dwarfs and now this ogre had come to devour him.

But the giant only burst into deep rumbles and peals of laughter at the speed with which Vasek had taken the staircase and fallen down on his back. The sight of the boy sitting half-raised on his elbows, thoroughly frightened and ready to burst into tears, only made him roar with laughter.

"Hé, mon p'tit, tu as fait une belle courbette! Mais tu n'es pas du métier, quoi? Du bist nicht von Zirkus, was?"

Vasek immediately sensed the change in his tone and in a flash grasped that it was not a question of his life. He also understood the giant's last question, and now rose to ward off the final danger which still threatened him. The fellow might want to give him a thrashing.

"You're wrong," he answered the Captain's French-German in his own Czech-German, "We are in the circus, my father and me, but we're new here."

"Well, everybody who is here a couple of days knows that when Captain Gambier pulls his blue flag up on the mainmast, then everything all round is to be silent, for Captain Gambier sleeps. Understand?"

"No, I don't," Vasek answered in German, but added in Czech, "But if you try to lick me, I'll run and get Papa and he'll soon deal with you."

"Je ne comprends rien," chuckled the giant, and asked in German, "From where do you come?"

"From Horní Snezná," answered Vasek.

"Quoi?"

"From Horní Snezná!" Vasek spoke louder.

"Nom de Dieu—qu'est-ce que cela? What do you tell?"

"From Horní Snezná!" cried Vasek. "From Hornísnezná, from Hornísnezná, from Hornísnezná!"

"*Ah, est-ce qu'il n'est pas rigolo!*" The bearded giant laughed and, in a good mood now, added in German, "Want some coffee?"

Vasek understood this perfectly, and at once realized that he was terribly hungry.

"Hm." He nodded. "I'd like some."

"Come on then," said the giant, backing out of the door.

"But that monkey will bite me," Vasek answered cautiously.

"Jock bite? Jock will not bite, Jock will go in his cage. Come!"

The giant picked up the monkey, which by now had quieted down, and Vasek went in. The houses on wheels had been a great mystery to him; in all his life he had never seen one. But he had heard his father say that they were going to live in one. And now that one opened up before him his boy's curiosity was aroused. And O Lord, it was beautiful inside! It struck Vasek that this was the third part of the fairy tale: first the dwarfs, then the ogre, and now finally a kind of a gingerbread house.

On the right and left were beds, behind them a little table beside a curtained window, and then a wardrobe, on top of which stood a cage, into which Captain Gambier now thrust Jock. At the far side stood two chairs under a second window. On the floor lay animal skins, yellow with black stripes, and across both walls over the beds two more skins with stuffed heads were stretched. Over them, almost at ceiling level, hung an entire head of the same kind of beast, with open jaws and protruding fangs.

Captain Gambier threw on a broad, dark-red gown which he tied with a cord.

"Sit down!" He pointed to a chair beside the table for Vasek.

Then he walked over to the opposite window, opened it, and pulled and wound something on the outside. Vasek noticed that they were strings he was winding. In a moment two flags, one red and the other blue, appeared in the window. The giant unfastened the blue one; the red one he hoisted up again.

"Here is the blue flag," he said to Vasek, laying it down on the table, "and there is the red flag. The red flag signifies that Captain Gambier is in his house. The blue flag—Captain Gambier sleeps. Understand?"

"I understand. But why didn't you sleep last night?"

"Last night, *hé, mon p'tit,* last night there was much work, understand? The lion Natasha had some little ones, she has cubs, understand? Three cubs, little ones, lions' children, understand? And Captain Gambier is a man of lions and tigers and bears, do you understand? He had much work with Natasha—the whole night, *mon cher,* the whole night long!"

The giant was already fussing by the little stove. He set two mugs on the table and poured coffee into them from the pot. Then he added cream, brought out a sugar bowl, a plate of butter, and a small basket of rolls.

"Take some, *mon p'tit,*" he urged Vasek, and himself sat down opposite him. "And take some butter to spread."

Vasek was not the sort of boy who has to be asked twice. He was accustomed to take everything he met in his young life just as it came along, and had learned to adjust himself to circumstances immediately. He understood that the shaggy giant was a kind man who was fond of children, and that he was master of the lions and tigers in the circus. He stirred his coffee and bit off a piece of roll eagerly, meanwhile examining his host.

"You are an animal-tamer?"

"*Oui, un dompteur, oui.*"

"And you were in the cage yesterday when the lion was walking on the ball?"

"*Oui, mon p'tit,* the cage . . . the lion on the ball. It is me."

"But where do you keep that beautiful blue suit with the silver in front?"

"Ohoho, that blue suit is now in its wardrobe, and the red one with gold and the purple one with gold. . . ."

The Frenchman, highly amused by the boy's visit, jumped up and pulled out of the wardrobe three gaudily colored, shining coats.

"Whooo!" Vasek whistled at this magnificence, and the spoon fell from his hand.

"*Oui, c'est magnifique.* Take some more butter," he added, coming back to the table. "I am a *dompteur,* but what are you?"

"I'm going to jump and walk on my hands and jump up and throw the other fellow through the air and do lots of things like that."

"Oh, an acrobat—*très bien*, that is a good métier. But are you working now?"

"No, Father works; he plays the trumpet in the band and he leads horses and cleans them. But I'm going to be a jumper when I grow up. . . . And I'm going to ride horses besides, and train them with a whip!"

"Ah, *c'est comme ça,* first you want to be acrobat, and now to be rider." Gambier smiled.

"Yes." The boy nodded, but at that moment it flashed through his mind that there was something a bit dull in choosing to be a jumper; that it would be much nicer to be an animal-tamer and wear beautiful coats and have a house like this one. To go into a cage with lions or tigers; how frightened everyone would be for him and what a hero he would be! And to be a captain into the bargain! As soon as he stopped speaking he felt that the best choice, the only one, was to be a lion-tamer. But he had one more doubt to assuage, and so he asked:

"And the lions and tigers—don't they bite you?"

"Oh, sometimes they are savage. Look at that one." Gambier pointed to the tiger head on the bed. "That one was wicked, he seized me by the leg. Look!"

Gambier stretched out his foot, pulled up his trailing trousers leg, and Vasek saw scars on his calf.

"What did you do?"

"Me? I hit him on his snout, again and again. . . ."

The Captain raised his terrible fist and demonstrated how he had struck him. Full of enthusiasm, Vasek saw in his mind's eye not Gambier, but himself, striking a tiger on the snout with his fist.

"What did the tiger do?"—he could scarcely whisper.

"Yusuf? He let go of my leg and ran into his corner."

"By golly!" the boy cried, and his mind was already made up: he would be nothing if not a captain over lions and tigers. He banged his left fist on the table, jumped up, and cried: "I'll do that too, by golly! I'll kill a lion and I'll kill a tiger and all the animals will be afraid of me!"

"Ohoho!" Gambier guffawed. "No more acrobat, but now *dompteur?*"

80

"Donter!" Vasek assented, and with this it was conclusively decided. But there was still one important matter which remained to be cleared up. And as he was finishing his coffee, Vasek plunged right into the subject.

"What are those pictures?"

"*Quoi?*"

"Why, those pictures you have there on your chest and arms and on your leg."

"*Ah, je comprends . . . ça, n'est-ce pas?*" His eyes glistening, the Captain opened his dressing gown and pointed at his chest. A girl, pricked out in blue, was lying under a palm tree, her loose hair waving; she was watching a sailboat which floated by on the waves.

"*Et ça?*"

He stretched out his right arm and on its side Vasek saw a crest with a rampant lion, with the letters L.G. along the side.

"Yes," he nodded.

"It is *tatouage,* you know, *ta-tou-age!*"

"Tatoowage. Yes. Were you born that way?"

"*Comment?* I do not understand. What do you try to say?"

"Did you have those when you were born?"

"Ohoho! *Non, non* . . . no, that is pricked on, prick, prick, the needle goes prick, prick, and later the color. It pains much, but Captain Gambier can stand it all. You wish to come with me to the lions and tigers?"

"Yes," Vasek assented, much relieved to learn that tattooing was something artificial. In his heart he had feared that perhaps there was a special race of people who were born with blue pictures on their bodies, just as in Hamburg he had seen people with black skins or yellow skins. And he had already reasoned that perhaps "donters" must belong to this race of "blue-picture skins." But if that was not the case, then nothing would keep him from being a "donter," for he wasn't afraid of pricks; at home the boys often pricked themselves or got stung by a bee—that he could stand. If only he could have an enormous beard when he became a captain!

Meanwhile Léon Gambier had thrown off his dressing gown and, with great spluttering and snorting, was washing himself in the tin basin. Vasek fished another roll out of the basket and thrust it into his pocket. Then he propped his elbows up on the table and gazed at the pictures the "donter" had on his back.

A hunter stood leaning against a boulder and was taking aim at a roaring lion which was crouching to spring. Behind the lion the sun was rising, although stars were still shining over the hunter. Below this scene lay a coiled snake with raised head. On each side of it there was a beautifully executed girl's profile. Then began some sort of woodland scene, but Vasek saw only the tops of some trees; the rest disappeared under the giant's trousers. On his neck there sat a chubby figure with his legs crossed and his arms folded. On the left shoulder lay an anchor; on the right, an ax. On the left arm there was another snake, this time uncoiled, then some kind of motto in a frame, a heart with initials, and finally a rose and a bird.

"Hm." He puckered his mouth, continuing to rest his cheeks on his palms and continuing to observe and deliberate. "Honza Bláhu can paint like that. When I'm a 'donter' I'll have him paint me. But I won't have snakes. Snakes are silly. And girls are silly, too. How can a 'donter' have girls on his skin? An anchor on the shoulder, though, that's all right. They had an anchor like that sewed on the altar cloth at home.

"But the main thing will be to have a lion and a tiger painted on, each pulling a 'donter' by the leg. And the 'donter' will hit them on their snouts. Behind them I'll have horses painted, standing in a row on their hind legs. And under that . . . maybe . . . yes, under the horses I'll have Father painted, blowing his trumpet. And in the evening when I take off my shirt I'll say, 'Look, Father!' And Father will laugh when he sees how he's blowing the trumpet."

The washing and combing took Gambier longer than all the rest of his dressing. Especially the combing; he had to reshape his Santa Claus whiskers into a handsome, masculine beard in the latest fashion, and to straighten out his gristling hair into a smooth, pomaded shape with a parting down the middle.

Meanwhile he sang, *"Oh, ma chère Marie, vous êtes une belle fleur . . ."* in a deep, rumbling tone, as if he were treading the bass pedals of an organ. But when he had thrown the comb aside, before you could say Jack Robinson on went shirt, trousers, shoes, and narrow dark-blue jacket with high collar and a long row of buttons. Then he set aslant on his head a strange-looking cap, a bit rumpled, with a long, broad claw on it.

"Voilà, mon p'tit, allons," let's go to the menagerie."

Vasek jumped down from the chair, caught up his cap, and ran out to watch the Captain pull down the red flag. Then he trotted along at the giant's side in the direction of the opposite building. The open space with its training ring was now empty.

Vasek had not yet been to the menagerie, and when he entered he stood still as if petrified. How was it possible that Father had said nothing of all this? A cage full of monkeys! A goat with a blue beard? Screeching parrots! Strange beasts in cages! Bears! Sheep! Here there was amusement for days on end, and Father had only taken him out to those wagons and those stupid dwarfs.

But now he had to leave it all to explore another time; the "donter" walked on toward the lion cages with great strides, and Vasek of course had to go with him. As soon as Gambier appeared among the great cats' cages most of the beasts rose to their feet, came over to the grating and, purring softly, rubbed their bodies against the iron bars.

"Bon jour, Bessie, bon jour, Corina, comment ça va, Mahum?" Gambier called to each animal with a quiet, caressing voice, and his hand traveled along their manes and into their fur, rubbing and stroking it. The beasts trembled with delight, but the tamer kept his eyes fixed on Natasha's cage. The lioness was lying down, sleepy and languid. Close beside her stood Anna Berwitz. Gambier disliked these whims of the directress, but had to admit that she had a way with the beasts and that she could take more liberties with them than anyone else could.

Nonetheless, he was better satisfied when, at the sound of his voice, the directress slipped out of the cage and fastened the door. Gambier greeted her, and Anna, giving him her tiny hand, told him the latest bit of news: the lion cubs must be taken away from Natasha; the lioness paid no attention to them and evidently hadn't enough milk for them. Léon Gambier nodded his head.

"We can try it. If she makes a fuss, we can return one of them. I'll take them to my place. I've kept lots of them before."

"No, Captain, you can't do that to me. I've already decided to bring up the cubs myself. Our caravan is bigger and more comfortable."

"As you please, madame, they are your lions, not mine. But you will have a lot of trouble with them. You'll have to take them to bed with you; they need the warmth, and they aren't pleasant bedfellows. They'll keep fidgeting about . . . and they aren't house-broken."

"I know, I know. But I love them. They're such helpless creatures. We must take some trouble with them; they are capital, you see. They'll be better off with us. And if none of us is at home, Helen will watch them."

Vasek didn't understand what they said, for they were speaking in French. He stood by the cage and watched the mighty animals, which he had never seen before so close to. Then he walked over and caught sight of several great, striped beasts. He realized that these were tigers.

"Golly," he said, "you really have teeth, you brutes, you could finish a man. But just you try; I'll smash you one on the snout."

The tigers looked the boy over lazily, and occasionally one of them yawned. The biggest of them pressed close up against the grating, trying to catch sight of Gambier and Anna, who stood off at a distance.

Suddenly a stir arose. Several men ran up, Gambier gave orders and the men dragged up an empty cage on wheels and placed it in front of Natasha's cage. Gambier went into Natasha's cage, stroked her, and coaxed her. The lioness half-rose to her feet and roared. The lion Mahum answered her. The lioness Bessie answered Mahum. The lion Sultan growled angrily at Bessie. The rumbling din from their terrible throats filled Vasek with anxiety. Gambier stroked Natasha behind the ears and coaxed her. Someone brought three pieces of raw meat. Anna took them and entered the empty cage. The opened door was set opposite the door of Natasha's cage. Three attendants stood along side with poles and pitchforks. Gambier walked over to the door and took a piece of meat from Anna.

"Viens, Natasha, viens, ma chère!"

He threw the meat into the other cage. Natasha got up, stretched, and walked to the door with a languid tread.

"Come, Natasha," Anna enticed her, "come, little one, see, there is meat for you."

The lioness sniffed the bottom of the cage, scratched her head against the grating, and then slowly, bit by bit, entered the opposite cage, treading noiselessly but with menacing growls. At last she jumped toward the meat, covered it with one paw, and roared more loudly. Everyone about, even Anna and Gambier, stood motionless.

"Don't roar, my dear, don't be afraid." Anna spoke softly. "It's yours, no one will take it away from you. And this is yours and this."

She threw the lioness a second piece and a third. The lioness sniffed at the meat, lay down by it, and growled. Continuing to speak tenderly to her, Anna slowly stepped to the door and passed into the other cage. The door fell to behind Natasha and the attendants dragged her cage away. Anna came out from the second cage and behind her followed Gambier, carrying three squalling kittens in his arms.

All the while Vasek had stood tense, watching everything that had passed with the keenest interest. His fists tightened unconsciously, and in his mind he resolved that he would throw himself on that monster if she should do anything to his Captain or to the lady. He was so entranced that he did not notice that someone had pulled him by the sleeve. Only when the tug was repeated did he look round and in sudden delight cry in a smothered voice, "Oh, Daddy!"

The directress looked round. Karas greeted her.

"Ah, Anton! Good day! So this is your boy? My sister-in-law told me about him. A fine lad. Come and look at the lion cubs. But don't touch them yet. When they grow up a little you can play with them."

Vasek stretched up toward Gambier, who bent down. On his left forearm, held there securely by his right hand, lay three ugly, damp kittens, softly squeaking.

"Natasha wants to go back to her nest," one of the attendants

85

observed. They turned round and drew back. The lioness, who for a time had been chewing and biting at the meat and dragging it on the floor, now left it unfinished and returned to the grating.

"Let her go back," Gambier commanded.

They dragged up the other cage, opened the door, and Natasha, the meat in her jaws, jumped in one great leap onto the bedstraw of her own cage. There she dropped the meat and began to sniff about for her babies in the straw. The door closed behind her and the workers hauled away the other cage. Natasha searched and searched, but at last came back to the meat and lay down to eat it.

· "A bad mother," said Anna. "Come, Captain."

"We must go to dinner, Vasek," his father told the boy. "How have you been?"

They walked slowly homeward, but the whole walk and the whole of dinnertime did not suffice for Vasek to tell his father and Rosa all that he had seen and experienced. And the single conclusion of it all was that Vasek would be a "donter."

"What's that, a 'donter'?" his father asked.

"For heaven's sake! Father! You don't know what a 'donter' is?" the boy scolded his father. And now for the first time came the piece of information that Vasek would have himself tattooed, that he would have a long beard and a flag on his house and would walk into wild-animal cages, and if they tried to bite him, he would give them one on the snout.

That afternoon, of course Vasek went to the performance again. Karas seated him in an empty place in the gallery and then ran off to the orchestra. He soon discovered that the program went off to a split second like yesterday's. Today he was more at ease, and in one march even permitted himself to develop an accompaniment to a short counter-melody, at which Mr. Selnicki nodded in approval. It was nothing more than one of those ta-boom-ta-boom-ta-ra-ra's he had played countless times with Milner, but Karas was overjoyed that it had been successful and that the conductor was pleased.

After the performance he hastened down below with the others to grab up his armful of covers. This time he was finished ahead of his partner, as he had made an agreement with Vasek for the boy to come and help him. And then followed the feeding and the evening cleaning, again a sight tremendously thrilling for Vasek. At last everything in the circus was finished, the night watches were posted, and both Karases were walking home together. Vasek was especially happy. Helping with the covers had been his first job in the circus, and a conviction rapidly grew in his mind that if it had not been for his co-operation, the circus would not have been left in order.

That evening, when he had gone to bed, he said just before falling asleep:

"You know, Father, everything in the circus is nice, but I'm going to be an elephant-trainer. Training elephants is the most wonderful job of all!"

CHAPTER SIX

THE NEXT AFTERNOON the two Karases dined at Frau Langer-mann's for the last time. After dinner they moved to the wagons according to the order. The parting was not a simple one. Karas had been a boarder here for many years and now was leaving on the threshold of the season he usually spent in Hamburg. It was a great event for these humble people that, as if by a miracle, he had hit on a job in the midst of unemployment; and on his side he knew that a bad summer was ahead for the good Frau Langermann now that she had lost the whole gang of Czech boarders.

And then there was Vasek, whom she had come to love in these few days, and for Vasek there approached a leave-taking from Rosa, the first little horse of his circus dreams. And so they were all on the brink of tears, and many promises were made. Should they return that winter to Hamburg, they would certainly look up

Frau Langermann and perhaps, it was to be hoped, they would lodge with her.

At the circus there was much bustle and noise. The whole circus was carrying bundles and that multitude of personal treasures from which people will not be parted, from a cage with a canary to a pot of flowers. Karas arrived with only his sack. He found his way to wagon Number Eight.

When he opened the door he discovered Kerholec inside, hanging up his clothes on the hooks at the back. Vasek climbed up after his father, and was extremely disappointed. He had expected a pretty, comfortable little house like Captain Gambier had, and now found a mere cheap lodging on four wheels. To the left and right there were three tiers of bunks, so that each sleeper seemed to be crawling into a drawer rather than a bed. At the back stood two tin washbasins on two chairs, two water pitchers, and a small cupboard with six drawers which locked and which served for the storage of small articles. Above this on all sides there projected hooks for clothing.

"Well," said Kerholec when he noticed the surprised looks of the two Karases, "I told you it wouldn't be the Grand Hotel; but you haven't such a lot of belongings that you can't get them into this dump. Whenever you want to sneeze, turn on your side so that you won't bump your head. If it's hot, we'll open the windows and the door and you'll enjoy the magnificent fresh air; if it's cold, we'll all breathe together and make it into a steam bath.

"Anyway, it's only for sleeping. From morning to night we'll be outside on the go. And if we only want to get out of the rain or something, the upper bunks can be folded in and you can sit on the middle ones as if you were on your own mamma's sofa. The main thing, man, is that it goes along with you all the time—no matter where you turn, your roost goes along with you, and that's something to be thankful for."

"Well, that's the way it is." Karas gave in to fate. "Where will we sleep?"

"I have Number Four. That's the middle bunk on the right. I have to be out first in the morning and at all times I have to be ready to get out fast, so I have first pick. You'll sleep in Number Six under me and Vasek in Two above. You can swap with him, but it's not easy to climb up there and a boy like Vasek can climb out like a squirrel. What do you say, Vasek?"

Vasek said nothing. But it was plain to see that he wasn't pleased.

"You don't like it?"

"I thought we would have a little house like the 'donter.'"

"Like who?"

"Like the Captain."

"Oh yes, like the *dompteur*. But of course, Vasek, you'll have a house like that, but only when you're a *dompteur* too. You will have to work hard and practice. Anyway, you see, you'll only be here at night; we need everyone we can get for the horses, even a fellow like you. Did you like the horses?"

"Yes."

"Did Hans give you a ride on that little striped pony, Mary?"

"Yes. Is Mary coming too?"

"Of course, Vasek. And if you like, you'll ride her during the day."

"Really? I'll ride a pony?"

"If I say so."

"Gee! Father, that will be terrific! Did you see Mary, Father? She's as pretty as anything."

"Well, but you'll have to learn to ride properly in the saddle and to manage her well so that she won't run away with you."

"How could she if I hold her tight? When I rode her before I didn't even have a bridle!"

"Well, run out now so that you won't be in the way here, and I'll tell Hans to teach you to ride."

"Golly, that'll be swell. I'm going to take a look at her. Can I go and take a look at her?"

"You can. And tell Hans that Mr. Kerholec said that you can ride Mary."

Exultant, Vasek burst out of the wagon, thrust on the new cap his father had bought him that morning, and, whistling,

89

trotted off to the stable. Karas Senior untied his sack and pulled out his things. Two hooks were enough for all his and his son's stuff.

"Who'll be with us on the other side?" he asked Kerholec meanwhile.

"All of them good fellows and countrymen of ours," answered Kerholec as he bustled around. "You know I wouldn't pick any rotters for my wagon. Number One . . ."

Karas had noticed when he came in that the bunks had little metal plates with numbers. This was another passion of Peter Berwitz's. The Latin blood in him tempted him to display and pompousness, while his German stock revealed itself in a constant drive toward order, precision, and perfect organization. He had begun to number his wagons when he could still count them all in the twinkling of an eye. Then, as he acquired more wagons, he had each bunk in them numbered and made Steenhouwer keep the list of which bunks were occupied and which free. Today after Kerholec's report Steenhouwer had made on his plan a cross over numbers VIII/2 and VIII/6, which stood for the arrival of the two Karases in Kerholec's wagon.

"Number One," Kerholec said, "is a certain Honza Bures, a former intellectual. Who he was and what happened to him to make him join up with the circus no one knows. And no one asks about it, either. Here a man's worth what he is, and not what he was. When you're with us longer you'll find out that the circus is full of all kinds of 'former people.' But no one pokes their noses into their business when they don't come out with it themselves. How can a man know what's knocked down another one and what hurts him?

"Anyway, it usually all comes out in the end. After a man's been on wheels for weeks, months, years, all the time under a different sky, there comes an evening when even a Trappist would dish out his secrets. As to this fellow Bures, we've only noticed that he's never gone to Prague with us. We've been there three times since he's been here, and three times he's always vanished into thin air before we got to Prague, and then showed up on the other side. And he always had such a stupid excuse that if he'd been any other man we'd have chased him out of here. But Bures is such a good fellow that I told the others to keep their traps shut and let him alone.

"Between ourselves, he's an actor—he speaks, preaches, declaims, waves his arms, rattles on—he's a marvel. But what's so funny is that he does it all just for us. You couldn't get him into any stunt in the ring for a thousand pounds. We've tried to make him, already; I even hinted to the director myself to get him into an act, but what happened? He stood like a rock, wouldn't look the director in the face; he wouldn't dream of it, he said, he was only here to do rough work and he wouldn't dare to try and be an artist in such a noble enterprise. But I'm sure that he was making a fool out of the director all the while.

"Well, he's a good fellow, but strange. They say—but look, this is just what's said, I don't know anything about it myself—they say that that time in Prague when they did in the Windisch-Graetz Princess, that he had something to do with it . . . but I don't know . . . that's just what people say. What's the proverb: 'If it isn't true, people will make it up'?"

"And the middle one?" asked Karas, who was very interested to learn something of the new gang.

"Three—Vosátka? Anton, my friend, I could go on talking about him all evening and all night. All I can say about him is that he's true steel; you'll see, he's worth knowing. But now I must go, and so must you too, in a couple of minutes . . ."

Kerholec was interrupted by the opening of the door. On the steps there stood an old man with stiff gray, short-cropped hair, a furrowed, weather-beaten face, and a load of some kind on his shoulders and in his arms.

"Hello, Papa Malina," cried Kerholec, "what are you bringing us?"

"I drew out our allotment of mallets and stakes," the old man answered.

"Bring them here," called Kerholec and added to Karas, "Those are the stakes we drive into the ground, posts or anchors onto which we tie the main rope. The main rope is the rope that holds the mast up, the main pole, you understand, and with that the whole *chapiteau* . . . the whole tent. And that's the job of us tent-stakers, and I like it when our equipment is always at hand.

And this is Papa Malina, Bunk Five. Get acquainted, boys. I have to run off."

Karas waited until the old man had put down his load. The mallets were good ones, heavy, with yard-long handles, the stakes were iron, with flat heads. Then he introduced himself quite simply.

"Karas, Karas," said the old man thoughtfully. "Once in Hungary we had a Karas with us, but that's many a year ago. . . . No, I've got it mixed up, that was a Parma, Jozífek Parma from Olomouc somewhere; but anyway, was he a relative of yours?"

"No, Papa, he wasn't. I never knew any Parma." Karas had to smile at the old man.

"Well, that's good. He was a villain, anyway, that Parma. Once he strewed powdered rose seed in Mamselle Arabelle's tricot and she had to scratch all the time during her ride. It's better to have nothing to do with such fellows. But where do you come from?"

"From Horní Snezná. That's near Budejovice."

"Ah, Budejovice. I know it. A bear got away from us there and we chased him to Jaromerice."

"That must be the Moravian Budejovice. I'm from the one in Bohemia."

"That's right, of course. There are two of them, to be sure. So you don't know Jaromerice. . . . Well, just imagine, that bear ran under the arcade in Jaromerice on Sunday morning, and all of a sudden darted off straight into the honey-cake shop. Yes, but wait . . . I don't know now what happened afterward . . . I've completely forgotten, just as if that bear got lost for me in that honey-cake shop. Do you think it's time to go to work? You know, whenever I have to start anything, then everything else stops for me, my brain, my mouth, everything. . . . Now I know I have to go to work, and I'll only remember the rest when I get started. So let's go."

The old man actually became silent. He locked the door after Karas, put the key in his pocket, and headed off toward the menagerie with long strides, forgetting his companion completely.

Karas was surprised to discover that he had arrived at the

bandstand just at the moment when Kerholec was clapping down below for the music to start. This time his playing went without a hitch; he was already beginning to feel at home. Meanwhile he reflected on the trio of strange people he had joined and whether Kerholec himself might not be just as much a mystery as the others. And he blew with great gusto and again played his own accompanying flourish, his ta-boom-ta-boom-ta-ra-ra. When he sat back someone caught him by the shoulder. Karas was almost frightened. When he looked round he saw old Malina in his blue livery, stretching over his neighbor's music stand with a tremendously serious look on his face. Karas nodded, and Malina put his lips to the other's ear and said in a muffled voice:

"He had got into the honey there. That's how we caught him."

Karas nearly burst out laughing, but the old man nodded twice to him now that the story was in order, and walked away on tiptoe.

Vendelín Malina was the oldest member of Umberto's Circus. He had been there longer than the goat Bluebeard or the stallion Pompon or the graying lion Sultan. How long he had been there no one knew, not even he. Peter Berwitz remembered only that when he was still a very little boy Vendelín Malina had lifted him up, set him on a donkey, and led him into the ring. Perhaps only Grandpa Umberto would have known when and where he had engaged Vendelín Malina.

In Malina's memory it was all a bit muddled. He had a magnificent memory for all the events and anecdotes with which Umberto's Circus had been associated, and for the crowds of people he had met during his life. In this respect he was a living chronicle of the enterprise, and often could relate things which sounded like legends, but which actually were truth. But the longer he lived, the more he confused names, and the times when the incidents had occurred. He was not talkative in the true sense of the word; sometimes he scarcely uttered a couple of words for weeks together; in his uncommunicativeness he would not even say hello, and if someone greeted him, he would answer only by muttering. But when something interested him, when some memory stirred in his brain, he would begin a slow, detailed narrative which went on interminably.

As far as his own history could be reconstructed from the stories he told, it seemed that he had been born somewhere in the Orlicky Mountains, and that as a young boy he had left his home for the road with his elder brother many long years ago. This elder brother, Stanislav Malina, had already been out in the world before, as a cooper's apprentice, it seemed, and had worked somewhere in France in the vineyard country, which he had liked extremely. After two years he had returned, a big fistful of gold pieces in his pocket, to his native village, made merry with his money, had a wild time, and danced at parties all over the region; but when he got the urge again for his red wine and food cooked in oil, he took the younger Vendelín Malina and they both struck out for France.

What happened there it was hard to say; evidently Stanislav had some sort of love affair which came to nothing, for he signed up as a sailor and sailed out to sea one fine day on a great, heavy, big-bellied sailing vessel, leaving Vendelín alone in the port. Where that was, the devil alone knew; once Vendelín mentioned Toulon, once Marseille, and once Bordeaux. It was certain that he knew all those cities; the circus people had already tested him, with the help of native Frenchmen.

Well, in one such city Vendelín made his living at all kinds of heavy work at the docks and in the shipyards, and perhaps he might not have got on so badly, but a terrible nostalgia for his native land seized him; he felt himself alone and deserted, nothing consoled him, and he thought always only of the journey home, home, home. But this was not so simple. From the boys' journey to France he remembered only an endless, crisscross wandering; how to go back he did not know. He could not read or write, and when he asked anyone there on the edge of the sea where Prague was, and how to get there, they only shook their heads, shrugged their shoulders, and often began to argue as to whether it was in the Russian Empire or somewhere on the borders of Turkey.

Only when Vendelín at last met a man who knew about Prague, and had even been there, did he discover that it was useless to try to make his way to Prague by sea. Then he began to pay attention to the land travelers he met: side-show men, traveling salesmen, carnival people, circus troupes, and all kinds of tramps and wanderers. Among them he at last found a talkative Italian circus proprietor who answered his timid question with a mass of cries:

"Ah, Praga! Si, si! Je la connais bien. La bellissima città! Le pont, le Burg! Grandioso! Magnifique! La città di Bambino Gesù! Guten Tag, gute Nacht, topri ten, topra noc, ecco!"

When Vendelín Malina asked the circus gentleman whether he might be going to Prague, the latter burst out into a new storm of cries and exclamations. Of course he was going there; he went everywhere, he went all over the world, he would go to Prague too, a beautiful land, a beautiful city, a noble people who loved great sights and could value true art. Then Malina asked quite timorously whether he couldn't go with him. The circus gentleman scratched himself behind the ear and said that that was a ticklish matter; the way to Prague was long and all sorts of things might happen.

Finally he asked if Malina knew any of the liberal arts. Malina said no, but that he could mend and repair everything on the wagons and anything at all that was made of wood, that he had learned on a farm how to care for horses, and that he would do anything which was required of him . . . and that he didn't want payment, only a bit of food, even potatoes would do. This last evidently pleased the circus gentleman the most of all, and so it was that Carlo Umberto became Vendelín Malina's master, and Vendelín Malina a part of Umberto's Circus.

Not that he wanted to stay in it. God forbid! Vendelín thought of nothing except of how to make his way back to Bohemia. But he had no idea whatever of how long the trip would take if he made it with the circus. At that time Carlo Umberto had his outfit packed on three wagons, with only two horses to draw them, which meant that everywhere they had to hire extra ones for the road. Now that Malina had joined them he began to travel by going a bit of the way with two wagons and then letting Malina return with one horse and bring up the third, while Carlo Umberto would try his luck in some village with a small show made up of the bear, the monkeys, and the dogs.

For his job Malina was given a skinny white horse, a simlík,

95

as he called it, since the other one, the black one, was prettier and was used in the bigger shows as a riding horse. And so it came about that Malina traveled each stage of their journey three times. He bore no ill will because of this, for he was happiest when he could be alone with his *simlík* and could speak to it in Czech. Before long he came to the conclusion that the *simlík* understood Czech, and was terribly moved by the fact that in the dumb animal he had found a fellow countryman.

And the *simlík,* too, loved Vendelín best of all; in the stable or when they camped under the open sky he would always greet him with a neigh and lick his face or his neck, all of which Vendelín patiently endured. Whenever he rode back on his *simlík* for the abandoned wagon a long conversation would ensue in which Vendelín would explain to his horse everything that had happened that day, and how completely different it was at home in Bohemia, and what a fine rest they both would have, Vendelín and the *simlík,* when they got to Žamberk and Vamberk. The *simlík* was so used to these conversations that should Vendelín sometimes fall into daydreaming and silence, the *simlík* himself would wake him up with a neigh and rouse him to further tales.

So together, traveling each interval between villages three times, they crossed all France, the Netherlands, and the various states of Germany, but of Bohemia, of Prague, of the Orlicky Mountains, there was no trace. Summer passed, autumn came on with its mists over the meadows and its campfires on the field stubble; then there was wet slush and snow, great quantities of snow, so that it was only with difficulty that the *simlík* forced his way through the storms, and Vendelín preferred to walk through the blizzards at his side to lighten his load.

They gave shows at inns, in sheds and stables, but nowhere did they stop for long, ever they journeyed on—according to Malina's belief, to Prague. Meanwhile he had learned to do all sorts of odd jobs in the circus and the menagerie; he put up the tent, fed the animals, helped during the parades and performances, aided the director's wife to obtain food and fodder from the peasants, toiled from dawn till dark like his *simlík,* his only reward his food and the hope of reaching his homeland.

Meanwhile spring came again and they journeyed up the River

Rhine and into Switzerland and south over its terrifying mountains to Lombardy and the land of Italy. The farther they went, the more fierce the heat grew; the *simlík* was worn-out and Vendelín could not find enough shade for him. He himself would complain to the beast during the summer nights, putting his arms about its neck, of what a long journey they were having to make back to their homeland, and what a faraway land of devils it was to which his brother Stanislav had brought him that the return trip must take so long.

And again came autumn and again they found themselves in the German lands. The director purchased a third horse and the return trips for the extra wagon now ceased, things speeded up, Vendelín had his own permanent wagon with his *simlík,* and again he began to hope that now soon, perhaps, they would reach Bohemia. But still he saw only the fields of Germany, now mountains, now plains, and only in the autumn of the third year, when they were in the town of Vratislav, did people tell him that the Czech land was not far away, that off there in those clouds stood the mountain peaks of Krkonose and Snezník.

The news tore at Vendelín's heartstrings and he almost burst into tears. At last, at last, he saw a bit of his homeland! And that evening when they had finished the show, he fed the *simlík* and went to see the director. Carlo Umberto received his excited announcement that tonight he would leave and go home with a terrible uproar; he crossed himself and called on the Mother of God to keep him from going, and called her to witness that Vendelín was committing sheer ingratitude and black treachery toward his benefactor.

When Vendelín stood his ground, Umberto swore by all the powers that though it would drive him to bankruptcy, from now on he was ready to pay Malina a couple of thalers a year, just to avoid having to change his personnel. Amid shouts and complaints he even raised this sum, but Vendelín stood his ground. Umberto cursed him with terrible Italian oaths, calling him the greatest villain under the sun, and then embraced him and kissed him and wished him a safe journey and reminded him that he could always return and Umberto's Circus would gladly open its gates to him.

More difficult was Malina's parting with the *simlík*. Here in the quiet of the stable he broke down and wept while he explained to the horse the great thing that had happened and how he could not take him with him without having to steal him from the proprietor. Vendelín Malina had collected only a tiny bundle of possessions during all the years of his exile. When he picked it up and threw it over his shoulder, the *simlík* turned his head after him and neighed, neighed so pitifully that Vendelín preferred to run off rather than to listen to that pitiful neighing. But nonetheless he kept hearing it.

The heavens were wide and starry and the night was cool when he walked, his stick in his hand, out of the inn stable where Umberto's Circus lodged its three horses. Vendelín walked all night and all forenoon, he climbed mountains and crossed forests, now and then eating bits of the bread and cheese the director had given him for the journey, and drinking from wells and streams. He walked on, crossed mountain peaks, came down into the valley—and all at once, suddenly, he heard a Czech cry coming from the fields. Great was his joy to find that at last he was among his own people, and when he came to a village he asked his way; it turned out that he was not far from his own village, only an hour or so away.

The good Lord only knows what Malina had expected from his return home. There was nothing really definite in his mind, only a vague, pleasant dream of some paradise of happiness. But when he arrived there and recognized the familiar hills and woods and fields and houses, and when he had entered the village and the dogs started their fearful barking at the sight of a strange vagabond, he was suddenly seized by the painful feeling that he no longer belonged to this place, that he had been away too long, and that his home had become quite different since the days of his childhood.

In his father's hut he found strangers, who told him that his father and mother were dead long ago, his father killed by a falling pine while chopping in the forest, his mother dead of fever, that Stanislav had never come back, and that the younger children had scattered over the world and no one knew anything about them. There he stood on the threshold of his own home, tapping his stick in bewilderment, timidly asking about this person or that of his old neighbors and friends.

Many of them were still alive, including his godmother, now already an aged woman living alone. He had nowhere to go but to her. He found her; she did not recognize him, but when he made himself known she clasped her hands and brought out some bread and butter and a little milk. They sat up together far into the night. Again he heard all the sad stories of what had happened, and whenever his godmother was silent he heard as if from far away in the distance his *simlík* calling to him with its plaintive neighing.

He stayed with the old woman overnight, sleeping in the stable; the next morning he went to look at the cemetery, at that poor little cemetery behind the church, grown over with weeds. Then he visited a few of his schoolmates, now already married and fathers of families, listened to all their complaints and grievances against their hard life, and again he heard the *simlík's* neighing from the distance. And he saw that it was indeed so, that he had cut himself off from his homeland, and his home had cut itself off from him . . . and that his true home was now on four wheels, and his only comrade the *simlík*.

On the morning of the third day he said good-bye to his godmother. From somewhere in a wooden chest she dug out two silver pieces which she pressed into his palm; then she made three crosses over him and Vendelín Malina went out of his native village. Slowly, almost without conscious thought, he climbed the mountains again, crossed the frontier, and marched into Vratislav. When he arrived there, he learned at the inn that the circus had gone off somewhere to Zitava. He struck out after them, asking in village after village where they had gone; when he arrived in Zitava they had already moved on.

He was already starting to spend his second silver piece, and was afraid that he would not reach them before his money was all gone and that he would be locked up by the police as a vagabond. However, he was catching up with the circus, that he already saw, and he hurried on with renewed strength. His tidings of the circus people led him on to a beautiful land, full of oak forests and waters. They could not be far now, perhaps a day on the road—though of course they were in wagons and he was on foot. He hurried on, taking short cuts and again coming to another wood by a river.

As he drew near it, suddenly—no, he could not be mistaken, a *simlík* was calling, his *simlík* was calling, and this time it was not a dream, this time it was real neighing. And then came the clatter of hoofs, and look, from the woods there emerged the *simlík*, without his harness and rushing to meet Vendelín. "Simlík!" cried Vendelín, and embraced him, and the *simlík* neighed and snorted and nudged against him. Two men and a woman ran out from among the oaks and with loud cries rushed along the path after the horse. Vendelín stroked him, patted him, and said:

"So come now, *simlík*, we're going to be together again." And after a while he cried, "Never fear, master, I'll bring you your *simlík!*"

From this time Vendelín Malina remained with Umberto's Circus; he witnessed its growth, and the arrival of Bernhard Berwitz; he drove him to his wedding at the church, and was there when the tiger Pasha attacked him; he had shared everything with them, even the Asiatic expedition. Often he could be heard muttering about the unheard-of innovations: for example, what good was an elephant to a circus—such a brute!—when in the old days they used to arrange a whole beautiful program with three wagons. His *simlík* had died years and years ago, and he himself now became a *"simlík"* and grew old and white, but he served on and on, was the first to begin working and the last to quit, this quiet old man without whom the others would not have been able to imagine Umberto's Circus.

When Karas now laughed and told Kerholec how Malina's "brain had stopped" when they first met, and how he had later come over to finish telling the story about the bear, Kerholec grew serious.

"Anton," he told him, "it's not as simple as that. That graybeard's brain works like a clock. That's why I keep him with me in my wagon. You don't need any alarm clock with him about. When it is time for some kind of work in the circus something ticks in Vendelín's head. If he were asleep, he'd wake up. If he were doing anything else, his hands would stop of their own accord. If he's telling you something, he'll forget what it is and look like an idiot until he takes himself off and goes to the job that is awaiting him. And we go with him.

"But there's more to it than that. Sometimes the old man will wake up in the middle of the night, get up, put on his shoes without a word, and go off like a sleepwalker to the stables or the cages or the tent. And every time there's something wrong there. Once the horses had got out, once the lions' cage was closed badly and the lions were out in the passageway, once smoke was coming out of a pile of rubbish behind the tent, and you can imagine what damage a fire would do there. And Vendelín always goes just like an automaton to the place where the danger is; he doesn't even know what he's doing there until he sees what's up and gives the alarm.

"The director says that he's the real guardian angel of the circus. And he brought him to me himself and told me to take him into my wagon. 'You know, Karl,' the director said to me, 'I don't believe in spirits. Discipline is the best spirit for a circus. When everyone does his own job we can all sleep peacefully. But there are times when everything goes wrong, and it is as if you walked into the ring backward; it is then that old Vendelín knows it somehow.

" 'If you ever see him crawling out of his bunk at night, don't be lazy; get up and follow him. It's possible he'll be just going out to powder his nose, but it also can be a matter of our hides,' Berwitz said. And that's just how it is, Anton. All the time I've been with that old man he's never gone out to watch the stars yet; he sleeps like a log, even when lightning strikes all around, but when he does climb out, that means something's up."

Today, when they had to sleep in the wagons for the first time, the musicians did not race so madly to the stables. They knew that they had their supper and bunk within thirty paces and not somewhere at the other end of Hamburg, and so everything was done more calmly. While he was attending to the horses Karas looked into the ponies' enclosure and saw that there were only three of them. He guessed that Vasek was outside riding again. To make certain he asked Hans.

"Yes," nodded Hans, and his face brightened up. "Vasek's on Mary. A fine boy, brave, and he'll make a good rider."

After giving in his report Karas went out and saw a number of people gathered around the outside ring. They were watching something with great interest, and crying:

"Hold on, Vasek!"

Karas walked up and caught sight of Hans standing in the center with the whip in his hand and urging the striped pony on to a full trot. On the pygmy sat Vasek, but the bridle was fastened to the saddle and Vasek had both hands behind his back. He could hold onto the pony only with his legs, and at the same time had to keep rising and falling to the rhythm of the pony's gait. Evidently this was not so easy, for his forehead was furrowed and his teeth were set; he did not see his father.

"Bravo, Vasek!" Hans cried now, and called to Mary, who slowed down her pace and came to a stop. "That's enough for today."

The boy jumped down, but as he did so he cried out. His whole body ached. Nevertheless, he went over to the pony, patted her, unfastened the bridle, and began to lead Mary off to the stable. Then he caught sight of his father.

"Father, did you see me?" he called to him with great pride. "She can go, can't she? I had a good ride, didn't I?"

"You held on well, they've already told me that. But come now, shake hands with Hans, thank him, and tell him that you'll curry Mary for him."

Vasek, his cap over his ear, walked over to Hans. He transferred the bridle to his left hand.

"Hans, ich danke dir!" and the child's hand stretched out to meet the great hand of the stable master.

"All right, all right." Hans shook it a bit shyly, touched by such good manners from a little boy. "For the first day it was really good."

He patted Vasek on the back and they went off to the stable together, Mary beside Vasek. Karas went to Number Eight and on the way caught up with Kerholec.

"Tomorrow's the gala performance before we go off," Kerholec informed him. "The newspapers are full of it. Our old man's good at that sort of thing."

"And where is it we're going?"

"Through Harburg to Buxtehude for the night and then to Bremen and Oldenburg. That's the usual beginning."

A thin fellow in a dirty red shirt was standing by Number Eight. He had a great bald patch over his forehead, half of his right ear was missing, and from there a scar stretched across his whole cheek to his nose. When Kerholec approached the fellow raised his right arm and saluted. Karas saw that the whole little finger and half of the ring finger were missing.

"Kitchen hand Ferenc Vosátka at your service," he reported in Czech. "I beg to inform you that supper will be ready in a quarter of an hour. On the menu there's goulash soup with potatoes, roast chicken with salad, and sweet rolls with brandy sauce. The chicken, salad, and rolls each one must furnish himself, while I'll provide the potato soup. Whoever's taste isn't suited can eat à la carte at the Hotel Ambassador. Decency would demand, however, that he invite us to go with him."

"Here's a new boarder for you, Ferenc." Kerholec introduced Karas.

"Sergeant Ferenc Vosátka." The fellow clicked his heels. *"Très enchanté,* Comte de Karas—how are the Countess and the young Countesses?"

And Vosátka marched off singing, while Kerholec smiled.

"Now you've met him; he's a character all right."

Vendelín Malina slowly approached from the opposite direction. When he came up to Karas he raised his bent head and said:

"His name was Mates."

"Whose was?" asked Karas.

"Why, the one we're talking about. The bear. We caught him in the honey and took him back to Budejovice. I only tell you that because you come from that part of the country. Is supper ready?"

"In a minute, Papa," Kerholec answered. "Vosátka's already gone for it. And here's Bures coming now."

Karas looked round curiously at Number One. He was a fine, sturdy man with a black goatee and long black hair, which kept slipping out from under his broad Calabrian hat.

"How do you do! Welcome to you, countryman." He spoke in a sonorous and melodious voice and offered Karas his hand. "Two more seedlings from our Czech land wafted to foreign parts? God give you both happiness on your wanderings with us. What comes to us isn't all sweetness and light, but it's a life of freedom. If you mind your own business no one will notice you, you are liberated from prejudices and chains, free and independent as a bird. And like a migratory bird you're here today and gone tomorrow, here you're madly in love and there, again, you forget."

"Only if you don't watch out," old Malina interrupted him, "the girl will chase you from city to city until she catches you. We had a rider here once—he said he was Spanish, but really he was a Hungarian from the plains. He turned the heads of all the girls. Once in Genoa he made a mistake—no, it was in Geneva, because she was the daughter of a Swiss pastor, and nowhere under the sun are the Swiss so pigheaded as in Geneva. So this fellow—Kösteny Imre was his name—talked the girl into believing he was a Count and that he would take her with him.

"The girl got mixed up with him; we went off and Kösteny went with us. He chuckled at the way he had got away with it, but that afternoon, when we were putting up the tent, all at once up drives a coach and the pastor climbs out of it. Where, he asks, is the director? So we called the boss. Umberto was some director; Lord, how he could talk! Once he talked a sergeant major of the frontier guard into lying down on his job, and with his own hands the fellow helped us to smuggle ten wagons over the border without permission.

"But with this Swiss pastor Umberto couldn't get anywhere; he argued with him in French, Italian, and German, but the pastor answered back in all of them and in Latin, Greek, and Hebrew into the bargain. He kept quoting the Bible and proving to the boss that Kösteny Imre could not back out, but must marry the pastor's daughter. That pastor made Umberto so dizzy with Holy Writ that he went and told Kösteny to clear out or it would be all up with him. Kösteny made a getaway to France and got a job in the circus with old Zanfretto, the one who always wore gold ten-franc pieces on his coat instead of buttons, so that at night they had to keep the coat in the office safe. But he was there only three days and all of a sudden there was the coach again, and the pastor, and the whole mess began over again . . ."

"Hot soup, good hot soup!" cried Vosátka, like a barker. "Who'll be the first to try some?"

In both arms he carried a good-sized pot, from which a ladle emerged. Kerholec, Malina, and Bures rushed to the wagon and each one came out with a tin plate and a spoon.

"Hell, I didn't think about a plate!" cried Karas. "I've got spoons, but no plates."

"Vosátka, run over to Harwey's for two plates," ordered Kerholec. "You can buy yourself some tomorrow, Anton."

"At your orders, Admiral," Vosátka answered smartly, setting down the pot on the landing above the steps. "It's obvious that His Excellence Karas III, Prince of Spain, has been brought up to eat with his fingers. And here, if my fiery eye doesn't deceive me, comes the Crown Prince, and it seems he's in trouble of some sort."

In fact Vasek was approaching, but he was almost crawling, with his hands clapped to his behind.

"Golly, Father"—he spoke seriously—"my whole body hurts."

"I think, Vasek"—Kerholec laughed at him as he handed out the first dishes of soup—"that you won't sit down any more today. When you go riding, the first few days you can only stand or lie down."

"So this is the young Karas," Bures spoke up. "Has he started to go to school yet?"

"He'd just started," Karas answered for Vasek, "but then we had to leave. But he can read and write a little."

"Well, we can't neglect him now." Bures spoke zealously. "It would be an everlasting shame if we did. Work and knowledge are our salvation. I have a few nice books in the wagon; what do you say if we go through them, Vasek?"

"Hm, why not?" Vasek answered slowly. "But only when I can sit down to do it. Daddy, I'm as hungry as a bear."

"And did you clean Mary thoroughly?"

"I've just finished."

"Here's a slice of bread for you in the meantime," Malina

pronounced, standing over everyone and cutting the common loaf of Number Eight. The soup in the pot and the plates had an unusual aroma, and now Karas too felt how his mouth began to water. Happily Vosátka had already returned with the plates, and Kerholec served both father and son with a heaping portion.

"Golly, that's good!" Vasek smacked his lips.

"Real Hungarian goulash soup," Bures confirmed.

"That old Zanfretto refused to listen to the pastor," Malina took up his story, "so the pastor went up on the platform and instead of the comedy act announced on the program, he began to preach to the people and tell them what a Sodom and Gomorrah the circus was. Zanfretto's family wanted to beat up the pastor, but he sent for the mayor and the police. For disturbing the peace Zanfretto had to pack up his tent and go on his way. Kösteny Imre they locked up. First they drubbed him soundly, then they ordered him out of France and sent him back to Switzerland, whence he'd come. And as the pastor was on the spot and offered the gendarmes the use of his coach, they took advantage of the opportunity.

"So back went the pastor, and with him Kösteny and the policemen, to Geneva. By now Kösteny saw that he wouldn't get out of it so easily. In Geneva the Swiss put him straight in the jug. And the pastor went there every day, roaring at him, threatening him with all the punishments of earth and Heaven, until the Hungarian was dizzy and promised to marry the girl. About two months later he came to see us with his wife, but only for a visit. He was going to Hungary, where the pastor had bought them a cottage somewhere near Kecskemét."

"And if they haven't died, they're living happily ever after," Bures added, as if to end the fairy tale.

"That's possible," nodded Malina quite seriously.

"Caramba, señores," Vosátka intruded, "what kind of system is this? Hungarian soup and a Hungarian tale, a man doesn't know which is the hottest. I'm for having another helping of soup without any stories, and for having the Crown Prince run out for a jug of beer for us. A moral tale like the one we've heard is tough sustenance for a young idealist like me or for our chief ladies' inspector here, Charles de Kerholec. We'll have to moisten it up a bit. And besides, today we're initiating two more worthy members into our royal society of the secret arts and sciences."

"Vasek, go and get some beer," Karas ordered him. "We must pay for our initiation into the guild."

"Bravissimo!" cried Vosátka. "The master is proving his right to wield the hammer and trowel!"

"Here's the jug, Venceslav Antonovic," Bures added in agreement. "And you'll find good beer on draught over at the Anchor Inn, straight across from the circus."

"And pay attention, Dauphin, that that scoundrel doesn't spoil the beer with any water," Vosátka reminded him.

It was the pleasant spring evening of a land near the sea, and from the Reeperbahn all sorts of noises floated toward them —the buzzing of the crowds, the calls of the barkers, the squeaking of the merry-go-rounds; accordions wheezed, the bells of the side shows clanged, and the fanfares of parades sounded forth.

The five men and the boy camped here on the steps of the wagon and involuntarily listened to this noisy harmony which came from without, the sound of the eternal fair, the carnival, and the festival from which they earned their livelihood. Around them milled the men and women who belonged to this vagabond society; from somewhere could be heard a song, or a mother's cry, or a child's weeping, and from the wagons yellow bands of light began to transect the growing darkness. Their world, the whole of their different world on wheels, was getting ready for sleep, for their last sleep of the winter in the city of Hamburg. Tomorrow evening their wagons would roll out one after the other, and again spring would begin for them.

When at last they found that they had talked enough for that evening, one after another they disappeared into the wagon and dragged themselves into their beds. The hum of noises from the Reeperbahn still sounded weakly through the opened windows, like a faraway hymn. Some of them were already asleep when Malina's voice spoke out in the darkness:

"Of course if they aren't dead they're living still. Nothing else is possible. But they're not living in Kecskemét any more. Now

I remember that we met them about ten years later, somewhere in Poland. They had a tent there for about a hundred people and they worked there at the fair with the 'shambles.' Kösteny Imre did a 'split' number on two horses, their three children did tumbling on the ground, while she, the Swiss girl, jumped through hoops."

"And throughout this whole beautiful evening I've been trembling with fear in case Swiss Puritanism is stronger than the circus," Sergeant Vosátka answered him. "Now we can go to sleep in peace."

Karas could not restrain himself; he burst out laughing and bumped his forehead against Kerholec's bunk.

"The new man has sounded his tom-tom," Vosátka observed. "Don't let yourselves be provoked. Sleep like kings, messieurs!"

CHAPTER SEVEN

THE NEXT MORNING Vasek rose and breakfasted with the others and went off with them straight to the horse stables. There Hans greeted him with a hearty *"Morgen"* and at once opened the door to the ponies' enclosure in front of him. It was as if they had already agreed, without any long speeches, that Vasek would take care of the striped ponies under Hans's supervision. And the boy began his assignment like a man who had spent his whole life with animals; in his pocket he had brought them a lump of sugar from breakfast and a slice of bread, cut off in secret. Mary got the sugar, with a piece of bread, the other three Shetlands, Fritz, Lady, and Miss, received at least a piece of bread from his tiny palm.

Karas Senior was already fully in the swing of the stable duties and all the rest of the bustling agitation. And this fine morning he had his day's work heaped up and running over, for they were wrapping up and loading things from the store-rooms. Everywhere Kerholec was giving orders, and he piled the work on Karas without mercy. The latter did not neglect to call for Vasek to come and help him. With Hans, Vasek finished the morning feeding of the ponies and then shot out like an arrow toward the menagerie to watch Captain Gambier's morning practice with the lions, tigers, and bears. But scarcely had he said hello to him and walked up to the cage when his father's "Vasek!" sounded.

Vasek was truly everywhere and nowhere. Only today did he begin to enjoy the circus to the fullest extent. He stopped at each cage to observe its inhabitants and then darted away like a trout so that he might not miss anything that was going on in the corridors or in the ring. Amid all the packing and moving the rehearsals went on as if nothing were happening; the director paraded his groups of stallions and mares and put them through their tricks, his wife led her Lipicans in a circle, Pablo Perreira rode in the High School on his Santos, the riding girls climbed onto the backs of their steeds in their work clothes, but with the same graceful motions as always, which they practiced for the enchantment of the now absent spectators, represented, however, from time to time by Vasek. The tumblers tried out their leaps and falls, and Léon Gambier had the great show cage hauled out, and there, to the growling roars of the big cats and the frequent cracking of the whip, he repeated with them their daily lesson.

Meanwhile the great Mr. Selnicki crossed the ring, passed all the rehearsals with an air of dignity and a complete lack of attention, came back with a glass and a bottle, and laid out both for himself in one of the boxes, where, with an air of languor, he now sat down to recover his strength. Shortly thereafter, at 9:30, something new turned up. Mr. Peter Berwitz arrived with the two dwarfs and presented them to Selnicki. From tomorrow afternoon on they would appear as the eleventh number on the program with three short dances. Mr. Selnicki rubbed his eyes with his hands.

"Have you got the music?" He turned and looked down from his towering height at tiny Herr Mittelhofer.

"Yes. And I have it with me, all orchestrated. Excellent compositions."

Frau Mittelhofer untied a package she was carrying and her little husband carefully took out a bundle of music.

"The first number is the *Lilac Waltz*, by Winterthal."

He handed the music to Mr. Selnicki, but instead of taking it the latter took a drink. When he had wiped his mustaches, he shook his head.

"I won't play it."

"Why not?" Herr Mittelhofer stopped and began to redden. "Excuse me, it's a beautiful composition, I spent a great deal of money for it, and now you don't want to play it?"

"No. You must dance something else."

"But we don't know anything else. We have been engaged to dance, in different costumes, a waltz, a minuet, and a country dance, and we'll dance the *Lilac Waltz*, known throughout the world as one of the most magnificent waltzes. I cannot understand how a man can be a conductor and refuse to play it."

"Well, here's one who refuses. I'm not going to play it."

"Mr. Director," Admiral Tom Thumb cried in his squeaky voice, "I am sorry that I must make a complaint at the very beginning. It is unheard of for the conductor in a circus to make a stand against the artists."

"Really, Selnicki," Berwitz said in a cautious and conciliatory voice, "have you any reason . . . ?"

"Of course I have."

"What is it?"

"The elephant!"

"What has the elephant got to do with it?"

"The elephant is the twelfth number on the program. And the piece to which he dances on the bottles is the *Lilac Waltz*. For the elephant I cannot play any other piece, and to play the same waltz twice running won't do!"

"Of course it won't do, you're right." Berwitz nodded. "I am very sorry, Herr Mittelhofer, but really it isn't our fault. You have bought the same waltz our elephant dances."

"But that is humiliating for us, too, Mr. Director!" both

pygmies cried in excitement. "Put us on some other place in the program!"

"I can't do that. You have Number Eleven just because it is the number before the elephant. It's a matter of production, you understand, the working out of the composition—the contrast, first pygmies and then a mastodon."

"Then part of our performance must be left out through your fault!"

"That won't do either. You've promised to do three dances, and besides, it's a question of the time. I can't throw away three minutes I've paid for, and paid dearly."

"What can we do, then?"

"What should we do, Selnicki?" The director confidently turned to the band leader, who in fact had already decided many similar problems.

"That's simple, Mr. Director. The gentleman and the lady will dance their waltz, but instead of the *Lilac Waltz* by Winterthal I'll play the *Estrella Waltz* by Goubin. It's the same to a hair, only the coda's different, and the gentleman and lady will soon get accustomed to it."

"Vasek!" resounded from the gate, and Vasek burst out of the dark gallery, flew past the dwarfs, and disappeared behind the curtain.

"That band leader is a grand fellow!" he thought; he rejoiced in his heart that Selnicki had settled those disgusting dwarfs so nobly.

His father sent him to the stable to Hans, and the latter had a pleasant surprise there for him: Mary was saddled and Hans permitted him to ride her out behind the buildings as long as he wished. Exultantly the boy availed himself of this permission. He circled the outside ring and then took Mary on beyond it, out among the wagons, now spurring the mare on to a trot, now stopping her to jump down, stroke her, remount, and ride off. It was not always riding by all the rules, often his stomach quaked within him and he felt that he would fall, but he did not fall, he always held on and was able to stop the pony.

The longer he stayed in the saddle, the more he seemed to himself to be a great lord. Already his childish playfulness was getting the better of him, and he wanted to call out from his horse at the people and give them orders about where to take things and what to load. Golly, if little Rosa could only see him now! This was something entirely different from that stupid game of the other day when he had chased her around in a circle and had cracked the whip on the chair.

He was roused from his playful dreams by a cry and an argument which came from the very end of the rows of wagons.

"Maybe somebody's having a fight," he said to himself at once, and was already spurring on Mary so that he wouldn't miss the sight. But he found something quite different; behind the last rows of the circus wagons there appeared a new one, resplendently blue, drawn by two horses. It drove up from the other side and its owner was loudly clamoring for the local wagons to make room for him so that he could get in.

"*Allah il Allah,*" cried the dark, bronze foreigner with a high fez on his curly head. "*Dove è il direttore? Il direttore! Padrone! Directeur! Patron! Principal! Mashallah!* Move over a little! *Anch' io Circus Umberto!*"

He stood beside his mares and gesticulated and cried, and the rear door of his blue wagon opened and from it rushed out a small black, curly-haired child, ragged as a gipsy, then another, a third, a fourth, a fifth, each one increasing in size. There were six or seven of them, and they all surrounded the man with the fez and they all shouted and chattered as he did. But already Kerholec was approaching.

"Achmed Roméo?" he called to the foreigner.

"*Si, si!*" nodded the newcomer, and raising both arms to heaven he cried with fervor, "*Roméo! Roméo! Achmed Roméo, fils de Mehmed Roméo, fils d'Ali Roméo, fils du grandpapa Roméo! Tous Roméo, tous Tunisiens, de Tunis de la Tunisie!*"

Kerholec called several people and ordered them to lift the backs of two of the wagons and drag them to one side. Thus a little street was formed which the blue wagon could now enter. The man with the fez turned round to his team and his flock of children, raised his whip triumphantly over his head, and cried anew:

"*Avanti, Roméos! Marchons vers la Victoire!*"

And turning back again, he moved the whip in his right hand like a drummer twirling his drumstick in time with the music and began his advance, the team with him, a cloud of black children to the right and left of the wagon, from inside of which there peered out an equally black and equally curly-headed woman with a baby in her arms.

Vasek understood that this was the new act they had said was to join them on the day before departure. Amid the mass of leaping children he caught sight of a boy who might be a year or two older than he was. In a flash he wanted to show this ragamuffin that he, Vasek, was at home in the circus, and was a great lord on his own land. So he headed Mary round, urged her on, and rode into the ring, which he now began to ride round with such an air of importance that it seemed that nothing else in Umberto's Circus mattered.

As soon as he had gone round the circle once in a trot the black boys immediately realized that it was a ring. Vasek heard their loud cry, and when he glanced round he saw the whole pack hurling itself at him. He pretended to pay no attention to them. But then something happened which he would never have expected in his whole life. The eldest boy, who had outstripped all the others, now ran straight at Vasek, shouting, wildly, rebounded, and jumped in one great vault over Vasek's head into the ring. Vasek did not realize that he had vaulted over him. He knew nothing of what had actually happened, for the frightened Mary had tossed him off her back and Vasek flew over her head.

When he collected himself, he was lying on the ground just as he had been the day before in front of the ogre's, and all around him the crowd of dirty children turned somersault after somersault with shrieks and exultations, stood on their heads and arms, and jumped over each other, while the eldest executed a series of continual rapid handsprings, and Mary, completely wild but still faithfully following the restraining circle of the ring, ran round and round.

Vasek felt that he must have really banged his head and back frightfully hard, and for a while it seemed that perhaps he might not be able to get up. But then with a jump the biggest of the gipsies stopped his handsprings, called out something, and ran over to Vasek, offering him his hand. The others rushed toward him from every side, fell on his arms and shoulders, and helped him to rise, felt his legs and arms and cried, "*Niente, niente!*" and the eldest pressed his hand and grinned at him with an irresistible smile and said, "*Scusi, scusi, excusez-moi, entschuldigen—io sono Paolo, Paolo Roméo, fils d'Achmed Roméo de Tunis!*"

Vasek was overwhelmed by this deluge of cries, good will, smiles, and foreign words, but when the other again and again pointed to himself and repeated, "Paolo, Paolo," he understood that this was the Moorish boy's name. Now he pressed his hand, and at once a word slipped out from him which he had already heard used many times in the circus: "*Bon . . . bon . . .*"

And Paolo laughed and embraced Vasek and the black brats all around them shouted with joy. Immediately Vasek felt the need to do something unusual to reinstate himself. Wishing himself luck, he called, "Mary, come here!" and the pony, who had calmed down meanwhile, actually turned at his call and came up to Vasek. The boys quieted down, Vasek mounted, and like a great lord looked down at Paolo, nodded to him calmly, and said in Czech, "You monkey, you!" With that he twitched Mary's bridle and trotted off to the stables.

He was not so calm as he appeared on the outside. Vasek had a great respect for adults, for their strength and skill, for the way they could surmount obstacles he himself could not begin to deal with. His constant promise to himself was: "When I grow up I'll do it like Father does, like Kerholec, like the Captain, like Hans." And at the same time he would watch to see how grownups did things, how they manipulated them, how they went to work. Their superiority he recognized as self-evident, but it rankled in him terribly when boys like himself triumphed over him.

Even though both horse and rider were small, Paolo's jump over them now irritated him vastly. Here was something in which he could not begin to compare with Paolo. And in general, the way those gipsy devils had jumped, turned handsprings, the way they had flown over each other—all of this was for Vasek something new and unheard-of. Vasek had been one of the most sprightly boys in the village, but what did he really know of gymnastics? He could knock over barrels, turn somersaults, stand on his hands, walk with his arms clasped under his legs like a frog, jump over curbstones, climb trees, run on top of logs, and jump from furrow to furrow.

At home that had been enough, but here evidently it was not. Now he must learn a great deal more if Paolo were not always to triumph over him. Again he recalled the jumps of the riders over the obstacles and the amazing tricks of the two men yesterday in the outside ring. Without question Paolo was already almost their equal, and unless Vasek wanted to let himself be outdone he must be able to do at least as well as Paolo. But how could he learn, where could he pick it all up? He felt that in this sort of thing even his father, his wonderful, all-wise father, could not help him.

Lost in thought, he was taking off Mary's saddle when he noticed that there were only three ponies in the enclosure.

"Hans, where is Miss?"

"Miss is working with Helen. Run over there and take a look."

Vasek ran through the stables and came out into the gallery. In the center of the yellow ring stood the director, with the whip in his hand, and around the edge ran Miss in a short trot. On her back she carried a small saddle and on it there stood a thin, pale little girl with long slender legs. She stood on her left leg and tried to keep her balance while bending her body forward with hands stretched out and with right leg raised at the back in a line exactly straight with her body. The pony trotted evenly beneath her, and with her left leg the girl had continually to compensate for the shaking of its back. There was a great risk of falling, but the girl's belt was fastened to a rope which ran from a pulley far aloft. The other end of the rope was held by the man who stood beside the director.

Three times the girl slowly bent forward and again straightened up. When she leaned forward the fourth time her exhausted leg quivered and slipped.

"Golly!" Vasek feared she might fall under the horse, but at that moment the man pulled hard on the rope, the girl in her short skirts flew aloft and sailed through the air to the center of the ring. There the director caught her and put her down on the ground.

"You must spring more, Helen." The director spoke sharply. "You stand on your left foot too stiffly. And turn your toes out more."

"Father, my back hurts me so," sighed Helen.

"I know," answered the director. "And for that reason we must repeat the trick until your body gets accustomed to it. So back on your horse. Run five steps and then . . . jump!"

Helen took her running start at an angle to the horse, bounded up, but did not reach the horse's back. The man pulled on the rope and in an arc she swung over toward her father.

"A quicker jump, girl, pick yourself up more! Again! We'll do the running start over again. Now . . . jump!"

Berwitz cracked his whip at that. But in the air Helen stumbled against the saddle and then floated back like a butterfly.

"Again. Running start, and now . . . jump!"

It didn't succeed. The six-year-old girl stood in front of her father and shrugged her shoulders with a guilty look. Vasek felt a tremendous sympathy for her.

"No help for it. Again. . . . Now!"

This time Berwitz did not even cry "jump!" Helen had lost the rhythm of the leap.

"Again. Run up, now. . . . Hop!"

Vasek almost cried out. He felt exactly how she ought to leap in order to reach the saddle, his legs even itched to run and jump themselves. But this did not help Helen. Three more times she ran with the rope on her back and three more times they tugged her away from a bad jump like a fisherman catching a fish.

"What's the matter with you today, Helen?" the director scolded.

"I . . . Father, I can't do it any more," whimpered the exhausted girl.

" 'I can't, I can't,' don't say 'I can't' to me!" ranted Berwitz. "One can always do what one wants to. That's enough for today."

And cracking his whip here and there, he turned and went

off to the gate. His assistant unfastened the rope from Helen, pulled it in from the pulley, and began to wind it up round his left arm and elbow. Vasek sprang out and caught Miss by the bridle. She stopped, tossed her head, and pawed with her hoofs.

"May I take Miss back to the stable for you, Helen?" he said to the girl, who was stretching herself.

"You're from here?"

"Yes. Me and my father, we're new here. But I know everything already and ride on Mary, and Hans has given Mary and Miss and Fritz and Lady to me to take care of."

"Then maybe we will ride together, because Fritz and Lady are one pair, and Mary and Miss the other. What's your name?"

"Václav Karas. But here they call me Vasek."

"Vasek. Is that a name?"

"I guess so."

"And you're coming along with us, Vasek?"

"Yes. In Number Eight. With Mr. Kerholec."

"Oh, with Karl. I and my mother and father are in Number One."

"I haven't any mother, but if she were still alive she would come with us and launder for us and hang the washing between the wagons the way they do here. Is it very hard to jump on a horse?"

"I used to be able to do it. But I balanced about twenty times on my left leg and I don't seem to have any strength left in it."

"But why don't you jump off with the right one?"

"I don't know. After five steps, then the jump always comes out on the left foot."

"Always?"

"Always."

"That's strange. I must give it a tryout. You'll be here at the performance?"

"No. I have to help Mother pack."

"And when your mother shows the white horses?"

"Then I'll be watching here by the curtain."

"Well, maybe we'll see each other then, maybe I'll have some free time and can come over. Good-bye, Helen. I must take Miss back."

"Good-bye, Vasek."

Helen hopped off and Vasek ran out with Miss like an old stable hand.

Behind the stable all sorts of boxes were lying about. Vasek kept thinking of the problem of jumping from the left foot on the fifth step. When he noticed the boxes, it occurred to him that with them he might try the jump on the horse.

"Come here, old man, you'll be Miss and I'll be the circus rider and jump on you. Come now, run and don't get scared. Pay attention, now, you thing, you . . . Miss; I'll take a run from five steps back, and now . . . jump!"

He bounded off from his left foot, flew up to the top of the empty box, which was lower than a pony, but he did not make it; he tripped on the box and it rolled over and he barked his shin badly.

"Golly, I knocked it that time. Well, old girl, get up. We must do it again. A quicker jump, and pick yourself up more. Again! We'll do the running start again! Five steps and now . . . jump!"

This time he flew up but did not stay there; the box swayed under his fall, then turned over, and he had scarcely time to jump away.

"Phooey, Miss, what a way to throw your hind legs out when you're carrying a circus rider! And you, sir, must spring more and turn your toes out. We'll do it again. Running start . . . now jump!"

Again he landed on the box and again flew off it.

"Golly, the brute always throws me! Stand still, Miss, stand still! Again. We'll do it again. Running start . . . now . . . jump!"

This time he flew up and the box swayed, but Vasek held it in balance with his spread legs.

"See, you brute. I'll tame you! Again! Do it again!"

He jumped off the box and again took a running start. Again it was successful. At last he was sure of himself; he jumped onto the box five times, eight times, and every time he held onto it. He noticed that each time he had bounded off with his left foot. Now he changed his stride and jumped off with his right foot. The left foot reached the box the first; he stretched out with the right one but it did not reach the box, and he fell off. Again he did it and again he fell off. A third time he jumped off with his right foot and held himself on only with the greatest effort.

"Hm, it really does seem better on the left foot. We'll try it again. Starting run . . . now!"

Vasek did not have enough technical inventiveness and experience to realize that the reason for this was that he was jumping from the left side, from the inside of the supposed ring. For him it was enough, as it was for most of the unscientifically trained circus performers, to know that you jumped better with your left foot, and from that day he always bounded off with his left foot. He flew several more times onto his wooden Miss, until his father called him for dinner.

Between the soup and the pudding he learned from Kerholec and the others who the inhabitants of the blue wagon were. Kerholec told them that Achmed Roméo was the descendant of a long line of Tunisian circus performers, whose Berber blood had long since mixed with Italian and French. With his children he did one of the best non-aerial tumbling acts in existence—a group appearance of father and sons with a rapid-fire outlay of acrobatics, in which even the three-year-old knew his tricks—how to stand, at least, on the top of the pyramid with one foot raised over his head.

"Say what you will," added old Malina to this, "what that Achmed does with his children is in the purest tradition of the good old school. It teaches a fellow how to do everything. It loosens up the joints in the body, makes the spine supple; a fellow like that can become anything . . ."

"Even a State Counsellor," added Vosátka with a grin.

"In the good old days," continued Malina without yielding, "it wasn't possible for anyone to get into the circus who didn't have that kind of training. It was called 'starting from scratch' when they twisted the joints of a four-year-old and bent his back. Then he could become a tamer or a ropewalker or a stupid clown, and if all those failed, he could still always earn a living as an acrobat. And the chief thing—nothing ever happened to any of them except by God's dispensation.

"I knew one fellow called Corini—his real name was Körner, but he worked as Corini—and he was trained from scratch. His favorite act was 'moving knot,' as he called it. He twisted himself up so that you couldn't see where his arms were, or where were his legs, as if someone had actually twisted and pulled him into a real Gordian knot. And then all of a sudden two arms would stick out from some place in the bundle and the knot would start to move. It had its rear on top, its head somewhere below, its legs on its back—it was terrible to watch it.

"And after some years this Corini took to being an animal-tamer as well and bought himself two tigers. Siberians, the fiercest kind. He went into their cage and trained them to sit up on stands like a pair of wooden soldiers. I myself told him, 'Körner, don't be a fool, a Siberian tiger isn't made for saluting.' But he answered that he wouldn't give up, even if it took him five years. So he drove them for maybe half a year, just to get them to get up on the stand and be soldiers, and all the time he whipped them and jabbed them, of course; it wasn't done any other way than that in the old days—not with caresses, the way Gambier does here.

"And those tigers were full of spleen, they kept spluttering bile at him. I myself would say, 'Lord in Heaven, someday there'll be hash out of Corini and a rug out of those tigers.' But he boasted to me; where did I get such ideas? he said. They were already raising their paws up to their chests, and one day they would really salute properly.

"But what I expected happened: the bigger one jumped at him one day. Corini noticed him when he crouched for the spring, and dodged. But then the other one got mad, stopped being a statue, and crawled down from his stand to attack Corini from the other side. Corini found himself between the two of them and at that moment dropped his whip and fork.

"We all looked on thunderstruck, but suddenly something stirred and Corini made himself into a moving knot. The tigers were so frightened at the unknown thing which suddenly appeared there that they jumped round the cage over each other, almost stumbled, and at last—hop!—up on the pedestals to make statues, and salute with the right paw, and the knot marched round in front of them as if on parade."

"You have enriched us, Comrade Malina," observed Bures, cutting a *knedle,* "with a truly inspiring narrative. So then this jumper of yours lived to a ripe old age?"

"Not a bit of it," answered Malina in the same calm voice. "Shortly after that business with the tigers Körner jumped off the box of one of the wagons, slipped, and the wagon wheel went over his right leg. It was broken at the shin. The doctors fixed it for him, but badly, so they broke it over again. It got infected and Corini swelled up all over and died. But I think I told you that a fellow like that could do anything except by God's dispensation—that you have to be careful of."

"All the same it's true"—Kerholec contributed his bit—"that it's a good thing if a boy can be trained from childhood for jumping and falling. If I were in your place, Anton, I'd really do something about Vasek. The thing for him is not to lose his chance. He can always be a staker, pound in pegs and pull ropes, but Vasek can be something more, the way he goes at everything. And it's a father's main responsibility to give a boy his chance. And the boy's job is not to miss it."

"General Kerholec speaks like the Bible," Vosátka put in, "like the most complete one, the Bible of the Royal British Bible Society, approved by the author himself."

"You fellows are all very kind," answered Karas hesitantly, "and I won't forget you all my life—how Kerholec here pulled me out of the soup and how you others took me and Vasek in. But it's not me who's the important one in all this. I've already got it figured out in my head that I'm with Kerholec's gang now instead of Milner's.

"It isn't quite the same to me, I'm not going to try to pull the wool over your eyes about that. Not one of you knows what a joy it is to take a well-made brick in your hand, weigh it, and set it in place straight with the others, and then stand and look at how a building is growing out of your work. Karlík Kerholec told me what a marvelous thing it is to put up a tent in a couple of minutes so that within two hours there can be a performance there, and then to take it down in a couple more minutes. I believe that's possible, and I'm looking forward to seeing it, but, if you'll forgive me, for me a trade will stay a trade, and I will always be jealous of other masons when I see them raising the walls of a house and doing the kind of building work which lasts."

After a pause Karas began again. "I'm only saying, though, that it's not a question of me. It's a question of what will happen to Vasek in the future. This change may alter his whole life. And this is my responsibility—should I, can I, dare I make him into a circus man? You see, the child doesn't belong just to me, he's Márinka's, too, and looking at it as I do, it doesn't matter whether his mother's dead or not, she has a claim to the child, and that claim lies on my conscience.

"It's true we never really talked about what the boy would be. And what could he have become, for that matter?—a mason like his father, with a hut for a home in winter when works stop. And now I'm worried; how can I go back someday to the village and say to my neighbors, 'Forgive me, people, but I've joined the circus and I've made an acrobat out of Vasek'? It's a very hard decision for me to make, I can't make it, my friends—forgive me, I really can't straight off. If this were only some kind of business, some trade . . ."

"My good friends".—Bures hastened to take the floor to obviate any sort of biting remark from Vosátka—"allow me in your names to state to our dear countryman that we fully realize the seriousness with which he accepts his paternal duties. The poet has it that that man is happy who has grown but one rose for his country, one apple tree. But dear Sumavian, do not forget that the things which bother you the most are actually prejudices, the stupid prejudices of human society against those who consciously reject their false environment.

"You speak of your native village and your neighbors there. But your mountain village can support only a handful of its children, and the rest must seek their bread in foreign lands. So far as they can they do this by practicing their trades. A trade has a golden foundation, but often that foundation is made of gold wires like a sieve, and much good will it do you. What do you do then, worthy compatriot? The only thing that's left to you: you hang your trade up on the hatrack. You play your trumpet for a living, and that, sir, is no longer any sort of trade, but an art the same as any art for which Vasek may be trained.

"Consider, friend, that we aren't advising you to make Vasek into a vagabond and a scamp; on the contrary, we advise you to have him trained properly, trained to master his art, for then he will be sure of not becoming a second-rate worker or a vagabond. And even if the experience should turn out badly he can always throw off the harness and go back to building. He won't waste the time. I'll teach him to read, write, and count, and as for the rest, he'll learn more than in any school."

"In my opinion, Anton," said Kerholec, "you'll get on better here with us than at building. And that's just the reason why you are here with us now. However, you said rightly that it's not a question of yourself, or of us. We're still only subordinates, while Vasek, if he began to train now, wouldn't have to be a manual worker like we are and could have a much finer life than we have. He could be a gentleman like Captain Gambier or Pablo Perreira or maybe even like Director Berwitz. The way up is open to him, and to that, believe me, even your late wife wouldn't have any objection."

"Worthy State Counsellor," Vosátka suddenly spoke up, "you are pleased to come to a decision about the future coronation and you still have not inquired of the young Prince if he's at all interested in the crown. I say, Vasek, which—the village or the circus?"

"The village?" Vasek grinned. "You can't compare them, even."

"But your father thinks that you should stay in your village and be an apprentice to a bricklayer."

"Father!" Vasek's gaze fixed itself on Antonín Karas's eyes. And Karas Senior again saw how the boy's pupils sharpened, as they did whenever he wanted anything badly. "You really don't think that! I have a pony already and Mr. Gambier promised me that I could play with the lion cubs and Mr. Arr-Shehir promised that he would give me a ride on the elephant. Please, Father, say we'll stay in the circus!"

Vasek stretched out his arms to his father and Karas softened. He caressed the boy with his rough hands.

123

"And you really want to stay with the circus all your life, Vasek?"

"More than anything, Father!"

"And do you want to learn to jump and ride and do all those tricks you've seen?"

"Yes, I do want to, Father," and Vasek's eyes shone. "To ride on Mary is nothing. That I can already do. And Mary's a pony. But to be able to jump on a big horse at full speed . . . and jump over it and the rider . . . and do the other things those black boys do—golly, if I only knew that, then I'd show them how!"

"But do you know that the training is hard and you have to practice a lot and that it'll make you hurt all over?"

"Let it! If I wanted to go to the woods to cut trees, the way the other boys do when they grow up, that would be hard work, too. And here I have ponies and lions and tigers and an elephant and I'll ride in a house on wheels."

Karas felt that his objections were growing weaker in the face of this childish eagerness. Vasek was so ardent, and the older circus men were looking at him with such favor.

"But Vasek, consider, what will your godfather say if you come back home a circus man?"

"What could he say! He'd stare perhaps, when I rode into the village, maybe on Santos, and Santos danced on his hind legs on the square. They'd all run there, the Sembers, the Blahas, the Cikharts, the Zelenkas, all of them, and roll their eyes at the most beautiful horse they'd ever seen. Or I'd come on the elephant, maybe, and say something to him . . . and the elephant would pick a rose and hand it to Nanny Cerha. And I'd jump off him and leap around so that all the boys would really stare. The big thing is that I must know how to jump. I've already jumped onto a box and pretended that it was Mary, but that's not much, I must know more than that. Let it hurt!"

"Bravo, boy!" Vosátka nodded approvingly at him. "Spit on your palm, and away with drudgery. Marquis de Karas, you mustn't thwart this descendant of yours, he may add a new brilliance to your shabby crest."

"So you liked the Roméo boys?" asked Kerholec.

"No, I didn't," Vasek answered confidently and as an equal

among equals. "They're such little runts that a man could knock five of them down with one blow. But they can jump like monkeys. And I'm going to learn to jump too, and I'll jump on a horse's back without bending my knees—maybe on Pompon's."

"Vasek"—Karas spoke with emotion—"God bless you! I won't interfere with your happiness."

"I think," Kerholec said to Karas, "that you should have a talk with Achmed Roméo. He'll be with us for at least a year and he could put Vasek to work. But maybe it'd be better if I arranged it with the Berber. You wouldn't know what exactly to ask for."

And that same afternoon Kerholec took Vasek and together they went over to the blue wagon. Mr. Roméo greeted them with extreme politeness, for he already knew that it was important to get on well with Kerholec if one meant to be happy in Umberto's Circus. Roméo lifted Vasek up and in a silence unusual for him felt over the muscles of his legs and arms thoroughly. Then he twisted his limbs and his body this way and that; Vasek almost cried out in pain as the gipsy tried to find out how far he could bend Vasek's arms and spine.

The outcome was that Roméo promised Kerholec that he would be glad to undertake the training of his protégé daily, and that he'd make him into a skilled acrobat. Vasek was not quite at his ease during their discussion. He felt that he would no longer be under his father's simple, rough, but good-natured care, but rather under the command of a half-savage tyrant who laughed at pain and would do anything to achieve his ends. But Vasek was now resolved to triumph over Paolo, to triumph over everyone, and even to undergo torture to defeat them.

That afternoon when he ran to the gate during the horses' act and found Helen there, he had good news for her.

"When you have to jump on your pony next time and it doesn't go right, don't worry about it. I'm an acrobat now and I'll show you how to do it."

This gala farewell performance was no less perfect than any other one, and none of the spectators would have been able to guess that behind the scenes a great organized departure was in progress, and that after every second or third number some part of the personnel and animals, now freed from their duties, was moving off. Only the stables remained intact, so that the noble guests might inspect them during the intermission. Director Berwitz walked through them in his Persian uniform and reminded the grooms of the procedure for their departure after the intermission. Meanwhile his glance had fallen on the enclosure with its four Shetland ponies.

"Who's taking the ponies?" he asked Hans.

"Vasek," answered Hans. "He'll ride on Mary and the other three will go with him. Anyway, I'll ride along beside Vasek and keep an eye on him."

"Vasek, Vasek," reflected the director, "who is Vasek? That's a name I've never heard." But he did not wish to question Hans, since if he did it might look as if Director Berwitz didn't know his own personnel. A little later they hauled the lion cage out of the ring and Captain Gambier returned from his curtain call. An intermission number by the clowns filled out this interval of preparations.

"The lion cubs are doing well," Gambier said to the director. "Madame tells me that they're taking to the world and are feeding well."

"Anna's giving herself a lot of trouble with them," replied the director. "Last night she hardly slept a wink; she had them in bed with her and the cubs were restless all night. If we succeed with them they'll be our first lion cubs. Up till now we've had no luck with them."

"Let's hope so, Director, let's hope so. When they get a bit stronger, you might send someone out with them among the crowd during the intermission to show them and pass the hat. The people will want to pet them and the money will pay for their upkeep. The best one for that job would be Vasek. Vasek's clever, and he won't be afraid. He's with me at every feeding."

"Vasek, of course, Vasek. That's a good idea. Thank you, Captain." So Vasek isn't a groom?

After his appearance Berwitz hurried straight to his wagon, the beautiful, spacious Number One, to change his clothes without delay. There Helen and her Aunt Elisa were packing some things. At once Helen raised her head.

"From now on, Father, when my jumping onto the horse

doesn't go right, don't get cross with me. Vasek's promised me that he'll teach me how to do it."

"Who? Vasek?"

"Yes."

"Oh, Vasek's trying his best." Frau von Hammerschmidt joined in the conversation. "I told myself at the very first that he would be a wonderful acquisition."

The doors opened, Anna had returned from the show.

"Oh, before I forget it"—Berwitz turned to her as soon as he noticed her—"Gambier's had a good idea, to show the lion cubs round as soon as their eyes open."

"Yes, he's told me already. Vasek will go round with them."

Peter Berwitz flushed and had to control himself to keep from pounding on the table. The whole circus and his whole family seemed to be wild about some fellow named Vasek and he, the proprietor, had never heard of him! However, he said nothing, but threw on his everyday clothes, burst out of the house, and headed toward Number Two. The second wagon was the traveling office of the bookkeeper of the business, the kingdom of his cousin Steenhouwer.

"Frans," Berwitz shouted at the bookkeeper, "who is Vasek?"

Steenhouwer took off his glasses and looked at him blankly.

"What do you want, Peter?"

"Tell me for God's sake who in our personnel is called Vasek, and what he is!"

"Vasek, Vasek? I don't remember the name."

To make sure, Steenhouwer pulled out the personnel list and opened it at the letter W.

"No . . . I see no Vasek."

"This is magnificent!" Peter Berwitz rolled his eyes. "This has never happened to me yet. A groom, an animal-tamer, an acrobat, and God knows what all, and I've never heard of him!"

Steenhouwer looked at him with perplexity. Berwitz turned and went out without taking leave. From the stable behind the menagerie the elephant Bingo came swaying along, his master Arr-Shehir in a white turban sitting on his head.

"Arr-Shehir! Have you seen Vasek?" called Berwitz as the elephant slowly passed him.

"Vasek? Yes!" nodded the Hindu with a smile. "There's Vasek."

And he pointed toward the main building. Berwitz rushed inside through the rear door. The performance was already over and the tiers of seats were empty and dark. Above over the yellow target of the ring the sun's rays gleamed in bright streaks through which specks of dust were floating.

"Vasek!" thundered the director.

It was the only method of getting to know this mysterious man.

"Vasek!" rumbled through the empty space. Berwitz went out into the center of the ring.

"Vasek!"

The curtain by the gate moved a little and a small boy with his cap over one ear rushed into the ring. Seeing the director, he stopped three paces away from him in the sawdust and saluted.

"Are you Vasek?"

Peter Berwitz, Emir of the White Horses and Colonel of the Persian Cavalry, Turkish Pasha and Inspector of the Sultan's Imperial Stables, director and proprietor of Umberto's Circus, lord of his stables and menagerie, stood here with his orders pinned on his well-pressed coat, and before him stood this tiny blob of humanity with its quick, attentive eyes.

"So you are Vasek?"

"Yes, Mr. Director."

Berwitz now remembered that in the last two days he had seen this boy darting here and there among the stables or passageways.

"And what do you do?"

"Everything, please, I'm given to do."

"Oh! And what are you?"

"Nothing yet. But I'm going to be someday."

"Hm, and what are you going to be?"

"Everything. I'm going to ride the horses and be a jumper and I'll tame tigers and parade the horses and do everything."

"But wait—how about the elephant? Don't you want to be an elephant-trainer too?"

"Oh, Bingo likes me, and if Mr. Arr-Shehir can't appear in his act I'll bring Bingo out and eat dinner with him."

"Well, one lives and learns!" the all-powerful Peter Berwitz cried, much amused. "And how about director—aren't you going to be one?"

"Yes."

"Director of a circus like Umberto's?"

"A bigger one. If I were director I'd have eight elephants and a gigantic cage with lions and tigers and lots and lots of horses . . ."

"Then we ought to be afraid of you?" Berwitz was already laughing heartily.

Vasek grinned and felt that he might concede something.

"You needn't be, I'll hire all of you—you, Mr. Director, and Frau Hammerschmidt and Helen and Captain Gambier and Hans . . . and Mr. Selnicki here, too."

The giant conductor had meanwhile appeared from the darkness and for the first time in his life was paying close attention to a performance in the ring.

"Then we'll all be all right in your circus, Vasek?" the director's voice resumed.

"Hm!" Vasek nodded with his mouth drawn up into a perfect circle, and he looked at the director with that roguish look which had already won him so many friends.

"Vasek!" sounded from the stables.

"Mr. Hans is calling me . . ."

"Well, if Mr. Hans is calling you I must let you go. So long!"

Vasek saluted and darted off. Berwitz turned round, his face wreathed in smiles, to Selnicki.

"Did you hear that boy? He's going to be worth watching, I think!"

"I've noticed him too, by now, Mr. Director."

"And whose boy is he, actually?"

"Kerholec hired a new staker—Karas is his name. He can't read music, but he's a real harmonist; you could pick him out among fifty. He can play a tune that sounds like a woman's caress. That's a Czech musician for you. And this Vasek is his boy."

"H'm, I see." Berwitz nodded his head. "At last I know something about him."

"I noticed him on Mary; the boy's crazy about her. And I'll tell you something, Mr. Director. This fellow Vasek on Mary and your Helen on Miss would be a better introduction for Bingo than those stuck-up dwarfs. If those children on ponies were to lead in the elephant, it would be a real contrast! I would play the *Gulliver among the Lilliputians* intermezzo with bassoon and piccolo solo—Director, it'd be worth a bottle of Rhine wine to you!"

"Selnicki, you shall have it. You're the only one who ever has any ideas. Man, where would you be by now if you were a bit more interested in the circus than in your everlasting drinking? I can't stand those dwarfs either. People like that are for side shows and fairs, and not for a high-toned circus like ours. I thought what we had arranged was good, but this would be much, much better. So long, Selnicki, I must find Hans at once and tell him to train the boy as soon as possible. Hans!"

"Hans has gone already, sir," Kerholec announced when Berwitz bounded behind the curtain. "Shall I take a message for him?"

"No, it's not necessary," replied Berwitz. "I'll see to it myself."

He pulled a pencil out of his pocket, thrust out his left cuff, and wrote on it:

"Helen—Vasek, Bingo, Selnicki, Johannisberger."

The last of the riding horses, covered with blankets to keep them from being chilled, were emerging from the stables. The menagerie was already shrouded in darkness; only old Harwey still limped about there, poking his stick into the different piles of rubbish to see if there was anything valuable left about. The open space behind the main buildings was almost empty. Most of the wagons had disappeared. Now about thirty horses stood there, tossing their heads and pawing the ground impatiently. The grooms and stable hands harnessed them in teams of four, climbed into the saddles themselves, and the beautiful cavalcade of graceful, temperamental animals started off at an easy trot. Then the first of the rear wagons moved out, drawn by a pair of horses, and slowly swayed along behind its team. The other wagons were already hitched up and the drivers stood by their horses.

The ones that remained carried the brains of Umberto's Circus: the director's family in Number One, the bookkeeping office in

Two, Three the cashier's and the wardrobe mistress's, Four with Harwey and his daughter, with the most valuable props, Five with Conductor Selnicki, the clown Hamilton, and the music. Next Kerholec's Eight stood in line, but there was no one in it. Karas was standing beside the driver waiting to sit on the small coachman's box with him. Meanwhile he held Kerholec's riding horse, for he and Harwey were inspecting all the rooms to make sure that they had not forgotten anything. The rest of the gang had already gone with the horses or the animal wagons and Vasek had ridden off on little Mary by the side of the coachman Hans.

Now Number One started out; then Two, Three, and Five, then Harwey climbed into his wagon, carrying two brooms he had found and a string of imitation pearls, and Number Four set off. Then Kerholec turned up with the permanent local watchman, slammed the gates of the building, locked them, and gave the bunch of keys to the watchman as the latter wished him a safe journey.

"All in order!" Kerholec called to Karas, taking the horse from him. "Drive after the rest, and when you're on the highway pass them, so that you're ahead of them all by tomorrow morning. So long!"

Kerholec's horse bounded off and after a few paces was lost in the distance. Karas climbed up beside the driver. When the horses started out he crossed himself involuntarily. At that moment he felt very sad. They had entered the crowded Hamburg streets, and caught up Harwey's wagon; swaying along the cobblestone pavement and out of the city, onto the rather muddy road, into the growing darkness, on to unknown lands, the last link of the long caravan of people, animals, and wagons slowly crawled along through the moist breeze, carrying with it so many hopes for good luck and success.

What was the name of the town where they were going for the night?

"Buxtehude," answered the driver beside him.

Buxtehude, Buxtehude, Buxtehude, Buxtehude. A strange name, like an enchantment. Secret and mysterious like everything which lay ahead. Buxtehude, Buxtehude. The shoes of the horses clattered out the name, the wagons rattled it. Everything was filled with its mystery: Buxtehude.

Antonín Karas sat back and gazed into the moist darkness. Already the birches, those strong and lissom birches, had vanished from the highway: nothing could be seen, nothing could be distinguished, but the lighted window in Harwey's wagon . . . Buxtehude, Buxtehude.

Remembrance after remembrance was born in him at the strange sound of the strange name, and each one whispered its message to him in the musical dialect of his homeland. How would Vasek be getting on on the pygmy up there? And what would his mamma say, Márinka? . . . Maybe she'd disapprove. . . . . No, for she was dead and her bones were laid in the soil of Horní Snezná, under the larch tree . . . and you, her man, were going to some Buxtehude or other. . . . Well, what must be, must, it couldn't be any other way . . . there was no gain in troubling your heart. You belonged to the world, and the world belonged to God.

PART TWO

CHAPTER ONE

On the road there were no important changes. But now a stranger turned up, whom both Karases saw for the first time that winter. His name was Gaudeamus. It was a strange name, but the circus people had no suspicion that it meant anything. Rather it was a bother for them to remember a word so foreign-sounding; Malina, who had known him the longest, called him simply Gaydamosh or the Runner. Gaudeamus had slender legs like a stork's, and his occupation was actually to be the legs of Umberto's Circus. A few weeks before the circus started out on the road Gaudeamus and one assistant would ride away in a wide landau to go over the route Director Berwitz had roughly traced out for them.

His task was to ensure the possibility of the circus's existence. It was his job to secure all the necessary licenses from the local authorities, make sure of a location, and circulate the first publicity. Gaudeamus had to know how to talk to town mayors, county officials, chiefs of police, to captains of the gendarmeries, owners of estates, and garrison officers, sometimes even to State Counsellors and Ministers. On his performance, on his fluency, the readiness of his arguments and his ability to find someone to put in a word for him, depended the circus's main success, the problem of choosing a consecutive route along which they would never be forced to make a detour and where in each city they might obtain the greatest number of successful performances possible.

Gaudeamus had to make an appraisal of each city, and of how it could spend, in order that Umberto's Circus might gain the greatest financial success possible. And Gaudeamus, after he had arranged everything, had then to visit the editors of newspapers, and with their help inspire the public's mood, and arrange for the hanging of posters, and often even for the delivery of provisions for all the circus and menagerie animals. His position was quite unusual; he ensured work and security for something which he himself might never have seen had it not been for its winter station in Hamburg. But even that was no time of rest for him, for in winter he went by train to certain important places to look over and prepare the ground for the future, especially when the circus made guest trips abroad. From spring until winter only the post and the telegraph kept him in touch with Umberto's Circus.

For these duties Gaudeamus needed and possessed not only unusual abilities, but also a real passion for the work. Tall and slender, with a fine beard parted in the middle, and a smoothly combed wave of glistening hair on his forehead, with the quick glance of his eyes and the constant smile on his lips, Gaudeamus well knew how to win people over. In exceptional cases, when all his personal charms and his eloquence failed, he would reach into a special compartment in the wallet he carried in his breast pocket and take out a visiting card which only a very few had ever seen, a visiting card with the brief text: "Knight and Baron von Schönstein." It was the last magical key which always opened the resisting lock.

The visiting card was not forged. Baron Max von Schönstein had served in the Austrian lancers, and ever since his lieutenant's days he had had to sweat out his service in the most Godforsaken, most deserted garrisons at Halicz and Bucovina. He, the handsome Max, who had started by dazzling the society of Vienna and had ridden haughtily on morning outings in the Prater. But one tiny mischance had upset his career: he had been present at the time when the "madcap Archduke" had jumped with his horse over a coffin carried in a poor country funeral beyond Brigittenau. His Majesty was enraged when his aide-de-camp brought him the news of the unpleasant incident, which had stirred up the people.

The wrath of the All Highest fell on Max as well; he was ordered at once off to Stanislawow. Now the wildest part of his life began: mad drinking bouts, gambling, insane rides over the country, vain trips to the capital to intervene for himself, and journeys back with inevitable hangovers, affairs with women, affairs which often bordered on abduction and other offenses in the criminal code. His service record was therefore rather spotted on the social side, but a soldier Baron von Schönstein was, it could not be denied, and a phenomenal rider; he always rode off from races with the laurels of victory. In this respect he was the pride of his regiment, which could always rely on him. These stanch abilities, working with a certain opposition element in the cavalry which quietly opposed the Emperor's decisions, ensured the handsome Max's progress in spite of all disfavor.

But it was a different matter when it came to his estate. He had inherited some millions in silver, but the greater part of this had been pledged long ago to pay the pack of bloodsuckers who had made possible the Baron's inordinate munificence. There were events about which whole legends were told; one of them even concerned Umberto's Circus, which Second Lieutenant Baron von Schönstein had hired in Lwow for a special trip to Kolomea, there to regale it for four days with food and drink.

It was after this event that the mishap in Mezöhegyes occurred. During a jump over an Irish bench the stallion Kolibri fell under him and broke its spine, and Schönstein was so badly crushed that for eight weeks they bandaged and plastered him in hospital. When he limped out he was a semi-invalid who could no longer ride a racing horse. They assigned him to office duty, which he considered an ineradicable humiliation. The next few years were bitter ones for him. His family estate had shrunk to nothing; his fame as a rider had disappeared; only his work was left.

In the embittered Baron there slowly began to awaken those talents with which his grandfather had won his barony. All kinds of rumors began to circulate concerning his purchases, but Baron von Schönstein remained that same handsome Max before whose shining, irresistible smile society forgave everything. Only he himself was cruelly dissatisfied beneath his alluring exterior; his occupation did not answer either to his ambition or to his restless blood, and besides that he felt that unless he could soon extricate himself from the financial machinations he had started, he would finish his career very shamefully.

At this time the young Berwitz came to see him. He had come to visit the well-known Maecenas to ask if it might not be possible for him to arrange another special performance for a garrison, and he found the noble officer on the brink of complete ruin. They sat and talked over several bottles of wine like gentlemen, but Berwitz, with his experienced eye, saw through the new state of affairs and did not hesitate to offer the noble a way to extricate himself. And Baron von Schönstein, feeling that the waves were about to close over his head, accepted it.

Within a couple of weeks he was installed in the bookkeeper's wagon of Umberto's Circus, and within a year he rode out in his landau into the world, equipped with his perfect manners and his worldly experience; and everyone who had anything to do with him felt that the charming Mr. Gaudeamus was wrapped in mystery. And the better did his efforts succeed, the better succeeded Umberto's Circus. Peter Berwitz rubbed his hands together; again he had recognized a useful man.

So the mysterious Gaudeamus was the first cog in the wheel of the travels of Umberto's Circus. The second was in the care of Karel Kerholec. He was the first to arrive at the spot Gaudeamus had secured, and as superintendent it was he who determined with his experienced eye on which side would be the circus's entrance and where its "behind-the-scenes" should lie. Soon with ropes and pegs he was tracing out on the ground the central circle of the ring, then the edge of the main tent, then the flat plan of the four-cornered front tent and the covered passageways behind which led to the stables and the animal tents.

Meanwhile the first wagons of workers and supplies had already driven up, the gangs of workmen had jumped out, and each one had plunged into its own special work. Four men with Kerholec's wagon began work with sledge hammers and iron stakes. Originally each one of them had pounded only one stake at a time, but Kerholec had hit on the idea that the work would go more quickly and the stakes could be larger and more secure if all four would drive in one stake together. For these men, most of whom came from the country, the rough, farmlike work changed into the gay work rhythm of hand threshing. Old Malina was the first to strike, and after him the three hammers of the others flew down on to the flat head of the "anchor": ramtadata ramtadata, the blows fell in 4:4 time and the iron drove into the ground as if into butter.

And then farther on a couple of yards to the second stake,

138

which lay already prepared in its place, and again the four-beat measure of this dance of the hammers whirled through the air. So in quick tempo they went around the larger, outside circle and stepped in toward the center a few paces, where they began to drive in the slanted poles which carried the canvas side wall.

In the meantime a second gang was digging a hole for the heel of the mast. This was the center pole on which the roof of the tent and the crosspoles were carried. In the circuses of those days it was the only one, and raised itself from the very center of the ring. Only years later did they come to the idea that there was no need to bury it in a hole, that it could simply stand on flat ground and be held in balance by four crossropes. And still later they discovered the possibility of using two slanting masts with a crossbeam, which held the whole tent on hooks and left the ring completely open below.

When the mast lay out on the ground, ready to be hoisted, Kerholec's most responsible task had arrived. He entrusted to no one else the fastening of the pulley ropes to the upper end. These were tied with a pair of knots on which depended the lives of all the people in the tent. Then the mast could be raised, the first four crossropes firmly attached to it at right angles, and the mast anchored by four slanting pegs driven into the ground.

Another gang quickly rolled out a star-shaped net of ropes, tied at one end to the iron stakes, at the other coming together at the top of the mast. And then everyone rushed to the wide sheets of canvas, which they unrolled on the ground and fastened to the main ropes.

Finally, Superintendent Kerholec drew out a whistle, with both arms clasped the pulley ropes, and with one short blast after another set the tempo to which the tent began to rise off the ground like a giant gray mushroom. Then it was necessary to fasten the pieces of canvas onto the side poles, and to straighten out the caved-in and slackened sections of the roof with slanting beams.

By now the wagons with the equipment for the inside were driving up, and the arc-shaped rails and tiers of seats were bundled out and installed in the tent in exact order, number by number, speedily forming a circular arena. The rails had still not been assembled or the round rim in the center, filled with sawdust or sand from the countless sacks, when at Kerholec's command they were already dragging up the covered gallery for the horses, with its long troughs, and were leading up the horses and standing them in the same order to which they were accustomed.

And the wagons with the cages now lined up together, some likewise sheltered by a canvas top, others in the open, and behind them stood the wagons of the personnel: first of all the big wagon of the director, and then the others, some of which were nothing more than little aged houses mounted on wheels. When circumstances were favorable and there were no hindrances, and if all the men could be used, Kerholec was able to erect and ready the main tent and the neighboring side tents in two hours and a half; needless to say, for this everyone had to pitch in and do his utmost.

Things went more slowly in the larger cities, where Berwitz loved to stage a colorful parade on their entry. Then only part of the working force could be used to put up the circus; the others had to stay with the animals. Somewhere on the edge of the suburbs the cavalcade would form, the men and women would put on their most brilliant costumes and then ride into the city to the sound of trumpets and the march music of their own band, most of them mounted on their resplendent horses. The wild beasts were dragged along in show cages, while the other animals were led in the procession. Finally came the giant Bingo, whose monumental appearance formed the climax of this strident and picturesque form of publicity, so dearly loved by all.

The way taken through the city was an extremely circuitous one, so that along its course as many spectators might be lured out as possible. And hardly had the procession arrived at the tents when the first to climb off her horse was the fat Frau von Hammerschmidt, who slipped down from her brown mare Admira, and picking up the heavy train of her riding dress, too much in a hurry to take off her little rococo hat or to pay any attention to the fact that in the summer heat the sweat was pouring and streaking across the great quantity of rice flour on her cheeks, she rushed off to her cashier's wagon to open the window for the advance sales and hang out her price list.

For it was her solemn duty to drum up trade as soon as possible and to sell, sell, sell—with the exception of one single instance: if an old woman ever appeared at the window as the first customer, Frau von Hammerschmidt had strict orders not to sell her a ticket, but to put her off with any excuse that she could think of. As firmly as Berwitz himself Frau von Hammerschmidt believed that such negligence on her part would bring to pass some unforeseeable misfortune that very day.

As for all the rest, they had scarcely thrown off their costumes when they had to rush to the tents, the majority to the menagerie. Gambier in particular had the natural responsibility to make sure that his wild protégés were quieted down in time. Although the beasts were used to the discomfort of the journey, it would often happen nevertheless that some big cat or other would grow nervous at the noise or the unexpected jolting, and it was very necessary that when they stopped they saw only the order to which they were accustomed and heard only the calming and tender murmur of their giant tamer.

The riding horses were relatively the best-contented on the road, for it gave them a welcome opportunity to move at a slow trot; and by now they well knew that on the road they would receive extra oats and hay and even a portion of beans and salted carrots.

The artists who did not work with the animals gravitated straight to the main tent. First of all, of course, arrived the two men from the Barengo Trio of aerial acrobats and trapeze artists. At that time in Europe these people were still not protected by a safety net, and their beautiful, graceful performance high in the air was a daily game with death. Frasquito Barengo was a broad-shouldered Spaniard from Córdoba whose cheeks and chin took on a blue tint after shaving. His wife Concha was a dazzling dark-browed beauty whom Frasquito constantly watched over with his silent, gloomy glance.

If it were ever necessary to expand the program, Frasquito Barengo could improvise a few chords on his guitar as a prelude, until there flowed out the rhythm of some popular allegro, garottina, or folias, to which Concha then danced with briskly whirling castanets in her hands, a yellow mantilla over her bright-red bolero, a great comb in her hair, twirling and slinking like a young tiger. And Frasquito stood behind her, motionless, brooding like a carved statue. His partner on the trapeze was the slender Marseillan, Hector Laribeau, in life a great braggart, but on the trapeze above cool and intent, with a feeling for the hundredth part of a second. *"Vanidoso, mas prudente,"* the conceited but cautious Frasquito would say of him with respect, and he especially praised Laribeau's firm, muscular hand with its secure grip.

On other occasions, departing for the moment from his silent meditation, a product of the Moorish blood which had blended with his Spanish character, he would say that "Hector has a sense for grace." And this was perhaps the greatest thing which he could say in his praise, for in Barengo's eyes all the splendor of the kingly art of the trapeze was contained in its gracefulness. He would also say that this was the only condition under which one could create that height of artificial beauty, the arabesque.

These two now appeared first at the top of the main pole to examine with care every rope of their trapeze, every beam, every hook, every ring, every piece of rope and every knot, to make sure that nothing should catch, or was beginning to rot or be worn through. Often Laribeau felt like saving himself this journey upward, but Barengo would not give in. "The Devil always has something to do at the altar and on the trapeze," he would say as he pulled himself up the rope ladder first.

But the ring also attracted those others who did not gamble their lives in the air above the spectators. In the circus every artist carried his skin to market in one way or another and if he did not stake his life, he staked at least the soundness of his limbs and his personal success. Everything might be jeopardized through some oversight or other, and so each took care that his apparatus was in readiness and in order. And when there was a little time left over they would try to rehearse at least the chief tricks, to make sure that their muscles, too, worked with complete precision.

Mr. Albert, the elder of the two Gevaerts cousins, who performed as tumblers under the name of the Bellini Duo (these were the two men who had so amazed Vasek Karas in the outside ring that first day), also played the part of the clown, August, during intermissions. So he too ran out into the ring, and there shouted and yodeled, to make sure that the tent's resonance was exactly the same in Mannheim as it had been in Duisburg. Even Mr. Selnicki crossed the new tent site with an air of dignity, to set down with his own hand his bottle of rum and thus prevent the mental agitation which would have arisen in his mind if his refreshment had not been at hand at the right moment.

The only member of the management who did not enter the tent was Frans Steenhouwer. This Dutchman, who had escaped from his studies with the intention of devoting his life to journeys through the wilds, to shooting tigers and killing snakes and beating his way through the primeval jungle, had come to the circus in order to find there at least a part of that romantic life of which his schoolboy imagination had so long dreamed. When he first entered the tent and the menagerie, a feverish trembling had seized him. It seemed to him that all the beasts of the jungles of Java, Borneo, and Sumatra were surrounding him in the persons of these, their representatives, and that he, Mynheer Steenhouwer, was standing before them as an unconquerable hunter, a famous trapper and killer.

Alas! it turned out that the beasts of Umberto's Circus had but small respect for this towheaded and bespectacled lord of the jungle. As he entered the stables and edged through the door Hamilton's ass, who stood directly opposite the entrance and in the stable had the reputation of a peaceful beast, kicked up his heels, struck Steenhouwer with his hoofs under the shoulder blades, and hurled him straight through the door. It was a powerful kick, which hurt, but even more painful was the smarting sense of humiliation when the director's cousin flew out of the stable and, to the loud laughter of all the grooms, flopped down on the ground on all fours.

On his next visit the elephant Bingo ate up his beautiful Florentine hat with its green ribbon. Then the lioness Corina clawed at him, and though he jumped away, she ripped to pieces the multicolored vest his mamma had knitted for him with her own hands. Then one of the parrots pecked him on the arm and drew blood. And a week later when he appeared near the monkeys' cage, the monkey Bobesh snatched at his carefully tied white tie and pulled it into the cage with such force and such an outcry

143

that Steenhouwer was certain Bobesh was strangling him. It was evident that the wild beasts were rising against the lord of the jungle and were in collusion against him.

Finally in Hamburg, when all the circus hands ran to the menagerie at the sound of the cries of despair which came from there, to find the bookkeeper fleeing desperately from the horns of the goat Bluebeard, the battle of Steenhouwer versus menagerie was decided, and never again did Mynheer enter the ring of the menagerie or the stables. He buried himself in his wagon amid figures and calculations; he began to compute all sort of statistics: how many trainloads of oats would feed Umberto's Circus over a period of ten years, how wide a longitudinal arc it encompassed on its yearly trips, how many wagons would have to be put on the scales to weigh the elephant Bingo, how many cubic feet of air the tent occupied, and how big a city it would take to house the people who attended Umberto's Circus in the course of a year.

From these amazing computations strange charts and diagrams appeared on the walls of the wagon, which Peter Berwitz examined with great interest and respect. When, however, Frans Steenhouwer began to calculate how much the circus would save if instead of seven pounds of oats daily, the horses were given only five, Peter Berwitz announced that his cousin Frans was a mathematical idiot, and that he had better not get in his way with any suggestions about economy when he, Berwitz, had his whip in his hand.

CHAPTER TWO

IT WAS A NEW WORLD for both Karases. From dawn till dusk, often far into the night, their life was filled with task after task, each following the other in a precise, unchangeable order and to all appearances taking all their time, hour after hour. And yet almost every day provided them with some unexpected event which demanded immediate intervention, quick improvisation, ready wit, and experience. At this Kerholec was truly an expert; he found a solution for everything, a way of attacking every problem. And his Czech work gang was the Iron Guard of the circus, always thrown in to attack the hardest and most responsible tasks. It meant real toil and concentration for them, but at the same time it meant exceptional position, for the other workers behaved with a certain respect toward the inhabitants of Number Eight, and the artists treated them as equals.

On the outside everything seemed the same, and yet how different the lives of father and son had now suddenly become! Antonín Karas quickly adapted himself, and with his native ingenuity made himself familiar with all his tasks. He cleaned the horses and cared for them, cleaned out Bingo's stable, ran messages for the horse-trainers and riders, put up and took down the tents, played in the band, and here and there doubled for others. He never spoke much, but everywhere could be seen the dexterity of his hands. He was never idle, and enjoyed this changing work just because here one job always gave way to another.

Whenever on their travels they passed some village where new construction was going on and Karas noticed a rural scaffolding and on it a workman with his assistant, he would watch with interest the way they manipulated their work, but no longer did he ever feel any envy for them. He had his own job now, to work fast and turn out reliable work, and it had got into his blood the way it had with the others. Even when they were traveling he was not content to sit quietly and be driven along; before long he took over the reins from the driver and learned to control the horses and drive the heavy wagon.

Then one day in some woodshed or other he came across a suitable piece of seasoned wood, and already he had a new task provided for him. For a few weeks this was his own secret, into which Kerholec and the others were not initiated. Then one day he called them together and winked at them as he pointed to the back wall of the wagon. They saw two carved horses' heads screwed onto each upper corner, and over the entrance a disk shaped like a plate; from it there looked out the head of an elephant with tusks and a trunk. It was beautifully done, and the entrance to the wagon suddenly took on the appearance of a gate to a hunting lodge.

The inhabitants of Number Eight looked it over from every angle and bestowed their admiration, then gradually brought the entire circus to see their festive splendor. Everyone praised Karas's skill, but it was Arr-Shehir who showed the greatest excitement when he noticed the head of Bingo. Before he uttered a word of praise he crossed his arms and bowed to the figure of the elephant. And afterward whenever he had to go near the wagon he would always glance at the top of the door and bow with respect, thus honoring the Holy One, whom Brahma had created on the First Day from the pure glory of Heaven, holding in each hand a half of the sun.

"We once had another woodcarver like that," Vendelín Malina recollected at his third inspection of the heads. "He was really a puppet showman and had learned how to carve puppets from his father. He too had educated hands. He came to us at the fair at Saint-Cloud or Saint-Armand, I forget just which saint it was. He'd come to see our old man to find out if he couldn't be taken on; he said he was a ventriloquist as well, and that he had two dummies with which he could make up a whole act, and could do lots of other things besides—he was a born showman, he said. He also told us he had left his father and his wife and that he didn't want to have anything to do with puppets any more, and he said a lot of other things which sounded confused.

"Old Umberto took him on. We knew him from before because we had often come across him and his father at fairs, when the boss still used to go to them. So this fellow joined up with us —his name was Kleinfisch or Kleintier or Kleinschnech . . . no, wait, it was Schneckerle, yes, Krispian Schneckerle; he was an Alsatian and could speak German as well as French. And of course we speculated what was behind it all. Old Schneckerle, the father, had quite a big show; besides his puppet theater he had a panorama of famous people, Napoleon, Louise, the Sultan, and other cuckolds of that sort, and some famous bandits and murderers besides, all figures, but just as if they were alive, and that, O Lord! really drew the crowds.

"And then Krispian had a young wife, and he'd come to us without her; something must have been up. But he shut up like a clam about it, just looked gloomy, and all he did was hunt for pieces of seasoned wood. His wagon soon looked like a woodshed, he had so much of it, until the old man gave him hell for it and told him he kept his wagons for the circus and not for wood. But that obstinate devil just kept rummaging around and digging up more pieces of wood, until one day he threw all of them out and only kept one for himself, a good-sized piece of wood it was, and from that he began to carve out a ball with his jackknife. A big ball, more than half a yard across.

"When he had it whittled smooth he began to cut out round holes in the ball, and through these holes he cut out the inside till the wood in the center was free from the shell. And then through those holes he began to hollow out the whole inside. We looked at it and saw another ball was beginning to shape up. Understand, a ball inside a ball. And again he began to cut into the inside ball and carve out a third ball.

"We were dying to know what he was making. It looked terrifically arty, three carved balls with openings, one inside the other; everyone was amazed at how each had got inside the other ones. Krispian kept carving at it for five years. For five years he didn't say a word except when he did his act and talked his ventriloquist stuff, and in that time he carved out seven balls with holes in them, each smaller and smaller, all of them inside each other, and still there was a little chip left in the middle.

"During those five years I had tamed him down a bit, so that he'd sometimes speak to me. When he'd finished with the seventh one, he told me, 'Now I'm going to carve that God-damned bastard in the center, so that he'll be damned and cursed and will rot in hell for all eternity.' I said to him, 'For God's sake, Krispian, whom are you carving there?' He answered, 'Who else but my own father?' I thought that lightning from heaven would strike us at that moment, so I rushed out of the wagon and never went back to see him.

"It seems it was this way: the young fellow, Krispian, had found a Gitano girl, a gipsy, somewhere in the Pyrenees and had carried her off. And then old Schneckerle, Andreas, had taken her away from him. He was a powerful fellow, with big eyes, a snout like a turnip, and whiskers like a Turk; he wore a gold nail in one ear, and across his vest he had a chain full of thalers; what was Krispian compared with him but a runt? They say the old man had some bags of ducats as well, and I think that that was the main reason why the girl wanted him for a father-in-law in the first place. The young people weren't wedded or properly hitched, and even if they were, then they wouldn't have been any obstacle."

"And how about Krispian, did he finish his carving?" asked Karas.

"Well, here's what happened. We were in southern Hungary then and were heading toward Belgrade in Serbia. Krispian was all wrapped up in his work—how could he carve a human figure out of that little chip of wood inside the seventh ball? It already had a nose and eyebrows, and he kept sitting and sitting at it in his wagon by the window and cutting into it and poking at it. And in Zemun we were crossing the Danube on rafts and everybody had to lend a hand with the horses, so Krispian left the ball on the table by the window and came out to hold one of the horses. When we were getting toward the other bank, suddenly his raft jerked hard to one side, the wagon leaned over, and I looked and saw the ball with its six other balls inside roll out of the window, bounce against the edge of the raft, and plop into the Danube. Krispian let out a roar and jumped after it."

"Did he drown?"

"No, he didn't drown, it was close to the shore, but that black-magic ball got away from him."

"What did he say?"

"Nothing. He looked sick, and when we got to the other side he started downstream to look for his ball. He walked and walked, and no one ever saw him again."

"But where could he go?" someone asked.

"How should I know where the Danube flows to?" Malina shrugged his shoulders.

"The Danube empties into the Black Sea," Bures informed them.

"That's no worry of mine." Malina waved his hand.

148

The day after this conversation Director Berwitz came during the midday interval to inspect Karas's handiwork. He looked at the heads of the animals and announced that the horses' heads had rather too heavy neck muscles for his taste, but otherwise both they and the elephant were perfect. And turning to Karas, he hinted that perhaps he might carve two figures of rearing horses when he got the chance, so they could be put in front of the circus gate or over one of the boxes, which could then be known as the "royal box."

"Why not, Mr. Director?" Karas answered. "I can do it at odd moments, if you'll furnish me with hardwood. But first I must carve something for Frau von Hammerschmidt. She was here this morning and asked for it for her wagon. It's for over the ticket window, she said, and I'm to carve some kind of goddess of Fortune with a horn. I promised her I'd do it . . . but I don't know what it's supposed to look like. I've never in my life seen any goddess with a horn."

"A goddess with a horn?" The director was puzzled. "What's got into the old fool's head? A goddess with a horn? But the stupid woman's got it mixed up, she's thinking of a goat with a horn, you understand, Anton, a unicorn—there was such a mythical beast. Just carve her a goat with one horn on the forehead, that will be just the right thing for her. A lot of use Hammerschmidt has for a goddess!"

Peter Berwitz walked off, still laughing as he went and planning to tease his sister-in-law about the mistake she had made in ordering a horned goddess instead of a unicorn.

Meanwhile Malina had climbed out of the wagon and heard the proprietor's views and, as so many times before, was not in agreement.

"Karas, don't let yourself be fooled. If she said a goddess, then she doesn't mean any goat, that's certain."

"All right, Malina, but what does this goddess look like? And where does this horn grow? On her head? On her forehead?"

"I don't know, brother. I never saw a horned goddess. Once we had a sylphide, a mermaid, but that was a fake; every morning we would fasten a fish tail onto her. But we never had anything horned."

Antonín Karas Senior was finding life good in the circus, much better than he had expected. But Vasek was a great concern to him. What was happening to Vasek, Karas did not want to think about, let alone behold.

CHAPTER THREE

The FIRST DAY of Vasek's training Karas had gone at once over to the blue wagon to see how things were going with his son. What he saw there gripped him with horror. That Berber, that Mohammedan, was standing there by the stairs, with his left leg planted on one step so that his thigh was parallel with the ground, and thrown over his thigh lay Vasek on his back, his head and arms hanging down on one side, his legs on the other; and this savage, this tyrant, was pressing down his chest with one arm and his knees with the other, exactly as if he wanted to break Vasek's spine.

"*La ilaha illallah*," he panted meanwhile, for he was leaning on the boy with all his strength, "*Voilà*, there it jerks, *mashallah*, the bones break . . . the joints stretch . . . It all hurts, I know, I know, *mio ragazzo*—only hold out, only hold out, we must *slogare il dorso*, disjoint your spine, *la spina, tutto scheletro*, the whole skeleton . . . *oh, oh la vertebra* . . . *bene, bene, benissimo* . . . *voilà* . . ."

Amid all these cries Karas Senior heard only the sobs, sighs, and moans of his son. He did not see how the boy's face darkened with the rush of blood, how it twisted with pain and how his teeth bit into his lips in despair and the tears involuntarily squeezed from his eyes. He did not see this, but he had plunged forward to put an end to this horrible tyranny.

However, Paolo, who stood beside his father and was watching everything, at once rushed out to meet him. He ran across

Karas's path and, calling *"Ecco, signore, ecco . . ."* threw himself lightly backward till his hands were touching the ground, even reaching round to his legs. And grasping his legs by the calves, and thrusting his smiling head between his knees, he began to turn and jump in front of Karas, at last righting himself in one upward-springing leap, to which he added a great theatrical bow and again cried, *"Fa niente, signore Antonio,* it's nothing . . . *schauen Sie. . . ."* And he turned three handsprings on the spot.

In point of fact he succeeded in holding back Karas by these stunts long enough for the latter to recover from his agitation and turn round so that he might not behold the torturing scene. He had shaken hands with Kerholec on his promise that he would not interfere with anything Achmed did to the boy. Kerholec knew that the training would mean suffering, and had insisted that the healthy boy would stand it all and that Achmed himself would let Vasek go if he felt that he was not fit for it. In the end Karas felt there was but one hope, that Vasek himself would declare that afternoon that he could not stand it.

He walked away on that first occasion, but his heart overflowed with grief. He confided his troubles to the first person with whom he could strike up a conversation. By chance this had happened to be Arr-Shehir, who came to see Bingo as Karas was cleaning his stable. The Hindu heard his complaints to the end with serious attention. Sitting down between the front legs of Bingo, who blew lovingly into his ear and on his neck with his trunk, he replied with the air of seriousness and meditation that derived from the wisdom of his far-off land.

"Sublime things are full of mystery. Only that man to whom the spirits have given the lotus flower may pass through the barred gates. And even he shall not pass them as he was born. The sublime opens only to the sublime. One man is born just as another—on the lowest degree. And he climbs upward only by being reborn. Knowledge is suffering. If you pass through knowledge as through suffering, you are another man, you are a degree higher. The path of transformations and the path of suffering are indeed as long as is the path to wisdom.

"Each art has its own laws. The art of love has the shortest law. The art of the care of elephants has the greatest law. This, it was written by a holy man twelve thousand years ago, while he lived in the heavenly jungle with the elephants as his equals, by the side of his mother, herself a goddess transformed into an elephant by an evil yogi. He who has been reborn in pain so many times that he has arrived at the last secret of the law, he shall become king of the elephants, who themselves shall follow him without a word so that they may serve him.

"But alas, one human life cannot serve for so many rebirths. It is necessary to be born many times and to suffer many times for a man to become king and master of the Holy Ones. Wise men accept suffering and become yet wiser. I have seen Bingo when he breathed on your Vasek's face and examined his hands. Bingo sees what we do not see. Bingo knows that Vasek carries the lotus flower. Bingo waits that Vasek may be reborn. Bingo will see it. Vasek will hold out."

Arr-Shehir had passed into a chanting voice and the elephant over him rocked to the sound of his chant. Leaning on his shovel, Karas did not understand; yet it seemed to him as if he were listening to some soothing gospel. Arr-Shehir finished his chanting and raised his arm. The elephant embraced his body, lifted its unfettered left leg, and placed Arr-Shehir on its knee. Arr-Shehir raised his palm with its fingers stretched into an arc and lightly stroked the lid of the elephant's eye. Bingo's ears trembled. Arr-Shehir bowed to him. And the Holy One took Arr-Shehir and carefully set him on the ground. Again Arr-Shehir bowed to him, and left the stable.

Karas felt soothed, but his conscious brain immediately indicated to him that this fellow had not told him very much. He was back where he had been before. He put down his equipment and went to the tent. In the gate stood the Gevaerts cousins, waiting until the ring was free for their practice. It occurred to Karas when he noticed them that they would have a much better understanding of the matter than that Hindu. Greeting Albert, the elder one, whom he already knew by sight, he asked his advice as to what he should do.

Albert and Gustave Gevaerts, the Bellini Duo, were Swedes who came from Friesland; their grandfather had somehow made his way to Sweden with General Bernadotte and had opened a store in Upsala, where he sold fruit, coffee, and tropical fruit. His two sons, Johannes and Lambert, were supposed to go to school. But in the course of time it turned out that neither project succeeded, neither the father's store nor the sons' studies. Both young Gevaerts enjoyed gymnastics more than Latin, and when their father was forced to admit that he had no money for their schooling, that he himself would even have to work his way as best he could, he came to terms with the reality that the boys must earn their living at their favorite pastime.

Johannes and Lambert together prepared a strong-man and acrobatic act, and under the name of the Frères Gevaerts went off to Paris to try their luck in the circus, then at its height there. Both were fine light-haired boys of slender athletic figure, and were able to "sell" their performance. They made good, became successful, married, and from their dual household there came the cousins Albert and Gustav, who refined the athletic prowess of their fathers into a more graceful act with leaps, pirouettes, and vaults, and who could even "play the fool." Like almost all true artists they were not talkative; their whole life was lived in their performance in the ring, and what they did outside this quarter of an hour was in fact only constant preparation and concentration on their act. So now Albert answered only in monosyllables. But soon he began to listen to Karas's complaints with interest and even called Gustav over.

"Come here, Gust, this is interesting. Anton here is the father of that Vasek, you know him, and is letting Achmed train him. And Roméo is starting out by breaking his spine. How does he do it? His leg on the stairs and the boy thrown over it? On his back, of course? And he squeezes him as if he wanted to break him in two? And throws him up and down over his leg?"

Karas nodded painfully and the two acrobats looked at each other.

"Of course, Bert, that's the right way!"

"Yes, Gust. Father always said that the older acrobats had special methods for every trick."

"And we started out with the monkey jump. That stretched spine is just what we always lacked."

"And it's marvelously simple: you just twist him over your knee. Father did that to me, only upside down, when he gave me a licking."

"A man's always learning. Too bad, it's too late for us to start now. But if I were to get married, Bert, I'd start breaking the kids' spines when they were five."

"Of course, Gust, the sooner the better. That's a tremendous discovery you've told us about, Anton. We can't go and stare at the Berber when he's working. But now you can look on every day and tell us every time what Achmed and Vasek are doing."

"Tell us everything, Anton, everything—how he crushes him, how he holds him, how he bends him, how he twists and stretches him, if he wraps him up in a somersault, if he kicks him—they say they do kick, too . . ."

"For God's sake . . ." Karas was terrified.

"Yes. If he kicks him now, tell us about it, where, on what part of him, how many times. I imagine kicking is a wonderfully satisfactory method for some things."

"And the chief thing is, whether he kicks with the toe or with the flat heel. I think with the heel."

"And when they punch each other . . . well, Vasek can show us that himself, how Achmed teaches him to punch . . ."

The Bellini Duo was suddenly full of life and craved with relish for all the tortures they could call to mind. Karas, who had come here to find consolation, was almost sick.

"Mr. Albert, for God's sake . . . how can the boy endure it? Can I really let him?"

The two exuberant acrobats stared at him, at first without understanding.

"Oh, I see," Albert cried at last and returned to his taciturn seriousness. "Don't be a fool, Anton. Either Vasek's got it in him or he hasn't. If he hasn't he'll run away from Achmed and you won't be able to get him to go back even if you whip him. But as he hasn't done that he evidently has what it takes. And when he's been through it for a week or so he won't even feel the blows and the falls."

"That's right, Anton," added Gustav Gevaerts, "and believe us that it's the best school. Aren't I right, Bert?"

"You're right, Gust. Gambier's finished cleaning out the cage, so let's jump out on the double, before the horses come."

Karas had the painful impression that he had failed, that he had erred when he had looked for advice from these two. At that moment Captain Gambier was passing him. Karas said *bonjour* to him.

"*Bonjour . . . oh, c'est Anton . . .* I see Vasek's at Achmed's . . . félicitations . . . *famos, famos . . . il est vraiment magnifique, ce petit gars . . .* Vasek is a brave one, very brave."

Karas bowed at this praise, but he felt still worse. No matter where he went in the circus afterward, he found that everyone heartily approved of what Achmed was doing with Vasek. He found only two people who understood him to some extent. One of them was Frau von Hammerschmidt. She clasped her hands and wrung them when he told her of what he had seen that morning, cried, "*Schrecklich! Entsetzlich!*" and again, "*Das herzensgute Ding!*" and she promised him that that afternoon she would bring two doughnuts from dinner for Vasek so that his existence might be made a bit sweeter.

And the second person who did not agree with Achmed's brutality was Selnicki. The conductor's gaze was a bit misty as he listened to Karas. Then a tear made its appearance, but Karas already knew that this could not necessarily be attributed to any emotion on his part. Then, too, Mr. Selnicki calmly listened to the end, took a drink, smacked his lips, and said:

"Well, but what could you expect? In my opinion a seven-year-old boy should be taught to play the piano. But a piano in a menagerie would be throwing pearls before swine. It's this whole devilish mess-up between life and art that's the trouble. Here's to you!"

After all these conversations the deciding factor was still what Vasek would say when he came home at midday.

When Karas hurried back to Number Eight Vasek was already sitting there on the steps.

"Vasek, my Vasek, how did you get on at Achmed's?"

"All right, Father," Vasek answered with unusual seriousness. "It's all right."

"And what did you practice?"

"We spent two hours learning how to do dancing steps and to bow to the public."

"What? Bow to them . . ."

"Yes. Mr. Achmed says that the hardest thing is to thank the public and bow to them so that it will look right from every direction. He wants it to be done well, according to the rules, and he says that no one here knows how to do it properly."

"But I was there this morning and I saw something quite different . . . the way he crushed you . . ."

"You were there, Father?" Vasek looked at Karas and his eyes grew sharp.

"Yes . . . and I saw . . ."

"You mustn't do that. You mustn't do that, Father."

Vasek spoke in a manner Karas had never heard before. Something of the adult, something decisive, sounded in that voice, just as it had in his mother's.

"But why shouldn't I . . . ?"

"Because you won't be able to stand it, Father," Vasek said firmly, and added, "But I can stand it." Then again a childish strain conquered him and he repeated with a child's headstrongness: "I can stand it and stand it and stand it. And I'll jump better than Paolo."

Karas Senior saw that something had come between them, some kind of barrier, and that Vasek was indeed quite a different person than his father had believed. If he did not want to lose the boy he must drop his objections and let him follow his destiny. This confused him, yet his heart was full of tenderness and love.

"But Vasek, I only . . ." he began quietly, as if apologizing. But Vasek immediately scented what his father was leading up to.

"Father!" he cried sharply, and tried to rise. But not for long, for at once he was gripped by pain and dropped back onto the step.

"Gosh!" slipped quietly out of him.

"You see," his father added almost in a whisper.

"I know," said Vasek, and waved his arm. "It's just like I'd have felt if I'd been chopping trees at home."

And he said it in a way that completely subjugated Karas

Senior. And to put an end to this, their first and most serious disagreement, he added with false calm:

"Frau von Hammerschmidt said that you might go to see her after dinner; she'll have some doughnuts for you."

Vasek wiped his nose with the back of his hand.

"With jam?"

"With jam."

"Fine!"

And so with the matter-of-fact business of a few doughnuts the tension between them disappeared and they returned to everyday life.

"And Mr. Albert of the Bellini Duo is very interested in your work and what Achmed is doing to you. He says I'm to tell him about everything, what you do, and how you do it."

The boy's eyes narrowed and he was silent for a moment. Then he raised a finger and said with boyish importance:

"Don't do that, Father!"

"No? Why not?"

"Mr. Albert and Mr. Gustav—"and Vasek bent over and spoke softly and insistently—"they will want to copy how it's done. But that won't do, Father . . . that's our secret. . . ."

Karas was silent and stared straight ahead. In his mind he saw the trainer Arr-Shehir between the black columns of the elephant's legs, and heard his chanting voice:

"Sublime things are full of mystery. If you pass through suffering and knowledge, you are another man, you are a degree higher."

CHAPTER FOUR

PETER BERWITZ had not had such an easy time of it lately as circus director. His daring expedition to Russia and Asia had placed him in the ranks of the leading circuses in Europe, but this position was by no means a secure one. Berwitz knew that in the circus world one must struggle constantly for first place if one is to avoid collapse and ruin. Each artist has to battle daily in the ring for his success and for the continual improvement of his act, and the circus too, as a whole, must always be ready and alert for battle.

However, it was really a good thing for a man to live in continual activity, in the continual fire and heat of the struggle; Berwitz was happier when his circus people had put the quiet of Hamburg behind them and were in the middle of all the turmoil of their journey, with its multitude of obstacles, unexpected misfortunes, and unlooked-for difficulties. Then he could immediately jump into the fray, make decisions, save what needed to be saved, jettison the rest, give orders, act.

Again, it was not only a matter of accidents, and sudden decisions; the director had also to consider the whole enterprise as a unified and collective whole, so that nothing should be dispersed or diffused, so that it might preserve the charm of its perfection and the beauty of its performance, and retain its ascendancy over its rivals. At this point Peter Berwitz felt an unpleasant cloud at the back of his mind, the short name of which was Kranz.

And who was Kranz? He had been a mere rider in old Briloff's ring, then known as the Royal Prussian General Riding and Art Society, Incorporated, when Peter was already director, in association with his father and his grandfather, of a great circus and menagerie. And what was Kranz when Peter became the sole master of Umberto's Circus? Director of an insignificant side show with eight people and ten horses, with Kranz himself and his own family included among those eight people.

Of course he was a born circus man, the son of a tightrope-walker and himself a skilled tightrope-walker. He had later learned to ride with the famous Peter Mahyeu of unforgettable memory; he then became the first rider with Briloff for some years; he rode standing on four horses in full gallop, worked on a free swinging rope, raised weights, vaulted and jumped on the backs of unsaddled horses, and did the *batoude,* a death jump from a springboard over the backs of eight horses.

After Briloff's death he had gone into business for himself with his white horse Soliman, and his whole circus had possessed no more than one equerry's uniform; his men were forced to change their clothes constantly so that one might appear before the public when another was finished. At that time Berwitz might have dismissed such an enterprise with a smile; but when he made his three-year expedition abroad and returned home to Germany he found to his amazement that Kranz had grown in the meanwhile—now his headquarters was in Berlin and he had entered into competition with the greatest French circuses, which at that time had a gold mine there.

Such circuses as Cuzent and Lejars or Dejeans were elegant enterprises, luxuriously equipped, holding fast to the old circus traditions, with excellent performers and outstanding horses, enterprises which operated with ostentatious perfection and with unerring taste. And now this pigheaded, obstinate ex-tightrope-walker, who had once torn off a wagon shaft as if it were a switch to strike a rebellious employee, had taken it into his head that he would drive the Frenchmen from the favor of the Court and the aristocracy, that he would surpass them, outdo them, defeat them! It was sheer madness—but in the end it became a reality. In fact, Kranz conquered Berlin, elbowed the Frenchmen out, established himself in their place, grew and strengthened, became more and more venturesome, and now was actually a serious rival of Berwitz.

He feared nothing, nothing frightened him; he filched the best riders and artists from under Berwitz's nose; he had just seduced from Berwitz that fellow Léotard—that French flying-trapeze artist who had been the rage of Paris for five years, so that people wore everything à la Léotard, ties, hats, shoes, canes. Léotard had won his fame because he carried out daily on his swinging trapezes an unheard-of, an almost unimaginable jump across a space of twenty-seven feet, a true leap of death, high in the air and without a safety net.

Now that Léotard was no longer with Berwitz, but with Kranz, Peter said contemptuously that he could not understand what people could see in the little runt. He had no body, his legs were short and weak, while above he had those huge bulging muscles on his shoulders and arms. Even Léotard himself said that he was happier up on the trapeze, for there he did not look so hideous as he did on the ground.

But now Peter Berwitz felt he must keep his eye constantly on Kranz. He too had his own permanent building in Berlin; eight years ago it had burned down and had been rebuilt; this was actually a great advantage for him in that it was more modern, more comfortable, and more luxurious than the old wooden construction in Hamburg. Just before departing Gaudeamus had sent Peter a confidential report that Kranz was trying to buy the building in Berlin instead of renting it. It dawned on Berwitz that now he must be on his guard even in Hamburg, for Kranz sometimes came there during the summer, and it was possible that he might even try to steal Berwitz's winter quarters.

Almost the last thing Peter did before going on the road was to give a commission to Hagenbeck's son to try to buy the old building in Hamburg for the circus, and in the event of being able to do so, to have it fitted out over the summer. The main thing was to equip it with gaslighting, so that during the following winter they could perform in the evening as well as by day, as was done in Berlin.

For the rest, Peter followed Kranz's activity very closely. This he did for the most part through Gaudeamus, who traveled to Berlin in the winter at his orders and there lived in brilliance for a few days as Knight and Baron, amid the "backstage world" of the Friedrichstrasse circus, worming secrets of every sort from the gossiping riding girls, not to speak of Kranz himself, for the latter was possessed with respect for the aristocracy, and would have jumped over his own whip for the Baron's favor.

From Gaudeamus Berwitz learned that Kranz was on the lookout for all kinds of human monstrosities he could hire as attractions, and that he was negotiating with a certain Julie Pastrana, a Mexican singer whose face was said to be all grown over with a thick black beard, who had two sets of teeth, and who sang old Mexican romances in a deep alto voice. Her sister rode and vaulted for Kranz.

And now the report arrived from Spain that when Julie had made her appearance there with some side-show freaks a certain Yorick had fallen in love with her, a man from the Cordilleran forests, a terrible giant with protruding tusks, a blue face, and a beard half red and half yellow. This Yorick wrestled in a cage with three bears at once, but when Julie Pastrana refused him he fought badly and one of the bears bit off his leg. The story appeared in the newspapers, and Kranz immediately ordered the girl rider to write to her Mexican sister with the full beard.

This piece of news was the main reason that Peter Berwitz had added dwarfs to his program, but ever since he had hired them he had kept regretting his action.

"They aren't circus people," he complained at the family dinner table, "they do nothing but whine and grumble to the director—as if he had nothing more to do than worry about them —asking whether that sawed-off little Herr Mittelhofer will get a carpet for his number, or saying that the bed in the wagon is too high for Frau Mittelhofer. The Devil must have wished them on me."

"It's not only that, Peter," Anna answered him, "there's more to it. You knew beforehand that dwarfs have nothing in common with a circus. You have a clear sense for what makes for pure style and grace. All style is lost when among your beautiful creations and perfect performances you put a couple of people to whom nature has been unkind."

"That was clear to me as soon as I saw them."

"Of course, it's perfectly obvious. We are always seeking to find beauty, strength, youth, freshness, charm, and suddenly you bring those two human monstrosities here, two maimed people who have the awkward forms of children combined with the peevish brains of spiteful old men. And you wouldn't have done it if you had acted on the basis of your own taste. But that Berliner, that fellow Kranz, is always haunting you."

"Excuse me, but Kranz hasn't any dwarfs!"

"He hasn't, but he will. Kranz has everything in which he can detect the smell of money. But would Wollschläger have put such monstrosities in his circus?"

"Don't remind me of Wollschläger. Wollschläger went bankrupt."

"Yes, but amid honor and glory. Everything he did had style. When Marie Anna and I rode after you to Antwerp that time, Count d'Ascensons himself said in the coach, *'Mes chères, ce que vous verrez, c'est un cirque qui a du style.'* Remember that: a circus which has its own style. And he also told us, 'Everything which has its own style is worthy of the respect and admiration of a cultivated man. The world is changing fast nowadays; they tell us of progress and revolution. But neither progress nor revolution will bring anything worth while if they do not at the same time give it the stamp of style. If we lose style, we are but the insignificant multitude, the heap, the mass, chaos. Only form, only style, can create the beauty of life.' Count d'Ascensons told us that, and the Second Chamberlain was a wonderful man."

"Of course, a count is a count, a big shot . . ."

"Not only that, Peter. A count can be a blockhead, too. But a man in the circus can only be an outstanding personality when he remains himself and doesn't crib from others. You cribbed those dwarfs from Kranz, and I've been waiting to see when you would realize it yourself. I would rather you realized that when you begin to act like him you have conceded him the superiority and unconsciously given in to him. I wish really that the two of you would measure your strength against each other and each show what he is worth. Perhaps Kranz will be the better businessman and will make millions, and we will come to the brink of bankruptcy. But we will have stuck to our own type of art and will not have allowed any sort of impurity to enter. Kranz is a great man and a powerful one; he knows a great deal, and you must not underestimate him. But let him call his circus an institution a hundred times over—you still know far better than he what a real circus is."

"You think that Kranz makes mistakes?"

"He makes them, just as you make them. We all make mistakes. But the thing is that you should make your own mistakes, and not Kranz's. You wouldn't show a two-headed calf, you would sense at once that that is another matter for a cheap side show and not for Umberto's Circus. I want you to act in your own way. These annoyances with the dwarfs are nothing; you can break the contract at the first opportunity, but leave Kranz's practices to him."

Peter Berwitz had the feeling that Anna was criticizing him sharply. To put an end to it he turned to her suddenly with the question:

"What are the lion cubs doing? I haven't looked at them yet today."

"They're getting on all right. Vasek could begin to show them, they're four weeks old already."

"Oh, Vasek. That's right. It's good you reminded me. I must find out how he's getting on with his riding. Then I could take those dwarfs off the program." Then he thrust out his left arm until the snowy white cuff protruded. "And one more thing, Anna. Please don't send my cuffs to the wash until I've copied down what I have written on them."

CHAPTER FIVE

BERWITZ made for the stable and called for Hans.

"How's Vasek getting along? Is he learning to ride?"

"Mr. Director, Vasek's been untrue to us. I'm sorry to say Vasek's gone over to the acrobats."

"What d'you mean?"

"To the acrobats, Mr. Director. I must complain about him. He's got tied up with that African fellow who tosses his own children up into the air with his feet, and instead of riding patiently, he's gone over to him for training and is letting him twist his body."

"Oh, ah." Berwitz shook his head. "Vasek's taking it more seriously than I thought. Did his father send him to Achmed?"

"No, it's not Anton's fault. He's very worried about it. I don't

163

want to complain, but it seems Kerholec fixed it up. He didn't grow up with horses, and it's all the same to him if you're a rider or an acrobat. But Vasek, if I may say so, has the right stuff in him for riding; a man can tell that from the way he goes at it, the way he takes to it. But you would see it, Mr. Director, most of all by the way the horses take to Vasek. Shetlands are rather stubborn, but with Vasek, Mary obeys at a word. That boy's a genuine horseman, Mr. Director, and it's a shame that he should be allowed to go over to the acrobats; it's a disgrace for the whole stable, Mr. Director."

Hans, his face red, had got worked up into a state in which Berwitz had never yet seen him, but in his heart he had to laugh at the way the coachman despised acrobats. For the most part equality governed in the circus, but in the ranks of the performers, as he saw, the old hierarchy and professional pride still lived on.

"Well," said Berwitz, "I'll drop in on Achmed and have a look at what's going on. If he's taking it seriously there must be something in it. But Vasek's still riding Mary?"

"Well, he rides, he rides," Hans answered. "It's all right at a walk or a slow trot, but of course he doesn't cut any kind of a figure, his arms droop, his soles aren't tight in the stirrups, he doesn't know how to catch the horse's attention—he has all that to learn. And now while the Arab's torturing his body, he crawls onto Mary as if she was an armchair and sits on her like a bruised monkey. It's a wonder that he has any desire left to get into the saddle at all; his bones must be nearly broken."

"The main thing is that he still hasn't lost his desire to ride. We must encourage him in that. Today there are all too few people who are born horsemen."

"That's why I'm mentioning it, Mr. Director. When I was with Wollschläger—and he could do the most terrific things with horses—he used to complain that a boy who could really ride hadn't come his way for years. And so I said to myself, 'Hans'— this was to be my own secret, but the director is the chief, yes, so how can there be any secrets from him?—I said to myself, 'Hans, you big bear, you, you've been working all your life with these animals'—and our horses are all marvels, Mr. Director, they are marvels through and through—so I said to myself, 'You've been working with these marvelous horses all your life and there won't be anybody to take over when you're gone, not a damn soul, and here's this boy, who one day might ride like the best of them—suppose you were to get an act ready for him?' "

"An act for Vasek?" Berwitz raised his eyebrows and looked more attentively at the enthusiastic Hans.

"I thought that people might enjoy it if, after all those grand acts with the stallions and the mares, all at once our four ponies could come out, free style, and if, instead of the director, a boy were to lead the ponies, dressed like a grownup, with a top hat, a dress coat, a whip in his hand, and doing everything like an adult. I would train the horses and get everything ready . . ."

Berwitz listened to him very attentively and now took him by the shoulder.

"Hans, do you remember that red waistcoat I wore when I paraded the spotted horses? You like it so much."

"How could I forget it? God, that was a waistcoat! With gold buttons! The most beautiful thing I ever saw. I used to forget to watch the horses, I liked it so much."

"Pay attention, Hans, to what I'm going to say. If you prepare an act with the ponies and Vasek for us, and it's successful, then you'll get that waistcoat."

"You can't mean it, Mr. Director." Hans was aghast.

"I never say what I don't mean. Only it must be a really good act—and the waistcoat will be yours."

"Mr. Director . . . let lightning strike me . . . let Santos kick me, if it won't be a real topnotcher!"

Berwitz only nodded his head and left Hans in agitated reflection over the act with the Shetlands. Actually the magnificent waistcoat with its little brass wheels in place of buttons had already been laid to rest in Berwitz's wardrobe, for ever since the time when Berwitz began to put on weight unpleasant wrinkles had appeared in it. So he had put it away for a rainy day, hoping to sell it profitably when a good opportunity occurred. Now he saw another use for it; so far the Shetlands had been only part of the décor, but in an independent number they might be put to real use.

He passed through the stables to the wagons with the animals, and then on to the wagons housing the personnel. Everything was in its prescribed order, so that he did not have to look for the wagon where the lame Harwey lived. He knocked on the door. It opened and the skinny man thrust out his mournful face.

"Good day, Harwey. I need something to fit Vasek. Right away. What have you got in his size?"

"Vasek . . . now, let me see. We have four pages here . . . a Persian falconer . . . an Arabian costume could be put together . . . there's nothing in knights . . . or in Romans . . . I've a woman's riding suit, but that wouldn't do . . . and then there's a Moraccan costume for a boy . . ."

"That's it, Harwey. Please have it tried on, and press it immediately. So long."

Berwitz walked on, heading toward the blue wagon. He wanted to arrive there unnoticed, but as he approached, a dirty little boy called out from between the wagons:

"*Il padrone!*"

The patter of bare feet sounded, and from all sides Roméo's boys ran out, each outshouting the other.

"*Il padrone! Direttore! Attenzione!*"

They all clustered around him, bowed, waved their arms at him. The window of the wagon opened and out of it leaned Mrs. Roméo, her dark face lighting up in a smile. And from behind the wagon Achmed Roméo appeared, and with him Vasek.

"*Che cosa c'è . . . ah, buon giorno, signore direttore, bonjour. . . .* What an honor it is for our blue home . . . Signora Roméo has still not yet had the pleasure . . . Felicia, Felicia!"

Berwitz cursed inwardly. He had only wanted to look in unexpectedly, and he detested family contacts. But Mrs. Felicia Roméo was already climbing down the steps with the infant in her arms and offering him her hand with a grand gesture. All around stood the flock of children, who waited with the greatest excitement to see what would happen.

"How do you do, madame?" said Berwitz, forcing himself to smile. "But please don't disturb yourself in any way. Actually I only came to ask how Vasek is getting on."

"Oh, Vasek's a brave boy," Achmed answered delightedly.

166

"Vasek, make the grand bow number four for the director . . . a great circle with the right leg . . . thaaat's it . . . both arms down away from the body . . . toward the chest . . . away . . . bravo! At the same time we've been practicing posture number three. He catches on very quickly. But the main thing is that he has patience."

Berwitz looked closely at the boy. It seemed to him that he could detect fatigue in the boy's look. Decidedly Vasek did not seem to be the same bundle of darting energy which had so pleased him the other day in the ring. And his smile, too, was a bit forced. Peter was well able to imagine how he felt, from the experiences of his own boyhood, and knew how much the boy needed encouragement. He walked up to him and put his left hand on his shoulder in a hearty manner.

"How's it going, Vasek? Your whole body hurts, is that it?"

"It hurts, Mr. Director." Vasek half-smiled.

"I know how it is. It's damned hard work, isn't it?"

"It certainly is," Vasek assented.

"Hellish hard work." Berwitz spoke with emphasis.

"Beastly," Vasek agreed.

"It's a dog's life." Berwitz played a trump.

"To hell with it!" Vasek went one better.

"But we won't give in, will we?"

"We won't give in."

"That's it, boy, that's right. Hold on and don't give in! It will ease up, one day it will ease up all of a sudden and you'll be able to do everything as if you were born to it. You can walk, I see. I have a job for you now. At the next performance you'll dress up in a costume Harwey will get ready for you, and during the interval you'll go among the audience with one of our lion cubs."

"Oh, the cubs. How are they getting on? I forgot all about them."

"They're taking to the world well and are already big enough to earn their own living. You'll carry one of them in your arms, show it to the people, let them pet it, and then collect from them, on a plate, money to pay for their milk and their meat. Understand?"

"I understand, Mr. Director."

"You'll turn in the money and the cub at Number One after the interval."

"Yes."

"Well, keep it up. So long."

The director patted Vasek lightly on the shoulder and turned to Achmed.

"Remember, Roméo," he said to him in French, "that we're going to need this boy for riding. Don't make a contortionist out of him, but a tumbler. The springboard, the *fricasée,* the *saut périlleux,* and that sort of stunts."

"I understand, Mr. Director—" Achmed bowed—"flip-flip-flop, rondada, and so on and so on. I'll give him the whole Arabian school, so that you'll be pleased and can see what Achmed Roméo can do."

"Madame Felicia, it was an extraordinary pleasure." The director turned to Mrs. Roméo, shook her hand as well as her husband's, and waving off with a gesture their protests that he must come into their wagon, he quickly turned back.

Achmed's boys rushed to Vasek, full of wonder that he had been chosen by the mighty director to walk through the tent with the young lions. For Vasek it was like wine that, among all these boys, who knew far more about twists and leaps than he, he had been chosen to stand out and excel as an accomplished tamer of animals. Mr. Roméo and Mrs. Roméo stood in the background, and when the director had disappeared from view they turned to one another, raised their eyebrows, winked with their eyes in Vasek's direction, and nodded their heads. Throughout the whole world, and not only in Tunis, this meant:

"Look here, this boy's important to them—we must keep an eye on him!"

The next afternoon Vasek entered the tent during the performance clad in the blue and red "Moraccan" uniform; in his right arm he carried a lion cub nestled against his chest, in his left a plate. As soon as the interval had been announced he started out on his journey through the boxes and then through the tiers of seats. Everywhere people were delighted at the chance to see a young lion, to touch it and take it into their arms.

And the boy who carried it earned no less a success. From all sides small and large coins jingled into the plate. When they finally counted up in the wagon the lion's first "take" amounted to seven marks sixty-eight pfennigs. Director Berwitz, dressed in his Persian uniform, with his Circassian saber at his side and his orders on his chest, nodded his head in acknowledgment, rummaged among the money, and taking out a twenty-pfennig piece, handed it to Vasek.

"Here, take it!"

His gesture was even grander and more kingly than the one with which the Sultan had once given him the royal sapphire.

Vasek ran joyfully over to Harwey's to turn in his costume. When his father came home to supper Vasek was standing on the steps with his palm stretched out and on it the shining coin.

"Look, Father! See what I've earned!"

Antonín Karas took the money, spat on it, pulled out his blue handkerchief, and carefully tied the coin into one corner of it.

Vasek was disappointed. He had had so many plans about what he could buy with the coin in the city, but his father announced that he would need new shoes. Vasek reconciled himself to this, but at least he could boast to Kerholec, Bures, and the others about how he had earned twenty pfennigs in the circus.

"When you bring twenty marks home, you'll pay for the beer," was all that Kerholec said.

CHAPTER SIX

THEY ALL had to admit to Achmed Roméo that he had not tortured Vasek needlessly. He knew that stretching the muscles, bending the spine, and loosening the joints were all terribly painful procedures, and he knew from his own experience how many children became so nervous in the process that with the stiffness of their bodies they lost the courage of their spirits. And there is nothing sadder to behold than a child who performs tricks only because he has to, and is afraid not to. The reason why the Arabian, Berber, and Moorish acrobats had triumphed so quickly when they invaded the circuses and carnivals of Europe was the fieriness of their performance, the wild ardor which they passed on, down even to the tiniest tots, who themselves jumped up on the raised legs of their father as he lay face upward on the ground, begging him at least to toss them up in the air.

A tumbling act should always look like a wild whirlwind of handsprings and leaps, and Achmed was careful that none of his pupils should lose that quality which he himself called their "fire." Often he too, as he lay on his back and caught his children, throwing them up into the air, where the boys circled and flew over each other, would be gripped by the wild spirit of the act as with a fever, would be caught up in the tempo as if possessed by a demon.

Suddenly he would begin to sing the horses' sura from the Koran, his head lying on the mat beneath the tumbling children. "The horses are snorting, flashing their hoofs, and are rushing in a storm through the morning, the horses are vanishing in clouds and dust, the horses are at the head of the warriors, triumphantly battling!" And then Achmed's legs kicked furiously; the children flew up like meteors; the whole act looked like a display of fireworks, and the people began to applaud before Achmed had even finished the sura.

"Allah is Allah and fear is fear," he would say, speaking of his method of training. "Fear is born in a man, and *not* to fear is his first lesson. And with fear you will not drive out fear. Fear must be overcome and put aside as you put aside weakness of the muscles. Train well, and weakness will pass into strength, fear into courage, a boy into a man. The Franks forbid children to work in the circus. Allah knows that that doesn't concern me. My five-year-old son is already a man in what he can undertake, and is already prepared to bear his fate."

To be sure, Roméo roared and yelled during the training

and rolled his eyes and bared his teeth, but Vasek soon discovered that it was all done only to encourage him or to stupefy him, and that Achmed's cries, like the way he squeezed his limbs, were full of sensitivity. And he also discovered that Achmed did not require him to learn all that he and his sons had mastered. When Vasek was already able to bend back so that his hands touched the ground Achmed was satisfied to teach him only how to hold this position firmly; whereas, in addition to forcing his children to bend back to this position, he made them stretch out their fingers farther and farther along the ground, a procedure which involved constantly increasing pain.

"Vasek won't be a snake man," Roméo said to Kerholec when the latter came to see how the training was going. "Vasek will be a tumbler and an acrobat and will have the cultivated manners of a performer of the old tradition. Good manners are on the decline in Europe. You Franks eat with forks and wipe yourselves clean with napkins and put on ties, but those are only the most superficial things. You don't know the difference between an entrance bow, a bow of civility, a small bow of thanks, a grand bow of thanks, and a bow before the Sultan. But my children, may Allah preserve them, know in addition to that the long reverence in seven measures, the short reverence in four, and the minimum and semi-minimum or brief reverence. Indeed that is part of the greatness of the art, that it trains people and shows them the perfect manners of the ancient and cultivated teachings written down by the wisest teachers of the holy city of Kairwan, in the oasis of Mursuk, in the city of El Obeid in Kordofan, in Cairo, and in Damascus."

"Good," Kerholec answered. "When Vasek grows tall it will only be a matter of . . ."

"Vasek will never grow tall." Roméo shook his head. "Allah ordained that the spine of man should grow straight. And when the great teacher of the art, Ali ben Rachmadin, asked the Archangel Michael to permit him to bend the spines of his pupils for the greater glory of Allah, whose name be praised, Allah sent word to him that he might choose one of two favors: either the firm spine which would grow, or the bent one, the growth of which would be brought to an end. And Allah's word remained. None of us is tall, for the body which is bent in a circle does not grow."

It dawned upon Kerholec that in fact all the first-class tumblers whom he knew were small in stature, but he did not stop to consider either Achmed's legend or the reality—that a child's cartilage turns to bone during acrobatics and slows up his growth. He had only wanted to inform Roméo that what Vasek needed most was a good foundation.

"*Mashallah!*" cried Roméo. "The best teachers can't give a child more than a good foundation. Look at this, for example." Roméo ran up three steps and did a handspring in the air. "*Ecco.* What was it? Mr. Kerholec will say a handspring. But in the middle of that handspring Achmed Roméo did a full pirouette, turning his whole body around. A pike's jump, signore, and not a handspring. And the take-off was done without any of your springboards. And the fall onto the ground was slow and gentle, as if the seven jinns had let me down. How long did I study that? Sixteen years it was, signore, *esercizio di sédici anni in totale,* before I could do that floating landing on the ground, and I must repeat it constantly, *un anno fa, una settimana fa, oggi, domani e posdomani,* today, tomorrow, the day after. Who could have taught me that? No, signore, the teacher only prepares the child, loosens his body, hardens his muscles, steels his heart, shows him the steps he needs to start out with, and all the rest is the pupil's affair. In truth Achmed Roméo will not give Vasek more than a good foundation, but it will be the foundation of the best school, signore."

All the circus people were right in one thing they had predicted to Vasek, that he would feel pain only during the first few days. Sometimes he had thought that he could not endure it, and his quiet "Golly" slipped out from between his clenched teeth hundreds of times. But behold, one day, as if by magic, his body suddenly loosened up, everything smoothed out, and his muscles and joints became adjusted. Now Vasek felt no more pain than he would have during some exhausting game.

This, of course, was a testimony to the fact that Roméo had exercised him very evenly and thoroughly. But Vasek did not stop to consider that. He suddenly felt as if he had been born anew, he now repeated persistently by himself the first tricks he had learned. He could now stand on his hands and hold that position without moving, even when Achmed took him by the arms and raised him. And from standing on his hands and bending over backward he passed to the first backward handsprings, which in the jargon they called flips. And then he learned the monkey jump, a backward flip on one leg, his body tied to a rope to prevent him from getting hurt and even more to give him confidence.

But the falls no longer hurt him, for he had learned to tense the muscles of his back and legs so that he dropped onto them as onto a well-stuffed cushion. Even his fingers strengthened, and he could fall straight forward on the bare ground without bending his knees or reaching out his arms; the fingers alongside his body still cushioned the fall and prevented a shock.

With the disappearance of the pain his former good spirits returned. Again he could no longer bear to sit still, again he ran about the stables and the menagerie so that he would not miss anything which was going on there, and again he came back to Hans to be trained to ride under his teaching. And this, too, progressed in a surprisingly different manner; Vasek swung into the saddle with a lightness he had never known before. And the training itself proved not the least bit tiring, though Hans put him through his paces according to old-fashioned, pitiless rules.

The most enjoyable thing was when Hans gave Vasek a ball, forced Mary to trot as fast as she could at the end of her tether, and then made Vasek throw the ball up and catch it, so that he could neither look down at the bridle nor at the pony. Vasek accepted this as a fascinating game, but in reality it was excellent training for a rider in that it loosened his hip muscles and gave him flexibility in the saddle.

In Achmed's school Vasek had learned something which would not have occurred to him before: to analyze each of the motions of his body separately. When he became engrossed in the training, he would observe successively the movements of his legs, arms, body, and head, as well as their co-ordinated effect on his balance. In his unconscious mind he had already developed a sense for the control of his body, and when Hans told him that a good rider kept his hands on the bridle over the saddle in a firm, unmoving position and didn't allow them to move, Vasek held himself motionless when he rode on Mary.

One day when he had jumped down from the pony and was taking the saddle off her Hans called him over, and Vasek was aghast—Hans was handing him a great trainer's whip.

"Take it, Vasek, you must learn to use it too. Take it outside and practice with it now without the horses."

Vasek nearly cried with joy. The whip, a real one, a gigantic one, was just like the one the director or Mr. Perreira used. The long whip, much longer than Vasek, was curved at one end in a beautiful bend with a white tip which shook and flew like a silvery snake. Vasek rushed out with it, his face glowing with triumph and excitement, first going to the side behind the wagon so that no one would see him while he was still struggling with it.

He soon found that this whip was much heavier than he had imagined, and that it wouldn't be easy for his boy's hands to learn to manage it. And besides, it turned out that a whip like this was a devilish thing; you lashed with it and crack, the whip end flew back from somewhere and cut you across the back or on the head. And to crack it, that really did take some strength! The first few days Vasek only fooled about with the whip, rather than actually learning to do anything with it. On one such occasion the lame Harwey stopped beside him.

"Hallo, Vasek, what a wonderful whip! A magnificent whip. Who gave it to you?"

"Hans, Mr. Harwey!"

"And you're supposed to practice with it?"

"Yes, Mr. Harwey."

"Hans is an old fool if he thinks that you can hold a whip handle like that. Come with me, Vasek, I'll find you something better."

Harwey headed toward one of his supply wagons, rummaged about in it for a while, then crawled out and gave Vasek an old, rather shabby whip, but one considerably smaller and lighter.

"This one will fit your hand better. It was Old Umberto's during the time when he had a small ring. You can really crack it—see, make it crack! . . . yes."

Vasek tried it, and in point of fact this one was just right for his strength. Once, twice, three times he made it crack like a pistol. He jumped for joy.

"Oh, Mr. Harwey, this one really cracks, doesn't it? Hear the way it cracks, Mr. Harwey? What do you think, Mr. Harwey, do you think Father will be able to hear it crack? Do you think maybe Father's wondering, when he hears it crack, who's cracking it? Do you think Father believes I'm cracking it? Or do you think Father thinks Mr. Berwitz is cracking it?"

"Oh, oh, that's a lot of questions for an old man. But don't believe that cracking is all that you can do with a whip. Of course, you have to learn to crack it too, yes. And in many different ways, not only one. Look, I'll make it crack twice with one stroke."

Harwey jerked with the larger whip and its white tip made two cracking sounds.

"And you must know how to crack three times with it, no less. And how to do it elegantly, so that the whip looks beautiful when it cuts through the air, yes. But that isn't all. Look."

Harwey took a piece of newspaper, crumpled it up, and threw it some distance across the ground. Then he stood a whip-length away from the paper, lashed, and the paper flew up.

"That's it! Hit it square! You won't be able to do that right away. You'll have to practice for three months or more before you can hit it every time. And you'll learn something else, too. You have to be able to hit any part of the ring from the center where you stand, and be able to crack it or only nip it or touch it. Very lightly. Then you have to know how to crack from above or from below, from the left or from the right. And how to lash your hardest with the whip, but so that it only cracks near the horses' ears and doesn't hit them. And then how to crack quickly three times in a row in different places, as if three horses were up to mischief at the same time.

"In a word, Vasek, the whip must speak for you, I might say, must tell the horses for you what it is you want from them: faster, slower, jump or don't jump; it must punish them sometimes and praise them sometimes. Yes. All of that's more important than just cracking the whip in the air. Our director has such perfect control of his whip that if you throw an apple up he can cut it in two in the air. I think that you'll be able to master the whip a bit by the end of a year. A whip, I tell you, a real circus whip, is a whole science. Yes."

So a new and prolonged subject of study began for Vasek, into which he threw himself with all his boyish seriousness. Roméo's boys soon discovered him at his work. At first they only looked on with respectful admiration, but then a great sport developed out of it: instead of striking at a piece of crumpled paper Vasek now lashed at Roméo's black offspring, who ran to and fro, jumping into the range of his whip from every side, daring him to strike at them, and roaring horribly when one of them actually got hit.

Vasek had his cross to bear with these boys. Already he put up unwillingly with their constant presence whenever their father worked with him. This Vasek did not like. At home he had been the recognized leader of the whole gang of boys from childhood up, and with a sort of boyish pride he had been careful to see that no one detected him in any weakness. And now he had suddenly met a new gang which could do everything better than he could. It was only a joke for them to do the tricks Vasek had to struggle and struggle to learn. They never jeered at him, it was true, but with constant shouts and cries they showed him how easy it was to do the tricks he could not perform—this already had irritated him, and inwardly he had vowed a hundred times that he would show the little wretches who was boss as soon as he could do at least the first jumps.

The worst and the strangest relationship was Vasek and Paolo's. There was a silent tension between them which perhaps had its origin in the fact that Vasek had nothing definite to which to attribute it. Paolo was somewhat older, and far more experienced, than Vasek and could do tricks in a way that left Vasek full of envy. Paolo was a good-looking boy, slender, graceful; when he stood he always stood a bit theatrically, when he did something his motions were always harmonious and pleasing. He was well aware of this and had already put his good looks to use.

Beside him Vasek felt quite awkward and clumsy. Paolo had

a bold, it might even be called an impudent, look, and in his gleaming eyes there shone a look of foxlike cunning which was at once ready to transform the look of impudence into one of innocent prankishness whenever he was reproved for his boldness or when he received a box on the ears. "Oh, you wouldn't be angry at handsome, innocent Paolo?" was his attitude. Vasek was direct and frank, and he detected the falseness and cowardice which lay behind Paolo's foxiness. He also conceived a deep suspicion that Paolo's joy at Vasek's progress was not sincere, but was only an attempt to flatter him.

Paolo was a sort of assistant to Achmed in Vasek's training, and when Vasek had caught onto some of the basic tricks (circus performers call a trick each part of an act which must be practiced over and over again until it becomes completely mechanical) and Achmed was absent, Paolo would supervise Vasek's rehearsals alone. This he did with great zeal. Again and again he would smile patiently and show Vasek the right way to start, and he applauded heartily whenever Vasek succeeded at the trick.

But this continual smiling eagerness, this attentive politeness, this extreme sympathy, seemed hostile and suspicious to the more restrained Vasek. None of the boys whom he had met before had ever behaved like this; his own child's world had been rougher, harder, perhaps even fiercer in its envy and jealousy, but it had been frank, open, and clear. With Paolo, Vasek felt he was dealing with a slippery eel which somehow kept getting away. And Vasek knew that Paolo did not like him, that he did not behave thus out of sincere affection, but on the contrary, from envy.

Why Paolo envied him Vasek could not imagine or even guess. Everything here seemed so natural and simple to him—this life of which he had so quickly made himself a part, the kindness which adults displayed to him and the share which he took in every common task. Actually he had been with Umberto's Circus only a few days longer than had Paolo, but he felt completely at home; he had made friends and comrades of everyone, of Hans, of the "donter," of Harwey, of Arr-Shehir.

And here lay the real seed of Paolo's envy: Vasek was at home here, he was a native, while the Roméo family wandered over the earth and were here only fleetingly. Roméo had a contract with

Berwitz for ten months, but if it had been for two years or for five, it was still temporary and would come to an end; one day their blue wagon would part with Umberto's wagons and they would wander about with another circus or open some side show at the fairs.

About Vasek and his father, on the other hand, there could be no discussion; *they* were anchored here for their whole life. The question of what constituted home affected their relative social positions, as it had already shaped the outlines of their future destinies. For Antonín Karas the idea of home was inseparably bound up with the hut in Horní Snezná; Vasek, whose child's adaptability could willingly accept great changes, felt that this great traveling circus was his home, a sort of village on wheels with all its people and its animals, a village far more enchanting than Horní Snezná. But Paolo, poor, handsome Paolo, felt that his only home was this wagon where he slept, squeezed up amid a heap of human bodies, which carried him now here and now there, in sun and snow, in rain and frost, over the whole earth, and which, almost every year, resounded to the squalling of a newborn child.

From this point of view Paolo envied Vasek and was jealous of him. The young half-Berber was devoured by an insatiable jealousy whenever he saw Vasek sit down to eat with such a powerful gentleman as Kerholec, whenever he saw him riding Mary or tending the Shetlands, when he found him in intimate conversation with Captain Gambier, when he noticed him during the intervals going round with the lion cubs. How he longed for all this himself, how glad he would have been to run so freely about the great tent, the stables, the menagerie!

But everywhere they drove tiny, handsome Paolo away. Hans behaved like a devil toward him and his brothers; he only scolded and called Heaven to witness that he would not answer for anything if those gipsies were allowed inside the stables. Captain Gambier had even distributed a special circular stating that the boys were forbidden near the cages and the wagons with the wild beasts. All of them had an entirely natural fear of this new quicksilver-like African element in which the desire to play tricks mingled with inborn, unrestrained curiosity. Vasek, on the other hand, was quiet and serious; the circus men felt the grown-up man in him, and behaved to him accordingly.

But if all of them were on their guard against the Roméos, one of them was filled with open enmity from the very beginning. This was Arr-Shehir, the guard and keeper of the elephant Bingo. While he was nearby the tiny, handsome Paolo did not dare even to go near the elephant's stable.

"Believers in Mohammed"—Arr-Shehir spoke in a worried voice—"are full of jinns who are hostile to the health of the Holy Ones. I have placed a moth's foot on the threshold of Bingo's stable, but the jinn could still pass over in Paolo's body."

The stable hands did not see the moth's foot on the threshold, but they did see the switch Arr-Shehir had placed near the entrance. When he struck out at Paolo with it for the first time the boy ran to Achmed almost in tears and complained to him bitterly that the keeper had chased him away. Achmed Roméo shrugged his shoulders.

"Revenge and retribution are in Allah's hand, not yours," he said.

During Paolo's short life he had already learned to dissemble, and in his childhood he had learned to bow to those greater than himself with the bow number three. At the very first glance of his sly eyes he had grasped Vasek's position, and this was the cause of all his sycophancy and zeal. It was in all of them, in all the Roméos; this was the reason why old Achmed welcomed Kerholec with humble bows, and all his children jumped round Vasek with bright smiles. But with his sure child's instinct Vasek sensed that it was unnatural and only play-acting, and more than once, when Paolo grinned at him in his heartiest manner, he inwardly breathed, "You snake!"

Amid all their helter-skelter flattery he now remained stolid and unconcerned, certain in the firm belief that one day these everlasting smiles would crack open, and then he would settle his score with all these Moors. And now, when he had learned to control the whip, and Roméo's boys ran up and cried to him to strike at them, a game began into which Vasek could put a part of his hidden fury. The boys were spread round in a circle; they ran up within range of the whip and Vasek lashed at them with blows which

179

were by no means meant to be gentle. Never would Vasek have learned to hit the target so quickly if he had used lifeless paper as he now did in this game which meant so much to him.

The game went on for weeks and Vasek's casts constantly became more precise and more quick, while the cries of Roméo's boys became all the more challenging. *"Vasek, ecco, Vasek, qui, Vasek . . ."* the voices sounded uninterruptedly whenever he appeared among the wagons with the whip. And the longer the game continued, the more vociferous were the shouts and teasings, the many jeers the little crowd indulged in, the protruding tongues, thumbed noses, and bursts of laughter. Without a word Vasek lashed and whipped as hard as he could, growing more and more angry at this crew which now openly taunted him when they succeeded in jumping aside or falling on the ground and avoiding the blows.

But one day their usual shouts suddenly changed into terrible screams and roars. The grooms rushed out of the stable and people ran from the wagons. There on the open field they saw a single scrimmage of fighting boys, and when they ran up to them they recognized Paolo at the bottom of the pile, Vasek lying on top of him and choking him, and on top of Vasek all of Paolo's brothers, whom Vasek kicked and shook off as best he could.

When they pulled them apart Paolo was quite powerless and out of breath and Vasek bristled all over with rage.

"What's up?" Hans went at them from one side and Achmed from the other.

For a long time no one wanted to confess, until Vasek answered to defend himself:

"Paolo called me a 'dawblecow.'"

"Dawblecow—what's that?"

"I don't know. But I won't let him get away with it."

"Dawblecow—what's a dawblecow?" Hans asked the people around them.

"Maybe it's the English expression, 'double cow,'" answered Harwey.

Further investigation proved that this was correct. The widely traveled boys had decided during their games with Vasek—or Vasku, as they called him—that his name was composed of the

French word *vache* and the German *Kuh,* and that therefore Vasku meant "double cow." And from this Paolo had invented the English expression.

The laughter was so great that Achmed Roméo completely forgot about cuffing and kicking the culprits. But Vasek, pale, picked up his whip again and stood among the others. Now that he had obtained an explanation of the insult he understood that the nickname was a dangerous one, that it could make his whole life here unpleasant. He cracked his whip and cried, "Whoever says it again will get hit!"

Hans, too, felt that they might have been ridiculing Vasek, and so he added: "Good, Vasek. Don't give in. And if I hear it from anyone I won't take a whip to him, but a belt buckle. . . . All right, let's break it up!"

And so Paolo discovered that he must go on hating Vasek, for all the great ones took his side against the boys who could do more than he could. But he must be careful, for Vasek had tremendous strength and perhaps he might kill the handsome Paolo.

CHAPTER SEVEN

The story of the double cow was a piece of fun which led to certain consequences—Vasek was beginning more and more to say things which belonged to no language whatever. In the circus everyone spoke a jargon made up of French, Italian, and English phrases, and the Czech workers mingled German words with their Czech conversations; but to this Vasek had added, beginning with the word "donter," all sorts of expressions from all the languages he heard about him. People shouted and talked in French, English, Italian, and Spanish, the Gevaerts often spoke together in Swedish, Mrs. Berwitz and Steenhouwer spoke Dutch, Roméo swore or called on God in Arabic and Turkish—

Umberto's Circus was like a linguistic Noah's Ark where each language was represented by a pair.

The older people were used to it, but a boy who lived in the midst of it all, as Vasek did, began to become confused in this Babel-like chattering. Sometimes he said things his own father failed to understand and which had to be translated for him. But when Vasek began to say *"Mashallah!"* then Bures realized it was high time to start to save his Czech soul from utter confusion.

From the back of Number Eight Bures dug out a bundle of books tied with a string, and began to read them whenever he had the chance. This happened for the first time when at supper Vasek told with excitement the story of how that day the tigers had almost fought one of the lions. Gambier had been training them for a joint performance, but today the ancient enmity of both species had flamed forth, and if it had not been for the attendants with their pitchforks blood would have flowed. The inhabitants of Number Eight discussed the great hatred which reigns among some species of wild beasts, and Bures suddenly remembered that there was a famous poem on that subject. Already he was on his feet and declaiming loudly about "Hermann from Bubno, a valiant lord, true to his king in his deeds . . ."

At first they listened with a smile to his declamation; but suddenly they became serious and followed the poetic narrative with rapt attention. The poem dealt with an episode in which Hermann saw two tigers attacking a lion. He considered the odds unfair, so he killed one tiger with his sword while the lion dispatched the other. Whereupon the lion was so grateful that he lay down at Hermann's feet.

At this point Malina stirred. He evidently had some objection, but he had waited to see how the story would end. Now they heard how Hermann tied a rope to the lion and how the latter followed him to the city gates, and how they then lived in Bohemia until the knight died and the lion "roared with great grief, did not eat, did not drink, and the third day passed away."

"Well, Bures, you've done a fine job of putting it together," Malina said. "Only I don't believe that that lion lay down at his feet. Everything, but not that."

182

"And why not?" Bures defended the imagination of the poet. "Out of gratitude . . ."

"He wouldn't have lain down." Malina shook his head. "What he would have done is hold onto the tiger even after its death. When a lion has booty he puts his paw on it and growls or roars. And then he takes it in his teeth and tugs at it and pulls and growls all the time. So add that to your poem: he dragged the tiger through the jungle and roared. I miss that part."

"And one more thing," Kerholec observed. "He wouldn't have lain down at his feet. Even if he were really tame, as Bures says, the most he would have done was rub his head against the man's body."

"Well, what about Corina?" Vosátka joined in with the air of an expert on the subject, a part not usual for him. "She rolls on the ground in front of Gambier."

"Yes, a lioness does," Kerholec defended his own theory. "But she rolls on her back and doesn't lie down at anybody's feet."

"Well, the male lies down in front of the tamer, too," Malina opined. "A lion *might* do that, but only an old and lazy one."

"But an old, lazy one like that wouldn't fight a tiger," Kerholec insisted. "He would roar and run away. I say it was a lioness."

"But friends," Bures defended the poem anew, "imagine that he did it out of gratitude when Hermann of Bubno saved his life and bound up his wounds!"

"They do do such things," Malina agreed. "Lions are grateful for kindness. The trainer Cervinka once had a young lioness—her name was Cleopatra. She got pneumonia and he was afraid he would lose her. He put her in his own bed and took care of her until she got well. And that Cleopatra was grateful to him till her dying day. Whenever he came to see her she got up on her hind legs, put her paws on his shoulders, and licked his face."

"You see?" Kerholec turned to the others. "It was a lioness, and she licked his face, but she didn't lie down at his feet!"

"In a word, Bures"—Sergeant Vosátka grinned—"you'll have to change that magnificent poem, and first make the lion mop up the forest with that tiger, and then make him change into a lioness and lick the fair countenance of your German of Bubno."

"That wouldn't do, either," Karas Senior joined in modestly "Why, she would have knocked him over!"

"Then we should reverse it." Vosátka accepted the change. "It was the knight Hermann who lay down at the lion's feet."

"I didn't recite the poem for you, you vandals with your menagerie wisecracks," said Bures at last. "I did it for Vasek. How did you like it, Vasek?"

"I liked it. It was very nice."

"You see? Youth still has some feeling for poetry. What a consolation it is that there will always be people to whom poetry can still speak! And what did you like the most?"

"What the Lord Hermann said when he saw the battle."

"Two against one is not a fair fight!"

"Yes! Two against one is not a fair fight! And when I fought Paolo I had seven of them on top of me. But I would have licked all of them if Hans and the others hadn't run up."

"And you liked the Czech lord's bravery?"

"Oh yes. But in his place I wouldn't have run the tiger through. I'd have hit him one on the snout and kept hitting him until he let the lion go. It's a shame, really, to kill a tiger."

Bures saw that Vasek was completely wrapped up in circus life, but he comforted himself with the thought that in his young soul there would also be room for loftier feelings. He resolved that from now on he would work diligently to save this boy's soul for higher tasks and awaken his love for his people.

The next day at midday, he started reciting old heroic poems for Vasek in the Czech tongue. Bures did it well. Vasek gazed at him with pious reverence and involuntarily felt that these wonderful, unparalleled verses carried him off to lands filled with quite different beauties from the entrancing charms of the circus and the menagerie around him. For the most part Bures recited from memory, and an expert would have noticed that his repertoire was a bit out-of-date and that Czech poetry had made considerable progress since his day; for Vasek it was all new and uplifting, it filled his mind with new interests, and before long he was sitting with Bures and his books every day and slowly spelling out their contents.

To everything he gave Vasek to read Bures could add some

184

commentary, for the most part drawn from Czech life itself. It was strange; the two of them had traveled far from their true homeland; around them sounded the various dialects of Low German, Frisian, Dutch, and Flemish; the canvas of their tents swelled in the damp sea winds, and often their wagons swayed only a few yards from the surf of the wind-swept sea; but here, in these strange lands, this dark-haired man, shipwrecked on the sands of life, sat and told the young boy of his love for his fatherland which lay beyond far-off mountains and rivers; and in the boy there flamed up a love for his own people, of which there were only his father and four outcasts about him. But each of these men was such that he had to love them; each of them excelled in something, each had lived through many experiences and knew many stories, each was firm and tough, and treated him as a man and as an equal.

Bures told him of the old man who had uncovered the past and written it down in the beautiful *History of the Czech Nation*. Again he would speak of the brave fighter Havlícek, or with tears in his eyes tell of the sufferings of Josef Kajetán Tyl, who had consecrated his life to the Czech theater and preferred to die of hunger rather than desert it. Vasek gained the impression that all these were people with whom Bures himself had been acquainted. Once he actually asked Bures this question, but Bures glanced to one side, waved his hand, and cried in irritation:

"Oh, that would be a long story."

As their evening talks continued, they grew longer and more serious. And whenever Bures tried to depict for the boy the beauty of golden, hundred-towered Prague, or tell him some memorable event from Czech history, the other roving wanderers would be silent and listen quietly to the story of their home, the story of their fatherland.

They never talked of it; they were accustomed to their rough battle with life, and had no time for sentiment. But now that this boy was with them, this child whom they did not wish to deprive of a knowledge of the things sacred to them, they threw off the hard shell they wore and involuntarily adopted Vasek's simple attitude, shared his child longing for faith and for legends.

185

CHAPTER EIGHT

ANNA BERWITZ was sad; one of the three lion cubs had died. From birth it had been weakly and feeble and did not take kindly to the world as the two others had. She ran with the news to Captain Gambier to gather sympathy. He simply shrugged his shoulders.

"Madame, it's all in the day's work. To keep young cubs alive while you're traveling is a job which requires more care than you can give. Success is mostly a matter of good luck and a miracle. But the others look thriving."

"Yes. I hope I'll be able to bring you at least those two, and someday I'll give them to you to be trained."

"Thank you, madame, I will do what I can. But only to give you pleasure. And I hope the lions will give you satisfaction. Of course it's not very certain that I can do much with them."

"Why do you think not, Captain?"

"I've had some experience of my own with them. There's nothing better than raw beasts, you know, real wild animals brought from the jungle. They know nothing of man, they instinctively fear him, and when they find in the tamer a creature who will not harm them they grow to trust him and obey him. But a lion born in a cage and brought up among people will be used to them, in his own way he will be sophisticated, and you cannot rely on his instincts. For him, man is no special being, but only a creature like any other, and if he takes it into his head he'll spring at him as he'd spring at a goat. I know how pleasant it is to play with the cubs, but when they grow up it will be different. From all my experience I've come to the conclusion that I only want to work with 'raw' animals. With them I know what I'm dealing with. A lion or a tiger you bring up yourself is unreliable."

"And Berwitz and I told each other that you could train them to do miraculous stunts if you brought them up from babies."

"Too bad, but that's wrong. Human society spoils an animal's good manners."

Old Malina was ordered to bury the little dead beast. He called Vasek to see it.

"He did not eat, did not drink, the third day passed away," Vasek recited, stroking the head of the gaunt little body.

"But in this case there will be two others to follow him," Malina muttered. "Death always wants to make a triple performance."

Malina was evidently upset by this trifling incident, and that evening again and again he led their conversation back to the subject of who might be struck down. In vain they tried to shout the old man down.

"In the circus," he answered stubbornly, "no one ever died alone. I found that out long ago. It happened the last time: first the tigress Miuma, then the Bengal Pasha, then Old Berwitz. In the circus death likes to hang about for a while."

The agitated old man fell to meditating and spoke no more. However, nothing happened in the circus or in the menagerie, the program took the prescribed order, the journey through Holland passed off without accident. But Malina kept to himself, only muttering a word now and then. One evening during supper he stopped eating suddenly, his spoon in mid-air. He put down the spoon, got up slowly, and walked away. Kerholec nodded to the others.

"He's going to the animal wagons. Run after him, Vasek, and come back and tell us what's going on."

They kept on eating, but with a sort of painful constraint. After a while Vasek came back running.

"He went to see the goats. Bluebeard is dying!"

The four stakers lost their taste for their food. The goat Bluebeard! The glutton and mischief-maker, who had given them trouble so often. How many times had he got out of the goats' enclosure! How often had he gulped down some man's dinner or supper, how often had he eaten up the circus posters or nibbled at Berwitz's whip when it was lying about! Once he had chased that secretary round the whole tent! Could it be possible? It was possible. Among the circus animals he was a real Methuselah; no one actually knew how long he had been leading the goats through towns and cities in their parade entries. For the last few years he had looked like the devil Mephisto, but for a long time it had been observed that he was growing lazy and lethargic, and that he spent most of his time lying down and sleeping.

Kerholec got up and the others after him. Among the animal wagons they found old Malina. He was sitting on the ground and held the blue-bearded goat on his lap. Bluebeard's eyes were shut and he was breathing heavily. Above him stood Anna Berwitz, petting him and rumpling his hair between the horns and speaking to him tenderly, but the goat took no notice of her. The men all slipped away; only Kerholec came back and handed Malina a blanket. Malina nodded his head and covered the gaunt body of the goat. The latter's white harem had crowded into one corner and were bleating.

At last Director Berwitz arrived. With a firm hand he felt Bluebeard's neck and belly, bent his front leg, and shrugged his shoulders. He tried to persuade Anna to come to supper, but Anna allowed him to go off by himself. She remained with Malina, and when it grew dusk she brought a wrought-iron carriage lantern, lighted it, and wrapping herself tight in her cloak, she sat down beside Malina. At intervals the watchman would come toward them and then go off into the distance. Slowly the starless night flowed along, the moths flew round the yellow light of the lantern, somewhere in the distance a tower clock struck, to be followed each time by the tinkle of chimes. At half-past twelve Malina put his hand to the goat's face, straightened up, and said:

"He's gone. . . ."

"Poor Bluebeard," Anna whispered. A part of her old beloved world had died, the world into which she had married; a part of Umberto's Circus was dead. For a while she stroked the cold body. Then she raised her head.

"Vendelín—couldn't we bury him? . . . now . . . the two of us . . . ? Bluebeard deserved it!"

Malina nodded his gray head. He disappeared somewhere in

188

the distance and returned with a pickax and a shovel. Anna picked up the dead goat. The old man took the lantern. And quietly they walked out between the sleeping wagons onto the sandy slope where the white birch trees stood.

"Here, Vendelín!"

He put down the lantern, examined the spot, and began to dig. Anna set down her burden, took the shovel in her firm, toughened hands, and turned over the loose sand and clay. They were in the southernmost tip of Holland, in the hill country around Valkenburg, not far from the borders of Belgium and Germany.

About half-past two the old man Malina climbed into wagon Number Eight on tiptoe. The sleepers stirred and raised their heads.

"How is he?" whispered someone in a muffled voice.

"Tomorrow the third one will die." They were Malina's first words to them for many days.

The next day was a day full of bustling activity from dawn onward. They had to travel to Aachen; they would have to cross the frontier, and it was necessary to make up in advance for the delay there with which they must reckon. Peter Berwitz had been on his feet since earliest morning, but before they set off he went to Valkenburg for the post. The handing out of the morning post was a rite with him, and he preferred to perform it in the big tent. He stood on the surrounding rim, called out the names in a loud voice, and with a grand gesture handed out the individual letters to the members of his community, or to the secretary, Steenhouwer.

Among other jibes at his expense it used to be said that he did this to prove to everyone that he could read and that he was superior to that tightrope-walker Kranz, who had learned only with difficulty to draw the five letters of his name; or like that notorious Director Ravanelli, who always spread the letters around the ring so that each one could take what was his; what was left he then scooped up, carried off to his wagon, and burned.

To be illiterate was nothing shameful in the circus, most of the members of which had never gone to school. In those days Umberto's Circus would nail up a sign for the illiterate on one of the supporting poles by the gate. This was one of Vendelín

Malina's many duties. He himself could neither read nor write, but with a slow hand he drew hieroglyphics on the coarse paper which were to designate the various acts: a rectangle with legs for a horse, a comma with a small circle for a rider, an arc for the elephant, two hooks for a flying trapeze, and a triangle for a clown's cap.

Today there was no time for any great ceremony with the post. Berwitz seized the bundle and looked over it rapidly before turning it all over to Steenhouwer. But toward the end he stopped and slowly pulled out an envelope with a black border. He looked at Steenhouwer and then tore open the envelope. He unfolded the letter and called in a stifled voice to the secretary.

"Frans, call Anna. Grandfather Umberto's dead!"

His mother had written to him from Savoy. The worthy Carlo Umberto had passed away quietly and happily among his dogs and cats, his training whip in his hand. For his eighty-nine years he had seemed to be wonderfully vigorous in body; he had enjoyed his bottle of wine and had still taken a delight in making speeches over it; but his mind was evidently growing feeble.

The year before he had started to prepare a wonderful scene which was to use both dogs and cats, but after a year and a half it still was not ready, for he had begun to forget what he could expect from each animal. For example, he had taught the fox terrier to do a rather high and dangerous jump, but then he demanded of it the carrying of two Angora cats in a basket, the traditional task of the bulldog.

Since spring he had been training them in the garden, seated in an easy chair in the sun, and more than once he would doze off at his work and sleep, until the dogs would jolt him out of his slumber with their barking when, in spite of all their training, they would start fighting with the cats.

And so it had happened that on Monday last Grandpa Umberto was sitting in the garden during the afternoon, while four dogs in ladies' and men's hats danced on their hind legs before him. The old man dropped his head on his left shoulder, gave a smile, and died, and the dogs danced on and on, timidly looking at him and at his cane, until their legs hurt and one after another they dropped down on all fours. The cane did not move, the punishment was not forthcoming; they stood and wagged their tails in perplexity until one dog in a Tyrolean hat suddenly sensed that something was wrong and began to howl. He was joined by all the others, the three dancers, the four jumpers, two which danced figures and two which were dressed as policemen—twelve performing dogs sat around the circle and howled until the women came and found the old man dead amid his blossoming oleanders in his sweet-smelling garden.

"Well, Grandfather Umberto!" said Peter Berwitz when Anna had finished the letter. "A beautiful life, a beautiful death. Sew mourning bands on the sleeves of all my coats. In ten minutes we must leave."

The death of the founder of the circus aroused a great stir among the personnel. There were many stories to tell and many people to recollect; of course it was Malina who remembered the most, he who had passed two-thirds of his life with the old proprietor.

"What did I say?" He gazed at his fellow travelers at dinner with a glance in which there was no pride of triumph, only the confirmation of an asserted truth. And although the old man was the most moved by the third death, still his worried unrest and his disquiet had passed, and again his tongue loosened up.

Karas was relatively the least affected by these events. He was a newcomer, he knew nothing of Umberto and listened with nothing more than interest to what Malina related and the others remembered. As a rule Karas now sat down to these evening conversations with a piece of wood and a knife in his hand, for ever since he had fastened the first ornamental emblems on his own wagon he had not had enough time to carve the mass of articles others requested from him.

The decoration of Number Eight aroused the envy of the occupants of all the other wagons, and all the circus people who had their own wagons now tried to beautify them and adorn them on the outside in one way or another. Some painted them with shining colors so that they would be equal to Roméo's blue wagon, others used contrasting colors for the window and door frames, and here and there an unsuspected master of ornamentation would appear, to paint a whole frieze round under his wagon roof. But most of all they longed for carved heads or reliefs from Karas's hand.

After the horse heads and the elephant relief a new wonder had made its appearance among the wagons: over the ticket window there stood a statue of Fortune, strewing apples, flowers, and something else which looked like banknotes from a horn of plenty. One after another the circus people came to marvel at this extraordinary creation of the carver's art. Among others Captain Gambier too came, and his beautifully combed head was tall enough for him to look without difficulty into the elevated window behind which sat Frau von Hammerschmidt.

He congratulated her on the beautiful ornament and immediately began to ask her advice about what he should order for his own wagon, a lion or a tiger or two bears. Frau von Hammerschmidt advised a lion as the true king of beasts and of heraldic emblems. Captain Gambier stated that he preferred tigers because they were much more dangerous. He boasted to her that he had the stuffed head of a tiger who had once attacked him, and that he had his wagon decorated with tiger skins. Frau von Hammerschmidt conceded that it must look magnificent and be much more splendid than the Berwitz's, the carpets of which were made of lion skins, which soon wore out and lost their hair.

Whereupon Captain Gambier considered himself obliged to invite the dear lady to drop in for coffee so that she might look at his tiger trophies. Frau von Hammerschmidt replied very coyly that it might not be quite proper, but at last promised on condition that she could bring her knitting. It seemed to her that a stocking in her hand would be the best defense of a widow's good reputation.

So it happened that one day during the midday rest Frau von Hammerschmidt started out, her knitting in her bag, toward the wagon on which the red flag flew aloft. Captain Gambier welcomed her very courteously. The white cups and the golden rolls lay shining on the table and the odor of coffee emerged from the pot. Frau von Hammerschmidt spoke French much more fluently than Gambier did German, and so the Captain was able to play the part of a cultured and animated conversationalist. While he talked Frau von Hammerschmidt did not even notice that the hour of rest had passed and that the wagons had begun to move again; only when the wheel of the wagon jolted over a stone, the wagon gave a lurch, and Frau von Hammerschmidt pricked her finger with the needle, did she cry out with amazement, snatch up her knitting, and get up to go toward the door.

However, Gambier observed that there was no sense in her leaving now unless she knew where her wagon was, and, at a loss as to what to do, Frau von Hammerschmidt admitted that she would have to stay in his wagon. To make up for this the Captain showed her all his tiger skins and took his stuffed tiger head down from the wall and told her of his struggle, even pulling up the leg of his trousers and showing her the scars from the bite on his calf. Frau von Hammerschmidt shivered with horror and admiration for the heroic giant, and wondered if the Captain was tattooed over his whole body as he was on his leg. She had always disliked tattooing and had spoken of it as an abomination, only fit for sailors, but now suddenly it seemed very romantic to stand at the side of a tattooed hero.

As a matter of fact she was being overcome by a long-forgotten but pleasant excitement. Outside the sun must have set long ago, for it had grown dark in the wagon and the little traveling room had acquired a special air of intimacy. As she experienced these sensations Frau von Hammerschmidt grew frightened; no longer did she hold in her hand her shield of matronly dignity. The stocking had long since been deposited in the knitting bag. Again she grew confused, and now there occurred to her something that no one could remember ever happening before—she lost her tongue. Her words grew confused and at last Frau von Hammerschmidt actually stopped speaking. She looked helplessly straight in front of her, directly at one of the two beds.

"My assistant sleeps here with me," Gambier said quickly, following her glance. "It's not the pleasantest sort of company I could have, but in the end . . . when a man's alone . . ."

This was the last straw for Frau von Hammerschmidt. She grew red all over, but regained control of herself only to make the unfortunate remark:

"To be sure . . . you deserve different sort of company . . ."

Gambier wanted to say something to this, but Frau von Hammerschmidt now breathed more easily; the wagon had stopped and now began to turn, and from the shouting it was evident that they had arrived at their destination. Now she was able to extricate herself from the delicate subject with the remark that they were there and that it had been a very agreeable afternoon, to which Gambier agreed still more vociferously. She thanked him for his invitation and took her leave.

When she climbed down the steps she discovered that all the wagons of Umberto's Circus were arranged in a circle, like the cottages of a village around the main square. Men and women were coming out of all the wagons, and their glances fell on Frau von Hammerschmidt. And just as if Umberto's Circus had been a real village, only one on wheels, the whisper traveled from wagon to wagon:

"Look, Hammerschmidt's just leaving the lion-tamer's. . . ."

Only one man did not notice her, though he sat on the stairs of the wagon directly opposite Gambier's. It was old Malina in front of Number Eight. Kerholec's gang had long since arrived and gone off to their work. And Malina, too, had his job. When Frau von Hammerschmidt came up to him she saw that between his legs he held a bearded goat and was painting his beard blue.

"Ah, the goat is redivivus!" Frau von Hammerschmidt remarked as she passed.

"Not redivivus, dear lady," Malina answered quite seriously, "but Bluebeard II. After the Grim Reaper's performances, Life must have his."

Frau von Hammerschmidt looked at him, but said nothing, and slowly walked off to the cashier's wagon. The figure of the tattooed Captain rose before her eyes. And she sighed.

"Malina's really a wise old man."

CHAPTER NINE

MR. SELNICKI got his bottle of Johannisberger.

The matter took quite a lot of arranging. The first thing in the chain of events was that one day Hans announced to the director that Vasek was fit for the ring.

"Of course," he added in explanation, "he's not ready for any jumping, but for an ordinary appearance in the saddle he won't disgrace us, either in the way he holds himself or in the way he manages the horse."

Berwitz nodded his head, and at the first opportunity he gave the order that Vasek would ride into the ring on Mary while he was there. Vasek understood that something was up, but he was so proud of his riding that without any hesitation he mounted his pony and rode at a fast trot into the ring. Three paces from the director he stopped Mary and gave a salute. With the whip in his hand, Berwitz nodded, and commanded him to walk the horse round the ring in a clockwise direction. Mary turned like a dancer, and Vasek sat perfectly motionless.

"Slow trot! *Allez!*" Berwitz cried.

Vasek bent forward slightly, pressed with his legs, and the little mare sprang forward.

"Fast trot! *Allez!*"

The speed increased. Vasek crouched forward but sat firm in the saddle.

"Gallop! *Allez!*"

An invisible pressure of the knee, a hardly noticeable movement of his body, and Mary struck out with both forelegs. Berwitz watched to see how firmly Vasek's feet were "planted" in the stirrups and how he rose and fell in rhythm with the pony's leaps. He followed the hoofbeats.

195

"Slow trot! *Allez!*"

"Turn and ride back! *Allez!*"

"Turn around, gallop! *Allez!*"

"Stand!"

Abruptly Vasek stopped the galloping Mary and held her still on the spot, her hind legs a bit forward, her neck bent, her every muscle in play. Berwitz turned toward the gate, where Hans was standing, and nodded in approval. Then he motioned to Vasek that he might go, and walked over to Hans.

"Yes, Hans, Vasek can appear. The way he stopped that pony and held the posture with her would get applause."

The next day there appeared on the bulletin board among the schedule of rehearsals:

"9:20—Helen Berwitz and Vasek on Miss and Mary."

Regardless of whether or not Achmed Roméo had been correct when he said that Vasek would not grow tall eventually, he was wrong for the time being; in front of the bulletin board Vasek stretched tremendously. And again and again he came back to read that magical phrase, "Helen Berwitz and Vasek." He still did not know what the number was to be, but already he was convinced that it would be the most beautiful on the program, over-shadowing even the director's black horses and his wife's white ones and Perreira's grand style. And no "team" which had ever been billed on the posters sounded so enchanting to him as that of Helen Berwitz and Vasek.

He rubbed his hands at this marvelous development for the two of them, but the task the director had assigned them proved to be a quite simple one: Vasek and Helen were to ride in together, greet the audience, ride round the ring together as if on a promenade, at the gate turn in toward the center, and on the other side separate, she to the right and he to the left; and after they had gone round the whole circle and come together again they were to ride back to the gate and make room for the elephant's entry. Then they were to come in with him to the center, point to him, and ride out in a circle. Actually it was only an introduction for Bingo's entry, but Vasek considered it the most important event of his life.

Their act was really a small one and both children knew how

to ride sufficiently well for them to be able to do it according to the instructions after the first rehearsal. But a mere "according to instructions" never satisfied Peter Berwitz's ambition. Everything he did he wished to be the height of perfection. And so again and again Helen and Vasek had to circle and cross the ring to synchronize the timing of their gestures and the steps of their horses to the split second. And Mrs. Berwitz, too, began to come to their rehearsals to correct their movements and smooth them out. Of Helen she was already certain, for ever since infancy she had been trained to bow and to greet people properly, but Vasek seemed to her to be a sturdy country "sapling" who would require a great deal of training before his movements could become easy and graceful. To her surprise Vasek greeted the unseen audience with perfect gestures. His constant practice with Roméo in the ten reverences had taught the boy to raise his hat gracefully and self-confidently with a sweeping and elegant curve in the air as he bowed forward slowly, to the lowest position. The director's wife was well satisfied.

The next day she invited Frau von Hammerschmidt to visit her; long discussions began between them as to how they would dress the two children. At last it was decided that for Helen they would get ready a wide, flaring skirt of yellow taffeta, a tight-fitting black bodice with a yellow rose, and a broad straw hat. The boy would wear long light-gray trousers, a short black, tight-fitting jacket, and over it a broad white collar; a black low top hat with a flat brim would complete his costume. Then Mr. Selnicki was called in to select the music for their entry. He watched their performance and announced: " '*Gulliver among the Lilliputians*,' just as I said before. And when the elephant enters, then the bassoons will come in."

Hans followed all the preparations carefully. His own pupil and a horse from his stable were at stake. But until the very last he had no idea for what the number was really intended. It was too short and poor for an independent act. Only when Berwitz gave the order for Arr-Shehir to bring in the elephant did Hans realize that it was an *entrée*. He watched the rehearsal; at first he was pleased, but when the ponies had finished their act an unheard-of thing occurred: Hans rushed into the ring before the director had finished the rehearsal. Berwitz looked severe and took a tighter hold on his whip, meaning to crack it in Hans's direction. But Hans waved his arms and cried:

"No, no, it's all wrong!"

Berwitz grew stiff with rage at such impudence, but Hans blurted out in agitation:

"That *entrée* has no close, Mr. Director, just look at it! What kind of close is it for a rider to wave his hat about? And Vasek's a real horseman, Mr. Director, and Helen's a riding *prima!*"

Berwitz's face was as black as thunder. The whip twitched in his right hand. But nevertheless he mastered himself.

"What are you saying, Hans?" he asked icily.

Arr-Shehir on the elephant, the director's wife behind the rim, and Mr. Selnicki on the bandstand stood dumfounded. They knew that an explosion would occur at any moment. But it was impossible to hold Hans back.

"Those children have no exit, Mr. Director! They deserve a rider's finish!"

"And what shall that be?" Berwitz controlled himself with difficulty.

"At the end the ponies must kneel down beside Bingo, kneel on their right knee! And then, and only then, should the children bow!"

"You fool"—Berwitz's anger could no longer be restrained—"since when do Mary and Miss know how to kneel?"

"They do know how to, Mr. Director!" cried Hans. "As God is over me, they know it, all four know how to do it. I've been training them for six weeks!"

For some seconds the director looked into the groom's face without moving. Then he turned abruptly to Anna.

"Madame," he cried, as if he were laying down the law on Mount Sinai, "report to the office that the groom Hans has received a fine of five marks for an unpermitted entrance into the ring."

Then he turned toward the gate.

"Arr-Shehir, Helen Berwitz, and Vasek, enter again. You will practice the close, which the groom Hans will direct. Mr. Band Leader, we will have to change the music."

"The music needn't be changed." Selnicki turned to the musicians. "Only after the bassoons we'll play a flourish in F major. Thank you, gentlemen, you may go."

Hans stood in the ring, hot and cold by turns. It was unheard-of. To be fined and at the same time to be ordered to take over the direction. In his simple mind there arose a confusion he could not control. The director walked up to him and handed him his whip. Hans took it without a word, bowed awkwardly, and walked into the center of the ring. Suddenly he found himself alone there, for with long steps the director went off through the exit for the public. Hans did not know how to begin. Spasmodically he clasped the whip, and then automatically his arm moved and the whip cracked three times in the air. The worst was over. Hans nodded toward the gate.

"Helen, Vasek, please mount again. You, Arr-Shehir, not just yet, wait awhile. *Allez!*"

Helen and Vasek rode in at a slow walk.

"Stand!" Hans commanded. And then he walked between the two children and showed them how with their right foot they were to signal to the animal to kneel down, how they were to loosen the bridle and bend back in the saddle so that they shifted their weight and at the same time assumed the posture for a parade salute.

The children tried it and Hans quietly chided the ponies. Mary and Miss snorted, but they understood; at the fourth rehearsal they dropped on one knee without a mistake, their left legs stretched forward, their heads bent down almost to the ground, and the children completed their greeting to the public. Then the elephant Bingo emerged from the opening and everything was repeated with him. From the very beginning it was a success. Mrs. Berwitz clapped her hands. "Bravo, Hans!"

Four repetitions, five, eight, ten—the ponies knelt faultlessly and began to toss their heads as the spirit of play and performance awakened in them. Above them the giant Bingo watched with concentration to see how it was being planned, how far he should come into the ring, and where the girl was to stand and where the boy.

"Bravo, Hans!" Anna repeated, coming out into the ring when

the groom had dismissed everyone. "Now it's really much nicer. I'll tell the director about it."

She took the whip and headed toward the director's wagon. Berwitz was not there, only Frans, who had come for a snack. He told her that Peter was in the bookkeeper's office and that the Mittelhofers had just come there to see him about a complaint.

"They picked the right time for it." Anna laughed. "It'll probably cook their goose for them."

Berwitz had walked out of the tent in a towering rage. An interruption of a rehearsal such as that old fool Hans had allowed himself broke up all discipline. How could a circus carry on when all its discipline was gone? And then that close to the number. It was natural that one brain couldn't hit on everything, of course, and Peter always told himself this when any of the personnel came to him with advice for improving an act.

But these matters almost always occurred decorously, and in private; and when the idea was adopted the greatest glory always fell on the director, who had actually carried it out. Peter Berwitz had trained himself to heed the advice and observations of his personnel, for very often wonderful developments arose from them, but it was terribly distasteful for him to let others know that these were not his ideas. He told himself that he had an actual right to the inspirations of his subordinates. He shouldered the responsibility for them when they made mistakes, why should he not have the glory when now and then they hit on a clever idea?

The way in which Hans had behaved today was unheard-of, impossible. A whole crowd of people had seen and heard how he, Peter Berwitz, the director, had worked out an act which had a poor closing, and how a groom, a stable hand, had had a better idea. How was it that others always had better ideas than he, Peter Berwitz?

When he thought it over systematically he had to admit that to the unique art of the circus he himself had actually brought very little that was new. Only external details were worked out in his head: how to dress everyone flashily, how to develop a new kind of publicity, what to add to a performance, where to give one. Then that trip to Persia—who among his competitors would have dared to do such a thing? Not even his late father could have brought it off, nor Grandpa Umberto. They had only hammered away and struggled over each rehearsal, never halting in their continual search for perfection, but they had not been great enough actually to attain it. But Peter had brought the circus up to the top—how many circuses in Europe could be compared to his?

And what did it matter if he accepted the inspirations of others, from Anna, from Gaudeamus, from Selnicki, from Gambier, from Kerholec, from Arr-Shehir, and now even from the groom Hans? What would these ideas of theirs have been worth if it had not been for him, who carried them out? And each one of them could be rewarded for their ideas—thank God that it was possible to pay for ideas and then be even; but for the *execution* of an idea his will and his resources were essential, and therefore he, Peter Berwitz, and only he, was the most important personage in the enterprise.

These considerations at last calmed him a bit, but part of his offended pride and vanity was still wounded. And in this irritable mood he was approached by the dwarf Mittelhofer and his wife, who requested a serious interview.

"You come to me just at the right time," flashed through Peter's head. "Just when the ax will fall." He nodded to the couple. "I beg of you to come into the bookkeeper's wagon with me."

If Herr Mittelhofer had known Director Berwitz better, he would have been very much on his guard against this "I beg of you." Whenever Berwitz began to say "I beg of you" to his employees, and to display an excessive politeness, everyone knew that anger was smoldering in him, and tried to find some way to pacify him.

"I beg of you, please, to be seated," Berwitz said to the Mittelhofers in the wagon. "What do you wish to ask?"

Herr Mittelhofer got to the heart of the matter quickly and briefly. Umberto's Circus was now entering the country of the Alps, where the dwarfs had great renown, and it was very important for them to have complete artistic success there. Now this would be impossible if they had to dance to unknown music.

The maestro was first-class, to be sure, but the piece which he had chosen for them was certainly not the equal of the one they themselves had brought and which was now being played for the elephant. Such a humiliation was offensive and unbearable, and the Mittelhofer couple now emphatically demanded that their act be moved in the program, away from the elephant's, and that their original music be played.

"Excuse me," Berwitz said, "but are you quite certain that in any other place in the program you would have quite the success you now have?"

"In any other place"—the dwarf jumped up with irritation—"in any other place in the program we'll have twice as much success if we have our own music. Won't we, Emilie?"

Frau Mittelhofer agreed emphatically. The director remained just as polite as before, but now his glance became cold as ice.

"You are pleased to consent to any other place. Assuredly. But what if it turns out that you have no success whatever in another place?"

"That is out of the question, Mr. Director. Give us any other place, but give us our original music."

"But what if I were right, nevertheless, and you had no success?"

"Then, excuse me," and the dwarf was red all over, "then, pardon me, it would mean . . . with no offense, excuse me . . . that pure art has no place in a circus . . . and we would . . . with your permission . . . we would be forced to consider our contract as not binding. That is evident, Mr. Director."

"Hm, on such an important matter we ought to draw up an addition to the contract, so that there will be no argument. Are you pleased to agree?"

Herr Mittelhofer nodded and Berwitz called to Steenhouwer, who had returned sometime before and was eating bread and cheese in the corner. Quickly Berwitz dictated to him two clauses concerning the added condition in the contract. Mittelhofer signed it very self-consciously. Berwitz scrawled his signature below.

"Good," he said, straightening up before the dwarfs. "I am happy that we came to an agreement without legal action. Tomorrow you will dance to your original music, and you will appear as the first number on the program."

"*Ach!*" cried Frau Mittelhofer. "That's impossible!"

"You want to kill us!" shouted Mittelhofer.

"I am sorry. The contract reads, 'In any place whatsoever.' I decide where. And that settles it. Good day. Frans, open the door for the lady and gentleman."

It happened as Berwitz had arranged. Before the Roman riders had rushed into the ring in their wild gallop, before even the usual opening fanfares had sounded, the two dwarfs entered the ring and began to dance. People were still streaming into the gallery, climbing over seats, looking for places, calling to one another, and buying programs. And those who were already seated and had their programs were rustling through the leaves. The curtain over the gate for the performers was still drawn, and the whole number looked like a poor fragment from a belated rehearsal or from a preceding performance.

The Mittelhofers danced one number, they danced a second, they danced a third. The spectators stirred and there was no applause. The band leader's hand was raised for a fanfare, but perhaps for the first time in the circus he decided at the last moment to lower it and set down his baton.

"A total flop!" He grinned to the musicians.

"I'll give you success!" Berwitz said at that moment to himself, apostrophizing the dwarfs as he stood in the entrance among the public, still dressed in his everyday clothes. Then he looked up at Selnicki.

"Let's begin! Fanfares!"

The brass instruments and tympani sounded forth, the curtain was pulled back, and two horses' heads with stars on their foreheads appeared in the entrance. Berwitz quickly drew back and caught hold of Kerholec.

"Tell Vasek to get ready. Today he and Helen can ride in the *entrée* for Bingo."

Oh, what a day of glory and triumph it was for Vasek! Like a tiny sprite he flew from one person to the other, starting with his father, to tell them all the great and wonderful news that today he would make his first appearance in the ring. The tigers, lions, and bears too had to be told, Bluebeard II, the worthy successor of old Bluebeard, Hamilton's dogs, the horses and the pygmies, and after all of them the great Bingo.

"Bingo, good old Bingo, today I'm taking you into the ring! Be good, Bingo, please, and try to do it well—and Helen and I will make a real parade entry for you!"

During the interval that day he collected a mark or so less than usual, for he was frightened that he would not have time to change into the beautiful costume which had been made for him. But he still had time after all to pop up into the middle of the bandstand, pull his father by the sleeve while he played his trumpet and show him how he looked in his white collar and black top hat. And when he had rushed down the stairs he had the added happiness of bumping into Herr Mittelhofer and his wife, who were making their departure with suitcases in their hands and sour looks on their faces, without saying good-bye to anyone. Oh, with what joy Vasek whipped into the grand bow number four, how he twirled his top hat before them and clicked his heels in their patent-leather shoes! He even jumped up three stairs to see them go, all the while waving his hat and calling:

"Farewell! *Mit Gott! Allez!* A happy journey! *Stia bene! Adiós! Glückliche Reise!* He did not eat, he did not drink, the third day he passed away!"

And from this he passed at once to the song:

> "Two little dwarfs
> Were smaller than small;
> Whatever they ate,
> They never grew tall."

He was still singing it when, under Hans's supervision, he mounted Mary.

The first appearance of the director's daughter and the common interest in Vasek attracted all the personnel to the entrance to the tent and to the gate. The band played the entrance march with one trumpet the less, for Karas could not sit still, and had obtained permission from Selnicki to look down below to see how Vasek got on.

He need not have worried. With unlimited confidence Vasek rode in before the public, and his tanned boyish face with its broad smile and the quick eyes which looked out from under his tilted top hat at once found admirers. And at his side Helen looked like a great lady in miniature, a charming little figure of fragile beauty. Both children rode magnificently, and their gesture of greeting had the graceful air of mature ostentation.

"Oh, *wie herzig*," sighed Frau von Hammerschmidt, "*so putzig!*"

"*Très 'ertsik, très 'ertsik*," Captain Gambier agreed.

"They look so charming," Anna said to Peter. "This autumn we'll send Helen to dancing school in Hamburg."

"It's a good *entrée*," Peter agreed in a whisper. "That boy, Vasek, who would have thought it, what bravado!"

Never before had Bingo been greeted by such a burst of applause as he was now in the scene Hans had devised. It was all a complete success, and Peter Berwitz rubbed his hands in satisfaction at the way he had got rid of the annoying dwarfs and at the perfect substitute he had found for their act. And before the program was over he sent Selnicki the promised bottle.

Next to Vasek the happiest person was the goodhearted Hans. However, after the performance a cloud came over him. It was salary day—in the circus everyone calls "pay" salary. There were four salary days a month so that people could manage their money better on the road: the first, the eighth, the sixteenth, and the twenty-fourth. Superintendent Kerholec paid the stakers, the grooms, and the work hands. He always carried the money in a large sack, for the circus receipts at the ticket window were taken in small change, and had to be paid out in change. Now after the performance and after the work was finished Superintendent Kerholec called out the individual names, but Hans did not appear. He had hidden away rather than hear about the fine. Nevertheless Kerholec had him sent for, and when he was found he read from the pay list:

". . . Fine of five marks deducted; bonus for directing the number with the ponies, ten marks; net bonus, five marks."

The inevitable result of this was that Hans invited Kerholec, Karas Senior, and Vosátka out for beer to celebrate Vasek's great day. Vasek spent the evening sitting with Bures and Malina in front of the wagon.

"And what did you think of it, Uncle Malina?" the boy asked the old man, unable to hear enough of the stirring event.

"What can I say?" the old man answered. "You rode like a hero."

CHAPTER TEN

Success! Success—what an incentive for Vasek's eager heart! How much longing for activity, for work, for distinction, now suddenly boiled up in him! Would this tent with its stables and menagerie indeed be big enough for him? It was all too small for a seven-year-old boy. In the morning he could not sleep, he had to be out by the wagons with the animals, or in the stables. The currying and feeding of the four ponies he had already taken over himself. At times Hans would stand by the pole and give him advice:

"Always brush with the arm which is nearest the horse's head. Never brush so long that white powder shows up. The curry-comb is for the brush and not for the horse. Always use clean rags for the eyes and mouth. The hoof must be cleaned and then greased with salve. Clean the hoof with a wooden knife only."

And Vasek served his four protégés earnestly, he curried their forelocks, manes, and long tails, he cleaned out their mangers, shoveled the manure, and picked out the longest-stemmed straw for his gang. In half a year he had learned all the practices of the stable, and now he often stood beside Hans as the great horses left the stable, watched their gait with the eye of an expert, criticized their step, noticed the horses of others as well, knew how to tell a flat-hoofed horse from one with a straighter hoof, like a goat's, and was constantly encouraged by Hans in the latter's conviction that the hoof is the most important part of the horse, for on it rests the weight of both horse and rider.

Vasek would have been content to stay all day long in the stables, but how could he desert Captain Gambier when the latter, clad in his blue apron, cut the quarters of horseflesh in ten-pound portions and distributed them on a fork to the tigers and lions! Of course Vasek had to watch—to watch the leaps of the animals when they smelled their food, listen to the hoarse roaring and deep growling of the great cats as they grasped the meat between their paws; he had to watch the zest with which they drank water after their meal, slowly bending over to the dish in a graceful, protracted curve.

And then he had to play with the cubs. They were now kept in Gambier's wagon, and already had names, Borneo and Sumatra, and they were growing like weeds. Soon Vasek would no longer be able to take them round during intervals; they scratched with their sharp claws, and since they were already eating meat their scratches could be dangerous. But in the wagon or on the fenced-in lawn in the sun they were a beautiful sight, playing, chasing one another, lurking in wait for each other, fighting, squaring up and then jumping back again. Mr. Hamilton had put a young terrier bitch with them and now there was much fury and scrapping among these three young ones. Vasek was the fourth young one; he used to get down on all fours and the lions and the dog fought with him.

Between the menagerie and the stables lay the elephant Bingo's stable. Vasek loved this great friend of his, who always greeted him with joyous trumpeting. And Vasek helped Arr-Shehir to pour tubs of water over Bingo on hot days, and crouched down beside him while he cut Bingo's nails with a great file. Arr-Shehir was almost constantly with his Bingo. But when he had to go away Vasek played with Bingo, and picked up his trunk and whispered caressing words into it. Then Vasek used to drag up a light pile of hay; Bingo would tear out bunches of it and throw them on to the top of his head. After a while his head looked as if it were garlanded and veiled, and below Vasek clapped his hands with joy. Then Bingo would bend down his head, stretch out his trunk and Vasek would snuggle up to him and be lifted up to the hay nest on his head.

Vasek would sit there happily, three yards above the ground, and dream of leading the sacred elephant to Sonarpur on the Ganges, the great trading center for elephants of which Arr-Shehir has told him so often; for it was there that his father purchased Bingo many years ago. Arr-Shehir loved to tell tales; in the course of the years he had learned to speak German fairly well, and everything he said turned into tales and sayings. After work he liked to sit between Bingo's legs, while Vasek sat on the ground opposite him. In a singing voice Arr-Shehir would begin to chant one of the ten thousand tales of the School of Life.

"Once there was a miser who stole an onion in the field. They caught him and brought him before the king. The king listened to them and let the evil-doer choose: either to pay a hundred dinars, or to receive a hundred blows of the stick, or to eat a hundred onions. Of course the miser chose the punishment of the onions. They brought him a hundred and the miser began to eat. He ate seven of them, and seven times seven, and became so sick that he begged the king to give him the bastinado instead. They threw him down and brought a cane and gave him seven blows and seven times seven blows. And the miser cried with pain and begged them rather to let him pay the hundred dinars. And so it happened that the miser caused himself to be punished thrice, hee, hee, hee!"

Arr-Shehir used to laugh in a thin, high-pitched voice and bare his teeth. When his laughter sounded, Bingo stopped rocking, raised his trunk, and trumpeted softly. Vasek sat opposite and noticed that Bingo understood everything that was said; for a long while he had believed Arr-Shehir's story that Bingo was a higher, more exalted creature than any other, that his ancestral mother flew through the air on wings before the yogi doomed her to walk on the ground, and that one must be respectful to Bingo on days of dry weather and of downpour, for Bingo was lord of the rain.

Then perhaps a clatter and a neighing would resound from behind the canvas of the stable tent. The director's wife would have just finished her rehearsal with her Lipicans and they would be returning. Whenever their work was done they neighed with pleasure, and the other horses answered them. Now Mr. Perreira would begin to practice, and Vasek would run off to watch. First came the Roman ride, a wild gallop about the ring with Perreira standing astride on two horses, two beautiful bays with white stars on their foreheads and white stockings on their forelegs. Vasek knew them already: they were the English half-bloods Leporello and Trafalgar.

When they had circled the ring twice the golden-light Valentine with his dark mane and dark stripe on his forehead ran in. On his left thigh a great S was burned, the brand of the Schwaiganger stables. With flying mane he galloped after the other two horses, which now moved apart a bit as they ran, to let Valentine run in between them, under Perreira's legs, so that Perreira rode with his legs spread over the three untied horses.

And now from the curtain the gelding Dahomey would run forth, a dun-colored horse with a pink skin and a white mane. He would chase the galloping trio, run in between Valentine and Trafalgar, and now Perreira would have four horses under him rushing around the circle at full gallop. The two dark bays would be on the outside, the two light ones inside, but after a while Perreira would transfer one leg from Trafalgar to Dahomey. Trafalgar would slow his gait and fall to the rear, then speed up again and slip in between Dahomey and Valentine. Then the same thing would be repeated with Leporello, and Perreira would finish his ride standing on the two light horses with the dark ones between them.

Next Alice Harwey, wardrobe mistress and rider, mounts the saddle. Already Vasek knows that all of these people know much more than it would seem at first sight. Her horse is the grayish-white Bonnaserra, with her black mane and coal-black head. The mare has Andalusian and Neapolitan blood, she has a proud stance, raises her knees high when walking and steps out with straight, tense front legs. Perreira says that she is evidently related to the Lipicans, and that it took a great while to find her and buy her for the High School, but that she is a bit weak "on the back hand."

It took Vasek a few weeks to learn what they meant by these

different "hands" of the horse when they spoke of the front hand, the back hand, the left and the right one: terms which designated the front quarters or the hind quarters or the horse's motion to the left or right. But now he already uses the most specialized terms of horsemanship; he says that Bonnaserra spurs high in Spanish style. For horses Vasek has eyes like a hawk, he notices everything and soon discovers that each horse has its own special peculiarity, its distinguishing feature.

And for hours he would have been content to watch the riders at work: Alice Harwey here, for example, as she stands on the horse, dances, and raises herself on tiptoe; or as she jumps through a hoop or over a barrier. It is strange; Alice is a plain girl, with a heavily freckled face, but here on her horse in shining flight she suddenly becomes a bewitching beauty, a firm slender body with long limbs, rising in rhythmic grace above the powerful figure of the dark-gray mare.

And then Perreira returns on Santos. The black seven-year-old Hanover stallion now flies in. His black hair is brilliant, his eye sparks with flame, his fine legs play under him as if they were dancing; but when Perreira holds him in the center of the ring he stands there as if made of stone, though his every muscle is tense as he waits for the signal to break forth again. The music begins and Perreira puts Santos through the rhythmic figures of the High School, himself almost motionless as he rides in a Spanish two-step, passes over at a trot into *passage*, at a gallop performs travers, renvers, passado, raises him in courbettes and half-courbettes, and finishes the first part of the act with graceful caprioles.

Vasek by no means understands yet what lies behind all this, but like a simple spectator he vaguely senses that before him is unfolding the perfect art of riding showmanship; each step and each motion is an artfully created beauty, something not given by nature, but cultivated to an ideal perfection by human inventiveness, human will, and human patience. He seeks to detect each imperceptible movement of the rider's arm or his leg, each motion in the saddle which has its result in the horse's dancing these unnatural but graceful steps. Everything is peaceful, calm, almost slow; trick follows trick and it all looks like an easy, charming game, but Vasek notices how Santos' hair dampens with the extreme strain, and several times he has been behind the curtain after the act when Perreira has thrown off his costume and two men with towels have rubbed down his exhausted, sweating body.

After Perreira, Barengo usually rehearses. Vasek feels a special respect for this melancholy Spaniard who is so different in every respect from the others. To be sure, the cheerful Mr. Laribeau is much more akin to Vasek; in the Frenchman the boy senses the gay blood of a young man, exuberant with health and strength, while Barengo is majestic and taciturn and performs everything as if it were a sacred rite. It is unbelievable how beautifully he soars up there on the trapeze, how he flies through the air like a silver flame, with what lightness he comes to rest, clinging there as easily as if he were only gracefully waving his hand.

But down here on the ground—no, never yet has Vasek known anyone so cut off from the world about him. At first the image of the priest at home came to his mind when he saw Barengo, but at once he discarded this comparison; how could he be like the village priest—who was after all only a peasant! Perhaps at Corpus Christi, when he walked with his monstrance under his canopy, you might compare him to some extent with Barengo when the latter, his wife, and Hector were marching toward the rope ladder.

Vasek would have been glad to climb up with them out of simple curiosity to see what it was like up there under the roof of the tent. When a strong wind was blowing outside, they said that everything murmured up there, the taut ropes about the mast hummed, the canvas trembled with a quiet music, the flagpole over the tent quivered, even the wood of the pole sang with its own sound. But when Laribeau once wanted to take him up with him, Barengo stopped him, stroked Vasek's head, and said:

"*Mi chicuelo,* don't leave the firm ground. The grave is farther off down here; up above we have it straight down under us."

He said this seriously and solemnly, and involuntarily Vasek bowed his head. So he stays below, climbing to one of the tiers of seats, so that with open mouth he can watch that enrapturing and exciting vigor of movement, that supple flight of white bodies, that noiseless whirling in which the effort of tensed muscles disappears, and there remains only a smooth grace of circling curves. This must be the way the angels fly, he used to sigh piously when first he watched them, but later, when he understood it all better, he said to himself:

"No, they're different from angels. How could angels manage a double death leap in the air?"

Everywhere there are things for Vasek to watch and try to imitate, not to speak of all he has to do himself! He has to ride Mary from one town to the next and keep an eye on the other three ponies who trot along at his side. When they stop for the night they have to put up the portable stable, and Vasek, too, has his sheets of canvas to join together and tie at the lacings. And then he goes with the grooms for straw, for oats, for hay, for water, rubs his ponies with handfuls of straw, and examines their hoofs daily as Hans insists he must. And the next morning it is all taken down again and loaded up and again he mounts the saddle and heads out into the road, in sun, wind, and rain.

And then they come to a city where they are going to perform, and he has to help to put up and equip the tent. Vasek struggles with the tiers and the folding chairs as he carries them into the boxes. Then they lay down the rim of the ring and the wagons with sawdust drive in. If the ground is level, five or six cartloads will go into the ring; the sawdust must be tramped down—the task of the heaviest draught horses—and sprinkled with water. There is no end of work for a boy like Vasek, and everyone calls him to come and give a hand, or sends him on a hundred and one errands.

When the evening rest comes and the men sit down with relaxed muscles to their supper, Vasek returns to his father's gang with the quiet feeling of satisfaction that he has done his share of the work. All the circus folk know that Vasek is more than pet and a mascot; he is the youngest worker, and they like him because he leaves his play quite simply, without arguing, and comes and helps them whenever an extra hand is needed. When he first came to live with them they smilingly accepted him for his charm, but now they have long since assumed a different attitude toward him. He has won their respect and regard; all of them know that in this little, agile body there is the seriousness and persistence of a grown man, and between him and all the others there is born a quiet man-to-man relation.

The circus is not the sort of environment where people mince their words. A sensitive boy might have suffered from the roughness of his surroundings. Strangely enough, even the African Paolo, experienced, tough, used to blows and cries, sometimes had moments of yielding sadness when he suffered from the fact that no one came to him—to stroke little handsome Paolo, caress him with a gentle hand and with silken words; how happy his little heart would have been if at least sometimes it could have felt warm affection and soft tenderness! But Vasek is hard as an oaken knot; his nature shows itself rather in swearing and spitting on the palms of his hands; he is never at his ease when a gushingly sweet woman like Frau von Hammerschmidt fondles and embraces him. His native element is with grown men, and most of all with the good fellows in Number Eight; with them he's an equal.

With them the nicest thing is when the air of a summer evening is cool and they camp outside in the open. Here the gang is free of the stifling air of the wagon, and one after another they bring out their blankets and stretch out somewhere on God's grass, under the vault of heaven which lies over them and the air which trembles with the pleasant chirp of the crickets. Remembrance after remembrance is reborn; the men talk and Vasek could listen to them until the stars faded.

Late summer has still other charms; they journey through the country and the joys of the farm boy triumph over the rider's pride—Vasek runs off into the fields to pluck the green peas or the pods of poppy seeds. And when autumn approaches and the days grow shorter, even the marauding lusts of Sergeant Vosátka are rekindled; he leads his comrades out to pitch a camp on some slope among the wild-rose bushes, makes a fire and bakes potatoes he has taken from some unguarded potato patch.

The oaks and the beeches are turning gold and red, the shining birches let leaf coins fall from their crowns, the gossamer threads of Indian summer touch the faces of the riders, the rain begins to trickle on the quietly trotting column of horses, on Bingo's head Arr-Shehir sings the prayer for the stopping of rain, and Achmed Roméo, wrapped in kerchiefs and shawls, repeats the sura of Saba in the twilight of sundown: "We have our appointed journey in the world. Go your way in safety day and night."

All of them know already that the prolonged hammering of the rains on the canvas is sounding an end to their journey and to their gay vagabond life. By the middle of October they must return to their winter existence. For some this means leaving the circus. Involuntarily melancholy comes over them as they make their way through the mists of the damp morning to tend the hungry animals. Only Mr. Berwitz walks among them with his shoulders haughtily thrown back as he rubs his hands; he has purchased the wooden building on the field by the Reeperbahn and has had it altered to suit him; now he is the master of his winter lodging and for the first time Umberto's Circus will spend the winter on its own ground.

CHAPTER ELEVEN

THE TWO KARASES were glad to return to Frau Langermann's flat. At last they would be able to stretch out again on the mattress of a decent bed! The widow welcomed them with great heartiness. Business had been poor for her ever since the Czech gang had dispersed. She had heard nothing of the fate of Milner's workers, nor had she known how the Karases were getting on in the circus. She had had no luck with lodgers; not a single respectable person had turned up, only transients, for the most part seafaring people—stewards and sailors who slept there for a couple of nights before they found a job somewhere or ran out of money and had to move to a doss house.

With the return of the Karases it was as if a gleam of the good old days had come back. Moreover, they were more important persons now, they were artists. The widow insisted on calling Karas an artist, for he played the trumpet in the circus band. She had a pious respect for music. Her late husband, the helmsman Langermann, had played an accordion so beautifully—how many times she had wept as they sat together on the kitchen couch, a cake on the table giving off its steaming fragrance, while the helmsman Langermann played on his sailor's piano and sang: "*Et wasen twei Kunnigeskinner, De hadden enander so leef.*"

Rosa had grown an inch or so taller during the past year. Her eyes popped out and she dropped her doll in joy when she saw Vasek walk in at the door. At first Vasek behaved with an air of extreme seriousness and importance, like a grownup who had already put all sorts of childish nonsense behind him. But after a few minutes the mask fell off, and over Rosa's playthings the child in him again made its appearance. Among the dolls, the toy kitchen, and the toy store he found a new world for his imaginative fantasy. He had lived among adults for eight months, had made himself useful to them, worked with them, and the longer he had been with them, the less time he had had for fun. Here now in Frau Langermann's kitchen, on the couch or under the table, the favorite games of his self-denied childhood opened up to him again.

In the circus he had always been intently wrapped up in the work which surrounded him, he spoke with the men like a man, he swore, spat, and did everything but smoke a cigar; but here with Rosa he melted and softened, he threw himself into the world of her fantasy, and played with her rag doll as if he were relaxing from the unnatural tension of a premature maturity. Only his desire to dominate persisted; it was he who must lead in everything, and Rosa who must submit. Fortunately Rosa was a devoted and submissive little soul, full of admiration for his decisiveness, and she willingly adapted herself to the changes he carried out. He decided that the doll's house should be a wagon, the toy store a menagerie, the doll's pram a cage of tigers. He saw everything Rosa owned through the spectacles of his own vision, and both children found themselves in the double charm of an enchanted world.

But one thing he could not enchant: Rosa's primer. She already possessed her first book with pictures and large print, with the words divided into syllables. Vasek knew some of the letters of the German alphabet, others he confused; but now he stared at its pages for long periods, and with all his persistence he continued to read some of it every day until he knew whole pages by heart. His father did not bother much with Vasek's new ambition, but Bures had moved to Frau Langermann's too, and every evening now he drew Vasek to the table and examined him on his German reading. And then, as a rule, he pulled out one of his own books and read something or let Vasek read some of the poems the boy liked. They read them again and again, and little by little they began to sound in Vasek's head like songs.

Vasek was far from understanding all he read in these poems. Here were a multitude of strange, unknown words which he could not associate with anything definite; he felt only that there was some sort of charm in them and that they stood for something powerful and glorious. When he read "and the lords of the signs of the star, the eagle, the lion, and the water lily raised their right hands," it seemed very lofty and elegant to him. When he read such Czech verses it was as if he were entering again the forests of Horní Snezná with their green brilliance, bluish dusk, and golden glow. Behind these unknown words great, seductive mysteries lay.

The boy asked Bures to read on and on. They went through all the books, until at last Bures pulled out a small pamphlet, all worn and tattered, and one evening began to read aloud from it. It was a long poem, a very long one, the longest of all to which Vasek had listened, and it was no less difficult to understand. He remembered only that it began with something like the statement that the Czechs were a good people; then it told of an evening in May on a blue lake, and how beautiful it was; then there was a bandit in it whom they led to execution, and he cried out that they should greet his land for him, his beautiful land, his beloved land.

More Vasek did not hear, for when Bures came to this passage his voice broke and he could not go on. Vasek thought that he was starting to cry, but he could not be sure, as Bures at once got up, put the book in his pocket, took up his broad hat, and rushed out. And he came back quite late in the night, and the next day Frau Langermann laughed at him for having taken one too many. Later Vasek begged in vain for Bures to read some more about that May evening; Bures abruptly refused and said that it was not suitable for him. So Vasek never learned what kind of a poem it really was. But none the less it sounded in his ears for a long time after that as something special and unusual.

Poetry was part of their evening leisure during their winter in Hamburg. During the daytime there was no thought of it, for they had to work hard. One would have thought that there would be less now that they had finished traveling and moving the tents, but many of the workers were only seasonal, and these now departed. The care for all the animals and the customary winter repairs of all the equipment fell on the rest.

Antonín Karas, too, had originally been hired only as a seasonal worker, but Kerholec was planning to keep him on somehow. However it was not necessary for him to intervene on his behalf. Karas had won Berwitz over with his carved figures, which slowly, piece by piece, decorated the exterior of the circus. And then there was Vasek. He was the "good measure" in the butcher's pound which weighed more than the main piece. And especially now when an independent act was being prepared for him.

Vasek had taken over the entire training of the ponies from Hans. They had been well schooled, they went through all their complicated figures almost automatically, for them it was only a matter of getting used to Vasek, and for Vasek of preparing them to meet every possible occurrence. During the first rehearsals he was not at ease, his head burned with excitement and his whip kept flying through the air. In a few days, however, he had calmed down, and he soon did better with the shorter whip the director had bought him in order that the whole act might actually appear to be a miniature imitation of a great horse show. He had to learn to use a whip in his right hand to set the tempo and impetus, and to use one in his left to slow up the figures the ponies described. And his pygmies, striped and shining like freshly shelled beans, followed his every movement with attention.

From behind the rim Hans corrected his posture so that while at work he should stand tense and straight like a real trainer, and not spread his legs, or bend his back. And then came the day when the ponies got new trappings of yellow leather, bordered with silver studs, with yellow and blue plumes on their curved necks, and when Vasek was dressed in a black dress coat. For him it was a day of the greatest excitement; first of all he ran to everyone to make them look at him, especially to those who had full-length mirrors in their dressing rooms, in which he could see every bit of himself; then suddenly he got terribly frightened that he might stumble and fall at some point and soil or tear his beautiful costume. But after some time this stage fright left him, and at last the time came for him to appear in the holiday Easter performance.

He had a distinguished claque of supporters by the curtain. The whole circus had appeared in white gloves, to add the final touch to the first appearance of their young protégé. They stood in two rows behind the curtain, clad in their sparkling costumes: Captain Gambier, Pablo Perreira, John Harwey, Mr. Hamilton, the two Gevaerts, Arr-Shehir, Achmed Roméo and Paolo, Mr. Barengo, Mr. Laribeau, and all the inhabitants of Number Eight except his father, who looked on from over Mr. Selnicki's shoulder. At the edge of the end box stood Director Berwitz with Hans, and on the chairs in the box sat Mrs. Berwitz, Helen, and Frau von Hammerschmidt.

Vasek was more frightened by this famous band than by all the audience put together, but as soon as he had crossed the ring, made his first bow, and cracked his whip as a signal for the horses to enter, his stage fright vanished. He paraded the horses with complete sureness; he did not rush; toward the end, when applause was already rewarding the individual figures his ponies were performing, his inner certainty had already passed into that easy nonchalance characteristic of the most accomplished trainers.

The audience was wild at the sight of the little boy; applause was not enough—they stamped their feet and cried "Bravo!"—it was a great success, the greatest success of the new program. Only one tiny fault appeared near the end. Frau von Hammerschmidt was responsible for it; out of the goodness of her heart she had sent Vasek a bouquet. No one had counted on such a thing beforehand, and when Hans handed it to him in the middle of the ring Vasek discovered with horror that he needed a third hand. In his agitation he did not know what to do with his whip, and for a few seconds he fell into a confusion which showed clearly how much of the child was still in him.

But this captured the public's fancy even more, and again the applause and shouts burst forth. And when at last Vasek returned from the ring, the giant Gambier caught him up, called to Laribeau, and the two Frenchmen raised their Vasek onto their shoulders and carried him off to the center of the whole gathering, to the applause of all the gloved hands.

Director Berwitz came up at this moment in his colonel's uniform and patted Vasek on the shoulder and told him that he had done nobly and that his father was to come tomorrow to his office to see him. Mrs. Berwitz patted his face and Helen shook his hand, and Fran von Hammerschmidt almost squeezed the life out of him the way she embraced him and kissed him. Above the exit from the bandstand stood his father, and instead of a trumpet he was blowing into a handkerchief and wiping his eyes. Hans strutted like a peacock at the entrance to the stables and shouted to the other grooms:

"Didn't I tell you? Old Hans has an eye for an act! I've seen something in my day, you lot of tyros! We haven't had a success like this for years!"

At that moment Vasek slipped out of the circle of women, ran over to Hans, shouted, "Hans—hop!" and in a long arc jumped into the groom's arms and with childish affection kissed both his cheeks.

"No-no-no! Vasek! You mustn't do that! You really mustn't!" the groom resisted, and the tears trickled down his cheeks and onto his uniform.

Poor Hans! On that day of his greatest glory he did not suspect what still awaited him. For after the performance the director came and with his own hands presented him, before all the stable hands, with the red waistcoat with its golden buttons, all wrapped up in tissue paper. Again Hans was beside himself with excitement; he put on the waistcoat at once, ran about the stable in it without his coat, and after work finished dressing and announced that today he must go and show it to the fellows at the Hippodrome. This was a show boasting six horses, to be found at the other end of the Reeperbahn; here drunken sailors and soldiers came with their pickups to ride a horse for a few pfennigs and play the cavalier.

It was a noisy place, smelling more of spilled beer than of horse sweat, one of the last places open to which evening carousers could resort, and as often as not there was fighting and bloodshed. But it was an enterprise with horses, and the circus grooms often came to drink a glass of beer with the grooms at the Hippodrome, to boast to them and talk big. It was here now that Hans headed with his red waistcoat.

But there were many bars on the Reeperbahn full of acquaintances of his who still knew nothing of the waistcoat. Where his way took him and how his fate came upon him no one knew. All that *was* known was that at half-past two the police delivered him at the circus, turning him over to Alice Harwey, bruised, beaten, with torn coat and missing collar. His left hand had been cut by a glass, his right arm had a knife wound, he limped on his right leg, he wore somebody else's hat on his head, his left eye was blackened. He did not say a word when Alice led him to the hay pile in the stables, nagging at him the whole way. Only when she turned to go did he stop her, slowly unbutton his coat in the moonlight, with an effort fixed one eye on her and, raising his fist, declared:

"It's all right . . . they had to carry three of them out . . . and the red waistcoat is in one piece!"

The next morning Vasek, rather than Hans, took care of the Lipicans and the black horses. After a while the director came along. He stopped beside the bandaged Hans and nodded.

"Hans, Hans . . . even I didn't know what a pig you are!"

"I am, Mr. Director," Hans agreed sadly. "I'm a terrible pig, but begging your pardon, it's just to have a good time, just for a good time. I never had so much fun before in my whole life as I did last night."

"And what are we to tell the police when they make inquiries?"

"But they won't, Mr. Director, they won't. It happened at the Hippodrome, you see. Where would the police be if they had to investigate every fight there? Only I'll have to find the Hippodrome three new grooms, so that the horses there won't be without attendants."

In spite of the way he was beaten up Hans put on his red waistcoat again that evening and went out for beer. This time Karas and the other stakers took him with them to drink Vasek's health. They went to the Sailor's Bride, where Moesecke greeted them with joy. Karas bought three rounds. This he was obliged to do, for that morning when he had gone to the office the director informed him that he had decided to engage Vasek as a boy rider.

This was part of Berwitz's principles: to make an offer himself before people came with a demand. He was convinced that in this way he arranged things more cheaply and made a good impression into the bargain. With respectful thanks rather than with any reflection, Karas had agreed to the figure Berwitz proposed. It was only a couple of marks, but then Karas thought in terms of kreutzers and pfennigs. Everything the boy could earn seemed to him like a gift from Heaven. The twenty-pfennig pieces for the trips with the lion cubs had stopped coming when the cubs grew up, but Karas still had all of them saved up. And now there would be marks to add to them. Vasek needed nothing and it would be better for him to have something saved for later on, if he wanted to leave.

In the depth of his soul Karas had never parted with this thought. As for himself, he was completely contented here. Vasek's successes and his good fortune had intoxicated him, but the thorn of old social prejudices still pricked deep inside the honest mason. Though he said nothing about it, he still thought of how one day they would come to some agreement and leave the circus to start something more respectable at home. Only one thing spoiled this line of reasoning for Karas: he still had heard nothing of how Milner's gang had managed the spring before. He had inquired eagerly about them in all possible places, but even Moesecke, who would have been the first to hear about them, knew nothing at all. They had gone off, disappeared, vanished from sight, and in the course of the year no one had brought any news of them.

As winter went on Karas remembered that before long Milner would start to go round the villages at home and collect the gang. Perhaps Karas could still catch them; perhaps they would meet here; and with their appearance the decision to leave could be hastened. But until then he did not dare to breathe a syllable of it, for everyone told him how well Vasek's act had turned out, how well it was liked, and how Vasek was improving it with daily repetitions so that now it went even more smoothly and easily than it had during the first few days. It would be a wonderful attraction for the spring tour. About this spring tour all sorts of rumors were going round, and Gaudeamus was kept on the jump; it was said that this time they were going toward the east, to Poland and elsewhere.

In his uncertainty Karas fell back on the thought that he would leave all to God's decision. If Milner should turn up before they went off, he would do everything he could to return to his trade; but if fate should decide that they should go away first, there would be no help for it, he would have to wait for another opportunity. But what he saw did not reassure him; construction was still idle in Hamburg. During his free moments he could not help going round the vacant lots in the city and in its vicinity, and he had to admit that there was nothing doing—not even a pickax was stirring to prepare the plots for building. If his countrymen came back, it was evident that it would turn out badly for them again, and the clear recognition of this reality forced him back to the circus again as to a salvation.

So he continued to waver in his uncertainties concerning his own future and Vasek's, until one bright day Kerholec gave the order to get the wagons ready for the road and to move into them. Milner had not turned up. Both Karases said good-bye to Frau Langermann and Rosa and started off on their second journey with Umberto's Circus.

CHAPTER TWELVE

THOSE WHO went on the road were roughly the same as the year before. Again Achmed Roméo shook hands with the director to bind the contract for a stay of an additional ten months. But much was missing, and Number Eight came near losing one of its most distinguished personalities: Sergeant Ferenc Vosátka was strongly tempted to leave the gang and the circus.

They were having beer at Moesecke's one day, chattering and laughing, when suddenly Vosátka caught his breath. In the middle of a sentence he became silent and motionless and his eyes stared fixedly at the door. They looked in that direction and saw a strange-looking man enter the tavern, dark, potbellied, with a nose like a tomato and with a mouth so large that it could have swallowed a chicken in one gulp. His mouth was soft as if it were laughing, and his right eye too smiled, but the left one was covered by its distended and swollen lid. Over his cheeks and his chin lay a scattered stubble, and his face was strangely streaked as if by dirt. When this powerful fellow with his blown-up stomach looked at their table, his face changed, and at once he rushed toward them, while Vosátka slowly rose to his feet as if hypnotized. The fellow came up to him, clicked his heels, saluted with his palm out, and thundered in a booming bass:

"General Vosátka, Sergeant Lebeda begs to report!"

Vosátka stood stiff as a board, mechanically jerked the three and a half fingers of his right hand toward the remaining half of his ear, and answered in a resounding voice:

"General Lebeda, Sergeant Vosátka at your service!"

With that both raised their arms, embraced one another and kissed, each trying to outshout the other.

"Amigazo! Qué alegía! Cielos, vaya una sorpresa!"

At last Vosátka tore himself away and turned to his comrades.

"Muy señores mios, make room for the guest of honor; this gentle soul must sit among us. Allow me to present *excelentísimo* Señor Don José Lebeda from Hlubocepy, my most trusty *amigo* in the whole of Central America. Why, we even made prisoners of each other there! Pepík, do you remember the battle near Pico del Espuela?"

"How could I forget it, Ferenc? That was really a story!"

Of course everyone at once wanted to hear the tale. And when they were seated again, Vosátka began to tell of the battle near the mountain Pico del Espuela.

"My noble comrades, it is distasteful for me to speak of my own fame. But eventually you would have to know, you canvas monkeys, you, what a distinguished personality has been traveling with you over this rotten world. And then, too, here is the witness for the prosecution. It all happened that time in Honduras, or was it Guatemala?"

"No, it was Nicaragua, Ferenc," Lebeda prompted him. "It was when we wore those plumes in our hats."

"Hombre, yes, Nicaragua. An enchanting republic, gentlemen. Made up of mosquitoes and half-breeds. At that time some sort of political upset was going on, and it seemed that there were two presidents. President Colador and President Almirez. What was at stake I never did find out, I was still a gringo then, a foreigner, I had just come there from Costa Rica, where Pepík and I had helped in a revolution. In Nicaragua I joined up with President Colador, who had just announced that the shame of the land could be wiped out only by blood. That was a speech to my taste, and so I enlisted as a sergeant in his army.

"General Chingolo was its commander, a proven patriot. The army was formed quickly enough; the only trouble was that some outfits kept running away from time to time. But since their members could be persuaded to come back again very easily, our reinforcements mounted to unbelievable numbers. At first we had thought that these figures would frighten the enemy off, but President Almirez made ready for battle and named a certain General Platudo as his commander-in-chief.

"We now saw that the only thing which remained was to fight. When some rifles and three cannon arrived from Colombia, we dragged them out into the field. At the city of Matagalpa we received the report that General Platudo was heading toward the Rio Grande. General Chingolo then decided to form his main camp and equipment in Matagalpa, and from there to send out a part of his troops to halt the enemy's advance. The commander of this expedition, gentlemen, was I myself, Sergeant Vosátka. I was given some twenty militiamen and my orders.

"The next morning we stood in the square in front of the church; General Chingolo rode up on a white mare, pulled out his saber and said, 'Sergeant Vosátka'—he spoke with energy—'go and wipe out the hydra of revolt. Fight bravely, like a hidalgo. The law must be enforced.' I marched out to meet the enemy. Here was Matagalpa, behind it a hill, behind the hill a whole sierra, in the middle of the sierra the Pico del Espuela. A bit farther on flowed the Rio Grande.

"When those twenty half-breeds and I marched up to the foot of the mountain we came to a *quebrada,* a gully washed out by the spring rains. And then a cry arose, and on the other side of the *quebrada* we saw a couple of ragamuffins with feathers in their caps run off and hide themselves behind boulders and cactuses. Gentlemen—we had come upon the enemy!"

"And what did you do?" asked Kerholec.

"I gave the order to take up battle positions."

"That's amazing," said Malina. "I'd never have thought of that."

"But you see I did. The order was useless anyway, because all twenty men of my militia had already run off and hidden, and I could scarcely see any of them. And so began the battle of the Pico del Espuela."

"Were there many dead?" asked Karas.

"Many. Mostly rabbits. They ran down from the mountains and we shot them from both sides, and then roasted them. Besides, we shot one mule. The enemy bragged that he also had bagged a vulture. In a word, we kept shooting all the time, but fortunately actual people were spared. And so we fought at the Pico del Espuela for perhaps a week. The advance of the enemy was checked beyond all doubt. Nicaragua could look forward to better times. But we saw worse ones ahead, for the rabbits had all disappeared and all we had left to eat was corn bread.

"At that point I decided on a certain measure: I sent a flag of truce to the enemy with the demand that he surrender. The truce party returned with the reply that in their position it would be better if we were to surrender, and that the best thing of all would be for both leaders to meet in the *quebrada* the next afternoon at three o'clock and come to an agreement. I consented to this honorable proposal and climbed down to the foot of the precipice, but I had to burst out laughing—across from me was this mass of rock here, Pepík Lebeda!"

"He was on the other side?" Malina was aghast.

"I was indeed," said Lebeda. "I stared a bit myself when I saw Ferenc! We hadn't seen each other for half a year!"

"You can imagine, gentlemen, how we threw our arms around each other in that gulch. We hugged each other and couldn't let go. And we both yelled, 'This is marvelous, this is wonderful! You're my prisoner!' We talked the matter over for three or four days. It wasn't easy to decide. I was enforcing the law and he was enforcing the law, and in the act of doing the enforcing we were against each other. And before we could make up our minds, our troops had all run off."

"They didn't have anything to eat." Lebeda guffawed. "So they slipped away like the rabbits."

"And we were left." Vosátka again took over the narrative. "All by ourselves in the virgin wilderness of Nicaragua. At last we came to the decision that the battle by the Pico del Espuela had ended with the complete defeat of President Almirez and that Pepík here would be my prisoner. We reached this conclusion for strategic reasons; the city of Cuicuina was far away and Matagalpa was close by, and we were hungry."

"And more important—thirsty." Lebeda chuckled.

"So we rode in together to Matagalpa and agreed that at the inn at the edge of the city Pepík would get off the horse and walk into the city on foot beside me, as my prisoner. In the inn we ordered some *queso de chanco,* a kind of pressed meat, and I asked how it was that I didn't see any soldiers, seeing that this was the main camp. And the woman at the inn told me that it had all been settled four days ago: the people had turned President Colador out and General Chingolo was in prison. 'Caramba,' I said to Pepík, 'the wheel of fortune's turned; you'll ride on the horse and I'll be your prisoner. Long live Nicaragua!'

"And then Pepík said—and fellow comrades, permit me to observe that this was a masterly stroke of statesmanship—he said, 'Be quiet, Ferenc, from now on we'll be rolling in clover.' And he looked at the innkeeper and said in a voice of command, 'Mother, send somebody to tell the priest and the mayor to prepare a welcome for two officers of the victorious army of the battle of Pico del Espuela, who have come to occupy the city!' "

"You rogues!" Kerholec pounded on the table. "Didn't they recognize you?"

"How could they?" cried Lebeda. "We had no stripes or officer's insignia; it all depended on your posture. A man just had to be courageous."

"And how did it turn out?"

"How did it turn out?" Vosátka answered. "We rode into the city together, as proud as two hidalgos. The mayor and the city council and the priest with his curate all welcomed us; everything was 'Your Excellency this' and 'Your Excellency that,' in the evening a banquet was arranged in our honor and afterward a dance."

"Were the girls pretty?" asked Kerholec.

"Oh," Vosátka raised his eyes to heaven. "Do you remember, Lebeda? That was a night, wasn't it?"

"*Cielos, vos sabés—qué chiche!*"

"And how did it all end up?"

"It ended by our giving the order to release General Chingolo, picking the two best horses in town for a ride out into the country, having a marvelous dinner at the priest's, and going off to Honduras."

"Yes, yes," Lebeda sighed, "those were wonderful days. New Granada, Costa Rica, Nicaragua, Honduras, Guatemala, Yucatán, Mexico, Texas, Arizona—plenty of revolutions, upsets, rebellions, wars. That was the life, that was sheer pleasure."

"How about Santa Anna—is he still alive?"

"I don't know, comrade."

"What saint was that?" Bures asked.

"A fine saint." Vosátka grinned. "The wildest dictator of Mexico, Antonio López de Santa Anna, general. He unmade half a dozen Presidents and then took things over himself and went to war with the Union. A crueler beast than any of Gambier's cats. But fighting was good under him, wasn't it, Pepíka?"

"Glorious. Do you remember that double hand-to-hand fight at Contreras and at Churubusco? San Diego, how we ran away from the Americans! You left your ear there, right?"

"No, later in Chapultepec."

"You were under siege there, and you surrendered?"

"Me surrender? I ran away. But half an ear stayed behind me, and still another piece of my irresistible beauty. Immediately after that we met in Pueblo."

"You're right. Now I remember the sequence. You were trying to go south then?"

"Yes. There were too many brass hats up there. So I went down to Uruguay with Garibaldi. There was still a decent partisan war there. But he was all ready to go to Europe, so I went off with him."

"And I, Ferenc, went off in the other direction. To the north. To California. That was the life then. They had just found gold there. A lot of it. A terrible lot of it. But you had to risk your neck all the time to get it. I wouldn't have come out of it alive if it hadn't been for a pal of mine named Hawkins. Did you know him? A terrific *compadriot*; in the beginning he was active in Ecuador, when it broke away from Colombia. He was older than we were."

"Hawkins? There was a Hawkins who made a big noise in Panama in my time."

"It's possible he's the one. That was his territory. But originally he was from the north; he had a quiet, Californian character. He didn't speak—just shot at sight. If it hadn't been for him I wouldn't have got away from 'Frisco in one piece. That place was crawling with robbers and murderers beside whom Santa Anna was a lamb."

228

"And how much gold did you plunder, you mameluke? Toss us a nugget or two to splurge ourselves on!"

"Yes, yes, Ferenc. There was, there was. But it's a very soft metal, you know, and when it comes close to alcohol it evaporates. That's its great drawback, Ferenc, its great drawback."

"So now you're a common hidalgo again, not burdened down by any estate?"

"*Vos sabés*. A common hidalgo. In my pocket there are no more than a couple of *cobres*. But there are great things in the air, and that's just why I've been looking for you. Why, I've been trailing you across half of Europe. As soon as I heard about it I said to myself, 'That's Ferenc Vosátka's specialty. His and no one else's.'"

"Don José, don't make me blush! In New Granada we'd have said *macana* to that; now I'd say that you're just flattering me along, Pepík!"

"No, Ferenc. It's really serious business. They're looking for old Mexicans."

"Well! Perhaps they want to found an incorporated society for the exploitation of healed-up scars?"

"No. But maybe, yes. Any way you want to put it. But there's trouble afoot in America, did you know it?"

"Between the North and the South, yes. They say they're fighting about slavery, but really it's over money."

"That's beside the point. But something's stirring in Mexico. Juárez is going to be put out . . ."

"That half-breed? It'd be difficult. He's a cunning beast."

"He'll be put out, I tell you. And now it's a matter of finding three hundred old Mexicans, like you and me, to get mixed up in it. It's a terrific thing, I tell you. The passage to Vera Cruz is certain. Then we only have to head up to Soledad, Orizaba, Pueblo, and Mexico, and be there when things get into full swing."

Vosátka stared at the adventurer, and all the others sat tense and silent. They felt that the greatest temptation which could come to their companion had arisen, from the world of his lost wild youth.

"Orizaba . . . Pueblo . . . Mexico . . ." Vosátka repeated as if intoxicated.

Suddenly it was as if he felt it through all his pores, as if the burning air of the sand wastes were buffeting him. He saw the white tops of the mountains in the clear air of the sky, smelled the peasants' huts, felt under him the trot of a striped *pingo*, his favorite horse. Strange flat temples and palaces of endless dimensions arose before his eyes, he heard the lowing of herds on the green plateau of the spring savannah, he inhaled the heavy air of the tropics with its jungle odors, and heard again the cry of the parrots, or the dry crackle of boat masts and the flapping of the tight sails. The odors, sounds, colors, and shapes of this zone of the earth came over him and merged into a single terrible intoxication, into a feeling of supreme freedom and independence, into a feeling of wild, stormy youth.

And as if it all sought to be incarnated anew, there circled before his eyes the provoking bodies of white women and brown men, sending out a mysterious summons from their dark, impelling eyes—their names themselves a dark, sensual music: Dolores, Rosario, Soledad, Encarnación, Guadalupe, Concepción, Eduvigis, Esperanza, Asunción, Gracia, Fé. The scar on his cheek turned red and the veins stood out on his neck and his temples.

Kerholec, Karas, Malina, and Bures had never yet seen their garrulous Sergeant in such rapture. They were convinced that his mysterious past was going to prove stronger than their present friendship. Involuntarily Kerholec thought of that unexpected whirlwind which had once descended on them in Hungary, like a bolt from the blue, breaking their cables and carrying the top of their tent far off into the broad heavens. Karas held his breath; now, perhaps, the moment had come when another would break the bonds which held him too a prisoner. Malina looked as if his brain had "stopped" again, but his instinct kept prompting him to go over and put his hand on Vosátka's head; but it was Bures who was to do this, though he did it indirectly. He felt that something must happen which would bring the Sergeant back to reality. And at once the right question to ask flashed through his head.

"And who, Mr. Lebeda, is paying your way to Vera Cruz?"

Vosátka started and fixed his eyes on Bures.

"What did you say?"

"I asked Mr. Lebeda who would pay your passage to Vera Cruz. He said that the way there was certain."

"That's right, Pepík," and Vosátka drummed with his fingers on the table. "Who's paying for it?"

"Vera Cruz has been taken and occupied."

"By whom? Surely not the Americans?"

"No. The French, Spanish, and English are holding it. Juárez is in retreat and will negotiate. But the French will go further. As to the others, I don't know, but Napoleon will. That I know positively, and that's why I'm here. They're hunting for a good-sized *montoneza*, an expedition of conquerors. Ferenc, now you can be a real general."

"Whew!" Vosátka gave a long whistle. "At the expense of France?"

Lebeda nodded.

"And he wants to take over Mexico?"

Lebeda looked round, then pulled his chair closer to them, and bending over, said almost in a whisper:

"It's still a secret. It's not to be a colony, but something bigger, something to put an end to all the confusion. Perhaps a kingdom or an empire or something. That I don't know. But it's certain that something can be made out of it. Nobody knows Mexico."

"And whom do they want to give it to? One of the Bonapartes?" Vosátka at once spoke in the same whisper, but directly and to the point. With amazement Bures sensed that their scoffing chatterbox must have had a great deal more political experience in the past than they had imagined.

"No," Lebeda answered. "A Habsburg has been found for it. The brother of Franz Josef. Ferdinand Maximilian. Both emperors have already made an agreement."

"So that's it," sighed Vosátka. And after a second of silence his hot anger suddenly flamed up. "The jaws of the great powers are again watering for plunder. The free states across the seas have tempted them and lured them on. Again they go to rob and murder in the name of civilization and order. The Mexicans have some fifty bloody years behind them. But they fought among themselves in the name of their freedom, and with every decade they came a step closer to their ideal. But now in place of blood-shed a yoke will be put on their necks; instead of shedding their blood they will sweat it. The hyenas of imperialism are already starting to howl.

"To such a cry Sergeant Vosátka answers with a rifle. No, Pepík, you were wrong when you came here for me. Santa Anna was a terrible monster, but I served him when he defended free Mexico. I won't let myself be smuggled onto the Mexican shore to help to bury its liberty. Form your *montoneza* yourself. I won't hold it against you. *Contra gustos no hay disputa.* But Sergeant Vosátka would rather stay in the stink of traveling stables."

"Excellent, friend," Bures cried softly. "And remember one thing: Should it turn out, as our countryman Lebeda says, that the Habsburgs are mixed up in it, it will turn out badly. It's a family that's haunted by a curse."

Everybody agreed emphatically. Lebeda drew his mouth into a wide smile and scratched his hair with a dirty hand.

"Well, well," he answered Vosátka peaceably. "Don't eat me up because I came to get you. I thought you'd be glad to take me up on it."

"No," Vosátka answered emphatically, "I don't want to have anything to do with it."

Lebeda was not the sort of person who was easily dissuaded, but evidently he knew his Sergeant and saw that all speeches would be useless.

"Another unrequited love in life." He grinned and raised his glass. "To your health, Ferenc—I shall go to Mexico without you."

He clinked glasses with everyone, and they drank away their disquiet. It seemed that Malina had been the most disturbed.

"My head's going round in a circle," he complained, putting his glass down on the table. "I don't understand it all yet, but it looks to me like that time with the python. But why, I don't know."

They all burst out laughing.

"What's this about your python?" they chuckled, glad to begin a new encounter.

"Well, once we had an Indian python," the old man answered. "I suppose you know what an Indian python is. This one of ours was a big fellow. Old Umberto would always say that he measured four hundred and eighty-five Florentine inches in length.

Whether that was true or not couldn't be proved, because there is no such thing as a Florentine inch."

"Pythons are big harmless snakes from the tropics," Bures rushed in to enlighten them.

"Just add that they're a kind of big worm." Malina grew angry. "If a python's a harmless snake, then Sergeant Vosátka here's a dove."

"Don't get worked up, Papa, and tell the story." Kerholec pacified him.

"Well, it's hard, when all the time others think they know better. This python was shown by the director's wife. But when she got into the family way she couldn't carry Bures's 'worm'— it was too heavy for her. So Umberto hired a girl, a very pretty girl, a real Italian. All the boys were mad about her. There was no room for her in the wagon, so she slept in inns or lodgings, and of course, as is the custom everywhere, the boys used to go to her window, rapping and tapping, hoping she'd let them in.

"But she had the job of taking the crate with the snake home with her at night so that the python wouldn't catch cold. And at night whenever the tapping sounded, or any kind of noise, the python would go Sss-Sss, unwind from the crate, and crawl around to find out what was making the noise. And when the girl opened the window and started to flirt with the fellow it wouldn't be long before the gigantic snake's head would come up between them, and the boy would let out a yell and run away.

"The girl was really broken up over it; in the daytime the Umbertos watched her, at night the snake. And she wanted to have experiences. So one day she came to me almost crying; she said she had a boy friend, but whenever he came to see her the snake would go Sss-Sss and head for the young man. I told her, 'For the Lord's sake, don't let the old man hear about it. He would be awfully scared that the python might rub his skin off, and he hasn't any money for a new one.'

"And poor Marie began to weep; it was all the same to her if the python rubbed his skin off or what, she only wished that he wouldn't go Sss-Sss and chase her boy friends away. I could see her point—it must be terrible to come to see a girl and suddenly that Sss-Sss, and there a python. So I told her, 'You stupid girl,'

I told her, 'tell your boy friend to bring a live rabbit with him this evening; he can throw it to the python and he'll eat it up, and for a week you won't have any Sss-Sss.' Marie thanked me for the piece of advice and went away. After a week or so I asked her, 'Well, how did it work—any more Sss-Sss?' And she said, 'Don't talk to me about those smart boy friends of yours. Do you think any of them would sacrifice a rabbit? They want everything for nothing, the misers, and the python's still going Sss-Sss.' "

"That's a wonderful story." The men chuckled. "But what's the connection with the Sergeant?"

"Well"—Malina got angry—"I told you I didn't know, that I didn't quite understand it, but it reminded me of that python. Anyway, let's go home to bed."

They agreed and got up. The stout Mexican was in no way dejected at the lack of success he had had. He and Vosátka drank another three glasses of rum at the bar on parting, then they embraced and kissed and Don José Lebeda from Hlubocepy disappeared into the unknown as he had come out of the unknown.

The stakers walked part of the way home together. On the Reeperbahn Malina turned off. Even in wintertime he slept in Number Eight, for he could not part with the circus. They had already separated when he called to them, "Come here!"

They went back a few steps and Malina, raising his finger, told them:

"Now I know what the connection was. As soon as I looked at Lebeda, at those jaws of his, I told myself, 'Good Lord, that fellow could swallow a live rabbit!' And then the python and the Sss-Sss came to my mind. And as for Marie, I have to add one more important thing before I forget it. What I told you about happened in Bavaria, I remember. When we came to the River Rhine everything was different. Different blood, different customs. There the boys brought rabbits every night, and the python was stuffed as full as a Christmas stocking and couldn't go Sss-Sss. And by the time the director's wife was back on her feet a bit, and could take over from Marie, Marie herself couldn't lift it; she was pregnant herself. Somewhere near Trier we had to let her go. Well now, I've remembered it all. Good night."

CHAPTER THIRTEEN

LITTLE HELEN BERWITZ had returned to her riding. During the whole winter she had been excused from it so that she could devote all her time to studying with Madame Delaglio.

Tereza Delaglio was a flashily dressed and painted old woman with black, witchlike eyes, a sharp nose, and a rough, rasping voice. She stooped a little now, but her feet in their high heels were firm and straight, and when she belted up her skirt she could still perform a *détiré*, an acrobatic ballet position with her leg raised up to her head and with her opposite arm lifted *en demi lyre*. Her life had been lived like a burlesque pantomime, in which she turned the heads of all the Harlequins and ran out into the moonlight with the Pierrots. She had come into the world in the anteroom of the ballet studio in La Scala in Milan, where her mother was a charwoman.

From the age of three she had imitated all the motions of the dancers like a monkey, and at seven she had appeared on the stage. At twenty-one she was the *première danseuse* in Riga, then in Warsaw, and then in Dresden. Her old prayer books were interleaved with love poems composed for her by the poets of six or seven countries. And throughout Europe there were many old and noble residences to which she could have paid a visit whenever she liked—a slender and fragile goddess of Victory at whose feet lay the estates and family crests of her aristocratic admirers. At last she married the bass singer Delaglio, who drank, beat her from time to time, and after he had squandered all her savings, died in a madhouse.

Now Madame Delaglio lived in an unclean apartment in Hamburg; her two daughters, Marietta and Gioconda, danced in the ballet troupe of the local theater. They were not as young as they had been, but Madame Delaglio guarded their virtue with the eye of a hawk. That is, she found admirers for them, arranged rendezvous for them in some clandestine manner, and then finally forced her way into the room at the right moment, so that, amid tears and cries, she could practice her refined blackmail. The burlesque pantomimes continued, only there were no more Pierrots in the moonlight, only potbellied Pantaloons, and Columbine had taken on the part of the old comic.

However many adventures the daughters had, and however late they were kept up, early in the forenoon Madame Delaglio chased them from their beds. At ten, often even at nine, her ballet school would begin. Young Hamburg girls came to learn from the artist whose glory their grandfathers and fathers had known. Amid the disorder of unmade beds and of evening dresses lying about, with their unfinished coffee on the table, the uncombed and only partly dressed Misses Delaglio sleepily stumbled. With her stick in her hand the old *prima* gave commands, the remains of last night's rouge still on her cheeks, her piercing eyes heavily painted, a haggard specter of the night in the gray light of the winter morning.

Here Helen and six other girls learned the five fundamental postures of the classical ballet; they twisted their legs with their heels turned in and their toes turned out, or, standing with one foot straight before the other, they raised themselves on tiptoe, stretching their body upward and dropping back down on their soles. Meanwhile the daughters showed them how to assume the six main arm positions. The painted old madame showed them how to make a circle with a leg and then gave the command for them to stretch it out in an *écart,* all the time pounding with her stick and croaking angrily.

The stick pounded on the floor and the girls learned the steps, the angel's step, the fish's step, and the first artificial steps and leaps, which included standing on one leg in an arabesque or an attitude and the execution of *petit, moyen,* and *grand battement.* These are only the first approaches to the royal art of ballet, but already the foundation was being laid for the innumerable combinations of poses and movements which would ultimately help to form the grace of their young bodies.

Of course the hours spent at Madame Delaglio's were not sufficient. Helen rehearsed everywhere. She was often to be found in the circus building leaning against the rail of a box and practicing her positions with her soles turned out, trying to keep her feet together the while, *collés*. Often Paolo, the son of Achmed Roméo, appeared out of the darkness of the building. He was filled with interest at the strange things he saw little Helen doing, and found that much of it was very similar to the exercises his father taught him in the school which preserved the most ancient foundations of formal perfection.

Only the names were different and their use was different. In Achmed's school everything served to produce a more violent movement, designed for leaping as if shot out from a gun; what Helen did was rather for the development of posture, for holding a position and for raising the body on the tips of the toes. Paolo was tremendously interested; his slender body was the body of a born dancer, and in himself he sensed the need for slow, graceful gestures, for free play with his own beauty. Paolo was already in love with himself, he longed already for praise; it pleased him to look at himself in the mirror, and when he talked to Helen it seemed to him that ballet would be infinitely more suitable for him than his whirling acrobatics.

In this he was Vasek's exact opposite. Vasek too came as a friend to look at Helen, to watch her practice, even try some of her tricks, but in the end he turned up his nose. These were only stunts for girls. To stand on the flat sole, stand on tiptoe, stand this way and stand that way, just to stand, stand, stand and look pretty—it wasn't the thing for a man. For a man there was the jump, the take-off, and the flight through the air. When you were flying above the ground—then you showed the charm of your body.

Vasek knew already which sort of charm he wanted to learn. Mr. Hamilton had to do it in his repertoire and the two Gevaerts of the Bellini Duo had it. He went to see them whenever they practiced it, and if it were on the program, he gaped at it with his arms folded. It was the *batoude*, a great jump from a springboard into the distance, over the backs of horses or over the heads of a whole double file of attendants, a jump with a beautifully twisting somersault. To line twelve horses in a row and then leap up and fly through the air over them! Or to line up twenty-four men in a double file, with rifles and bayonets which bristled criss-cross over their heads, and yourself be only half a yard higher than this living barrier! Now, boy, jump and get over them and past them; if you don't they'll carry you off as full of holes as a colander!

When you're over them with your flying body bunched up, your head between your knees, you whip over those flashing bayonets and the rifles, and boom!—the men fire, and you fly over like a cannon ball; and then it is time to straighten up and check your speed for the landing. That was a great feat if you like; a man had to have his whole body under control for it; and you won't do it, lad, if you don't take the board on the bounce, if you don't say to yourself, "Either I'll do it or I'll be a cripple." Whenever Vasek asked Mr. Hamilton how it was that he managed to fly off so fast, using his legs or using the springboard, Hamilton answered:

"It's pluck, Vasek—for a death jump like the *batoude* you have to have pluck. The men who shoot from below you are your twenty-four soldiers, and you must fly over them with the pluck of their leader; or else . . ."

But Achmed Roméo knew nothing of Vasek's premature longings. Schooling had to proceed in due order. Vasek could flip and do the monkey's jump—good, now he had to learn the flicflac, a front handspring, and the *saut perilleux,* a backward leap which was easier. And only when he could begin to do these automatically would he come to the *salto mortale,* a jump and a somersault forward, with the body bunched up and the knees under the chin. Hundreds of times Vasek ran up at Achmed's cry and leapt forward, and hundreds of times he felt that unpleasant, nauseating feeling in his stomach as the safety rope pulled him back from an unsuccessful leap. It felt as if something were hitting him in the stomach, and after twenty or thirty failures Vasek's head was whirling and he felt like vomiting; but Achmed laughed and said it was nothing, that Vasek must practice it again and again and one day he would suddenly get the knack, would get into the swing of it, and then it would all go automatically.

Vasek still thought that he failed because the force of his takeoff was too weak. He did not understand that inertia supplies the motive force for artificial jumps and that he had to learn to take advantage of this force which could carry his body through the air for him. Small movements are enough, and strength has another effect; under certain conditions it will turn you in space and bring you back onto your feet again. There is a single, invisible fraction of a second when your strength must enter into the interplay between inertia and gravity, and then suddenly the grace of movement will appear.

But this Achmed Roméo cannot tell him. Nor can Hamilton explain it, nor either of the two Gevaerts. All of them can do it, but they do not know how it is done. For them it is a "trick." The only one who could tell him about it, for he knows, was Frasquito Barengo, the trapeze artist. But Frasquito Barengo was silent. Frasquito Barengo was meditating. Meditating over the different curves the arms, legs, and head trace in the air when, after the sixth windup of the arm, they leave the trapeze and fly at liberty through the air, of how this flight might perhaps be more nearly perfect if a man were weaker in the legs and more developed in the shoulders, meditating whether or not Concha would betray him some day with that chatterbox Hector.

Frasquito Barengo came to no clear conclusion about all these matters; each time he came to a point where everything dissolved into mystery and his thoughts only lost themselves in a mist; into his brain and into the depths of his heart there penetrated from somewhere the insistent rhythm of a guitar accompaniment. And then Frasquito Barengo sat motionless like a carved statue and listened for hours to the music which sounded in him constantly, with its continual slow and intoxicating rocking, until there emerged from the music the image of home, of rocky wastes and burned grass and a dried-up riverbed, where Señor Juan Gonzalo Barengo, his father, rode on a great horse across a half-ruined bridge, erect, with a cloak thrown over his left shoulder; behind him his wife Rosita; and behind the horse a mule loaded with sacks of grain they were taking to the windmill.

So Vasek attributed his exhausting lack of success with the leap of death to the insufficient preparation of his muscles, and he plunged madly into new strengthening exercises. At the Gevaerts's he found a skipping rope and skipped persistently at every spare moment. He jumped everywhere that the opportunity presented itself, and one day he discovered a trick which had a special charm for him: the jockey jump. Whenever any of the riders rehearsed bareback vaulting, Vasek held his horse for him when he had finished, got up on tiptoe, rubbed the back of the horse with more rosin, and then practiced jumping up from the ground onto the horse's back without bending his legs.

It was much harder than his former jump onto the pony, but he found it easier to hold onto the broader back of the horse. After three weeks he developed a sure spring and a sure landing, and then Hans led the horse and Vasek learned to fly onto it while it moved. As far as possible he did all this in secret, at odd moments when no one was in the ring; his inborn ambition led him to want to surprise others with a perfect performance, and not to show anyone an act till he had mastered it thoroughly.

He practiced most often with the light-gray gelding Ajax. His back was somewhat lower and broader than those of the other horses, he was calm and reliable, and he paced the ring with a perfectly even step. It was for this quality that Berwitz had picked him for Helen's further training. In Hamburg Helen had been excused from her circus lessons, but now that the ballet school was over she went back each morning to practice vaulting. For the most part all went well, but when the ambitious Berwitz decided to demand the jockey jump from her as well, Helen was lost. As long as she could use the fork they fastened to the saddle girths she swung up onto Ajax lightly and gracefully, even when the horse ran at a trot. But she was evidently too weak for a direct jump.

However, Berwitz was dominated by the memory of how he himself had done the jockey jump in public when he was no older than she. He ordered rehearsal after rehearsal, but Helen could only perform the jump by swinging onto the horse on the safety rope. Berwitz did not shout or grumble, but slowly his good nature disappeared. Inwardly he began to reproach the girl for not having a firm enough will. It seemed to him that every success was only a matter of a firm, persistent will, of stubborn resolve. And he told himself that he should not have permitted the women to start all that ballet nonsense. He had let the girl go without practice for four months, and now this was the result; the girl was spoiled, softened, her calves were as soft as cheese, and it would take months before they would be firm enough for a decent jump.

Often when Helen, with tears in her eyes, took the run-up to no purpose for the twentieth time, two tiny figures would appear in the dark corners of the tent and follow her useless and exhausting attempts with great interest. They were Vasek and Paolo. Both boys considered themselves great experts at jumping, and Helen's clumsiness was an incentive to them to discuss the matter as experts.

"I," Paolo said one day when they were sitting together on a box at the back of the tent, "I could show her how to do that jump. But Hans won't let me near the horses, so that I can't try it out."

"A jump onto a horse," said Vasek, feeling his superiority on this score over Paolo, "is like any other kind of jump. There's nothing to it." But inwardly he thought, "Just you try it, you dirty chimney sweep; you'll break your legs."

"Well, I don't see," Paolo deliberated, "why Helen can't manage it. The take-off seems to be right."

"Helen's too weak." Vasek stuck up his nose. "And she can't find the trick to it."

"You think there's a trick to it?" Paolo asked.

"I don't think. I know."

"Trick? I don't think so . . ." The cunning Paolo pretended to disbelieve. And irritated, Vasek at once came out with his own special bit of wisdom.

"You fold your leg under," he said, as if it were the most ordinary thing under the sun.

"Fold your leg under? What do you mean by that?"

"Look—Helen goes at that jump like at a *suprasalto,* with her legs straight, *collés.* As if she was trying to get up into the air. But she won't go high enough that way. Her legs always strike the horse a little too low down. But if she bent in the right leg and pulled it up it would be easier for her. Then she'd land on the horse's back. And she'd have to straighten it up right away and reach out with the left one. *Non è così?*"

"How do you mean?" asked Paolo, still not understanding.

Vasek showed him how. They both understood examples better than words. Paolo clapped his hands.

"*Per vita mia,* that's right! How did you hit on it?"

"That's my business. Remember that Vasek knows a bit more than you think."

And Vasek walked away, his hands in his trousers pockets, kicking the stones out of his way. He was very pleased with himself for having put the ragamuffin Paolo in his place.

Paolo remained seated on the box, his eyes half-shut. "*Ecco,*" he said to himself, "how I got it out of him! It's a special big cat's jump up into the air. Now that I know I can risk jumping onto a horse without any practice."

The next morning when Helen took over the ring Paolo crawled into the tent and bit by bit edged closer toward the ring. Helen had finished her vaulting and was now starting the jockey jump. Three times she tried it, but all in vain. Berwitz looked gloomy, and began to crack his whip in the horse's direction, though Ajax ran like clockwork. Again Helen ran up, and again her jump was too short. And at that moment Paolo, burning to create an effect and unable to restrain himself, jumped out into the ring and cried:

"*Signore direttore . . .*"

Berwitz started. Someone had dared again to disturb him at a rehearsal and enter the ring! A barefoot boy! Berwitz trembled with rage and lashed with the whip.

"Ow!" screeched Paolo, and rolled on the ground. Then he got up and ran off, howling and yelling. His calf burned as if the whip had cut through it, and under his right knee the skin was actually torn and the blood was flowing. In the ring Berwitz continued to crack his whip into empty air to relieve his feelings; behind his back Hans cursed quietly, and Helen stood frightened and bewildered, her shoulders trembling, ready to weep; fastened to her string she looked like a trapped beast. Only Ajax continued to trot quietly in a circle round this scene at the same even gait.

242

Now the curtain moved aside and Vasek's puzzled face looked into the tent to see what was going on. Berwitz caught sight of him and at once sensed that he must put an end to this scene.

"Vasek!" he shouted at the boy.

Vasek ran out.

"You're not afraid to do the jockey jump?"

"No, Mr. Director."

"Come here and show Helen how to do it."

Hans untied Helen, but before he could turn to Vasek to tie him Vasek was already standing on Ajax's back.

"Again, Vasek. *Allez!*"

Vasek ran up beside the horse, jumped off, and his legs sprang up and reached the horse.

"Good, thank you. That's all for today. That's how it's done, Helen! And Vasek's only a year older than you!"

Berwitz left the ring. Ajax stopped. Vasek climbed down from his back onto the sawdust and then led him away to the stable to rub him down with straw. Hans soothed Helen with a few good-natured words and then went out after Vasek. Helen looked round and then ran off in the same direction in which Paolo had disappeared.

"Helen!"

Above on the top tier of seats sat Paolo, and he nodded to her. She ran up to him.

"Does it hurt much, Paolo?"

"*Ecco,* it's bleeding. He hit me, the brute!"

"You mustn't call him that. He's my father. Have you got a handkerchief?"

"No."

"I haven't either. But that wound ought to be bandaged up!"

"Why? Let me die. Then you'll have to bury me. Did I do anything bad? I only tried to help you!"

"That's what I thought. You're a good boy, Paolo. I like you."

"Better than Vasek?"

"Vasek's a good boy, too. And he rides with me. But what will we do with your leg?"

"Nothing. I'll put some spider web on it later. Come here and sit down."

243

Helen sat down beside Paolo. It was quiet there and dark; below the deserted ring shone dimly. Without a word Paolo drew the girl close to him and put his arm round her neck; a light trembling came over both children, a vague feeling of a sort of intoxicating madness. Involuntarily they spoke in whispers.

"What will you do, Helen, when you're grown-up?"

"I'll be a rider."

"I'll be a dancer. I've already made up my mind. I'll be the head of a great ballet."

"That will be nice!"

"You could dance with me if you'd keep on training."

"I'm going to, for certain. Mother told me so. We could be a team, couldn't we?"

"Yes. Of course. I'll have a lot of dancing girls, but for the solos I'll always pick you. And we'll be terrifically successful."

"Madame Delaglio says that I'm going to dance on my toes very well."

"That's good. You have to know how to do that. And how about getting married?"

"No—or do you think we should?"

"Of course. You like me, don't you?"

"Yes."

"Paolo is a handsome boy, isn't he?"

"Yes."

"And Paolo tried to help you and got whipped for it!"

"Yes."

"So, you see—Paolo likes you, Paolo will protect you, Paolo will make a great dancer out of you."

"That will be very, very nice."

"Will you promise, then, that you'll marry me?"

"I promise, Paolo. But what will Father say?"

"That doesn't matter. If he won't let us, I'll carry you off. We'll run away from him."

"Maybe on horses."

This suggestion dampened Paolo's enthusiasm a bit. It stirred up the old pain he felt at the realization that he was not a rider. Behind them a muffled sound arose. Evidently someone was get-

244

ting ready to practice in the ring. Paolo hastened to finish the conversation.

"Maybe on horses or in a coach. Whatever suits best. Now give me your hand. Do you promise?"

"If you want me to, Paolo, then I'll promise."

"Word of honor?"

"Word of honor."

"Well, remember. Now we belong to each other. Even if we get separated, even if Father and I go somewhere else, you must wait for me until I come and carry you off."

"Yes, Paolo."

Helen found all this quite proper. She liked Paolo, he was handsome, at home they said of him that he was a wonderful performer. And today he had been hurt because he had tried to help her with the jockey jump. Father might get angry, but Madame Delaglio would have approved. Madame Delaglio always told her pupils to be on the lookout to find a husband, so they wouldn't end up like those daughters of hers.

Down below Hamilton came in and called to someone that the ring was empty. The younger of the Gevaerts brothers appeared at the gate. For the last time now Paolo pressed Helen's hand. Both got up. It then struck him that he ought to kiss her, but they were on top of the steps and might have fallen. Now Paolo spoke aloud as they went off together.

"Did Vasek tell you how to do the jockey jump?"

"No, Paolo, he showed me, but he didn't tell me."

"He could have explained it, too. Last night I told him how to do it. But maybe he didn't understand. He's only a beginner."

"How can I do the jump and stop Father's being angry?"

"I'll tell you how to, Helen, so that you can see what kind of fellow Paolo is. You make the mistake of trying to make the jump with your legs straight. You must jump off on your left foot and raise your right one as you're going up. Look here."

And the handsome Paolo showed her the secret he had learned the evening before from Vasek. And Helen tried it out, pretending that she was jumping on a horse, and then ran off home. She was so happy she felt like singing. Paolo had promised her that she was to be *première danseuse*. Paolo would carry her off, and in general Paolo was a wonderful boy; he wasn't afraid of blows and he knew how to do the jockey jump.

CHAPTER FOURTEEN

BEHIND VOSÁTKA'S BACK the inhabitants of Number Eight spoke a great deal of the unexpected appearance of Don José Lebeda. They had uncovered a part of the past about which their friend had been silent.

"He's had a full life." Karas shook his head.

"I told you that," Kerholec agreed. "That fellow has a history longer than Napoleon's. Lord, that man's been shot at by everything from cannon down."

"I was pleased," Bures added, "by the way he came out and said that he always fought for ideals. It's important that our countryman Vosátka's more than a simple adventurer. A man must follow some sort of ideal."

"He should write it all down," Karas opined. "People would read it."

"Don't say that," Malina grumbled aggravatedly. "Maybe you don't think a staker's good enough, so you want to make a scribbler out of him? That'd be a low trick."

"Something could be made out of the story," said Kerholec and wrinkled his forehead. "It would be an eternal shame to let it go to waste."

Kerholec never said such things at random. It was true, Kerholec possessed the gift of the gab, but he never gossiped without a purpose. A clever quick brain worked in his head and he was full of practical ideas. Such conversations as this led him to ideas which were at first vague and nebulous, but which soon took form. And one day, without thinking out any long speeches

246

or making any preparations, Kerholec went during the midday rest to see Berwitz.

"Mr. Director, I may have an idea," he said to him, his hat shoved back on his head. Berwitz stood by his wagon, minus his coat and waistcoat, his leg propped against the steps and a cigar glowing in his mouth.

"Well, let's have it, Karel," the director said. "Ideas aren't meant for the wastepaper basket. Most ideas can be turned into an act."

Berwitz knew Kerholec, and appreciated him. If his whole circus were to fail and he had to start all over again, the first person he would hire would be this Czech staker who had ideas.

"We haven't done any pantomimes for a long time."

"That's right. We've played them all too often and everybody's seen them."

"True. We'd have to come out with something new. We've always done fairy tales or the Queen of Sheba, or stories of that kind, only for kids. We should find something that would interest the grownups."

"That's right, Karel, and it's what I always say, too. But what could it be? Have you found something?"

"I think I have. Not a fairy tale—this would have to be something really absorbing and to do with present-day life, something that people are always talking about."

"And is there any one thing that people are always talking about? My wife's always talking about her tigers, my daughter about her ballet, Frans about numbers, and Hammerschmidt about stockings—you won't make any pantomime out of that."

"No. But there's the war."

"My God, what war? Where is there a war? I hope to the Lord they don't take the horses. . . ."

"The war's in America, it seems."

"Oh, in America. Well, they can fight there, as far as I'm concerned. We're not going to America. So there's a war in America! That's none of my business. I haven't time for newspaper foolishness. Who's fighting, anyway? I always thought that was a paradise."

"The war is in the Union. The Northern States against the Southern. To stop slavery."

"Iyiyiyi. Are there still such things in the world?"

"There are, and everyone's interested in them. The newspapers come out every day with some piece of heroism or cruelty. If you got a pantomime about it ready for this winter in Hamburg, we'd do a big business."

"Well, maybe, but how would we do it? There would be Indians in it, right?"

"Indians and Negroes, riflemen, cowboys, and cavalry. The main thing, of course, cavalry. We could stage a whole battle in the ring."

"Wait, first there'd be the fleeing populace. So that we could drive in the sheep, geese and Bluebeard and his goats. That was always successful. And then the battle—and Karel, I could appear in it as a marksman. I learned to shoot from Father, and I still have all the equipment in the wagon. It would be a wonderful act. The elephant should be in it, shouldn't he? Maybe I could shoot at him."

"We'll have to ask whether they have elephants in America or not. Everything must be as true to life as possible, you know, realistic."

"Of course. We'll have the Negroes wear those Moroccan costumes, and for the Indians we might do over those Persian falconers."

"We can find that out from anyone who's been there."

"To be sure. But where can we get hold of someone?—every day we're somewhere different."

"He's here now; he travels with us. He's in my gang: the staker Vosátka."

"Vosátka? He's been there? Wonderful. Well, but how will he do it—will he write it out or what . . . ? I can't imagine how you'd put a pantomime like that together. Before this we always acted what we saw. But this is a completely new idea."

"I think you can leave that to me. I have another clever boy in my wagon, Bures; we'll put it together somehow and bring it to you all ready."

"Yes. But the fleeing populace has to be there, and the marks-

248

man, don't forget that, Karel. And what will we call it? That's very important, too."

"A name . . . a name . . . well, the best might be simply, North versus South."

"North versus South. That's terrific. Yes . . . North versus South . . . North versus South. . . . Wonderful. It's catchy: North versus South. But wait, won't it matter if the building's in a different direction . . . you know, I think the gate could stand for the North and the entrance the South, but suppose the gate's to the west?"

"That won't matter, Mr. Director."

"I know it won't. But you said everything should be realistic. Well, so be it: North versus South. And Karel, if it's a success, remember that Director Berwitz will show his gratitude. Let's say fifty marks. And if it's a big success, maybe sixty. So long!"

And Director Berwitz straightened up and went to look for his wife to tell her that he had just hit on the wonderful idea of creating a new, stirring, and realistic pantomime, North versus South, and that he had turned over the working-out of the smaller details to Kerholec and his corps of fellow workers. And that he himself would play the chief part, that of an expert sharpshooter, so that the thing would be bound to be a complete success.

Though Kerholec had had no difficulty with Berwitz, it was more difficult to get such people as Vosátka and Bures interested in the composition of anything so serious. He did not dare to come straight out with it; he had to act carefully, to approach the matter indirectly. He left it until evening, when they had finished eating a huge pile of noodles with sauerkraut and had lain down on the ground with their stomachs pleasantly distended. As every day, today too they began to speak of old times, and it was not difficult for Kerholec to turn the conversation onto the old pantomimes. It was Malina who, all unknowingly, helped him the most. The old man waxed eloquent.

"Yes, pantomimes," he at once took over the attack, "they were really beautiful. Little Red Ridinghood, Snow White and the Dwarfs, the Seven Cockroaches—that was a wonderful show, the people really liked that. In the Seven Cockroaches I played the seventh cockroach, and it was really a hard part, because the front ones always tumbled over in a pile with the last one at the bottom. But it didn't matter to me; old Umberto praised me for the way I interpreted the seventh cockroach, and for the feeling with which I acted. I acted with feeling all right; there were six fellows on top of me, with boots on, anyone would act that part with feeling, even if he were made out of cast iron."

"And now they don't act anything like that," added Karas. "I heard about Red Ridinghood myself from my grandmother, but I never saw it with my own eyes."

"Fairy tales are out of date now." Kerholec brought the conversation closer to his own subject. "Now you'd have to produce something completely new."

"Well, comrade, I have a sensational new idea," Vosátka plunged in. "Why not stage the flood of the world—that would make a real pantomime for the circus! Noah and Sons! The peak in animal performance! All the beasts of the earth in a joint appearance! A unique event in the annals of humanity!"

"And to that you must add"—Bures burst out laughing—"billions of cubic feet of water flooding the ring from all the floodgates of heaven!"

"Quite right, quite right. And as a special attraction an equilibrist act by the dove with the olive branch."

"And how about the background, Sergeant? The rainbow over Mount Ararat!"

"And a whole ballet of all the animals!"

"And at the end a living picture with Maestro Selnicki as Noah, doing justice to a goblet of wine."

These inspirations tickled them vastly; only Malina remained serious.

"The rainbow on Ararat's all a mistake," he pronounced when they had quieted down. "I'd heard about it, too, but with my own eyes I made sure that there wasn't any rainbow on Ararat. Those are old wives' tales. There are clouds on Ararat."

"You've been on Ararat, Uncle?" Vasek rolled his eyes.

"Well, I wasn't on it—who'd climb up a hill like that? But we were at the foot of it for maybe a week, and clouds kept rolling above us all the time."

"And did you see anything left from the flood?"

"Yes, boy. There was still a terrific swamp there in one place. Our Bingo rolled about in the mud there for a long while."

Vasek was silent, for he was busy deciding that he must go to see Bingo and ask Arr-Sherir what it was like when Bingo took a bath in the remains of the flood below Ararat.

"You see, fellows"—Kerholec now changed the subject. "Here you've been making up a pantomime just for fun, and actually all you would need now is the sign: 'Free admission to the righteous.' But suppose we were to think up something real, something that could be staged? Umberto's Circus could use something like that."

"God be with us and the Devil keep away!" Malina almost crossed himself. "Maybe you want us to write a pantomime for you?"

"Why not? Why is it impossible?"

"Stop kidding me, you're out of your mind. Did you ever hear of anybody making up a pantomime? Pantomimes are always acted just as they are; nobody ever wrote them."

"That's a good one, Malina. How do you think the old panto-mimes got started?"

"I don't know, but I'm sure no one ever wrote them down. Circuses and pantomimes are things which have always been, and you never introduce anything new into them."

"Look, Grandpa, what will you bet we *can* think of something completely new?"

"Well, I'll bet a keg of beer, you lunatics. You're mad and mad you'll always be. Just try and tell me that pantomimes can be written! They're made up of pictures and happenings and a terrible lot of things you have to see being done before you can make them up. You can't make something out of nothing."

"Did you hear him, friends?" Kerholec quickly turned to Vosátka and Bures. "A keg of beer—is it a bet?"

"It's a bet!" cried Vosátka. "The seventh cockroach had better take care!"

In this way Kerholec induced Bures and Vosátka to put their heads together, and from the erudition of the one and the living experience of the other they wrote a simple scene for the circus, in which the slave owners, with the help of the blacks, attacked a small Northern troop of cavalry. An Indian boy, played by Vasek, led up reinforcements which defeated the Southern rebels. Mr. Berwitz received a double rôle in this spectacle: first that of an extraordinary marksman whom the Southerners made their leader; then he came on at the end as a very important sheriff of the North. The piece was extremely successful, and North versus South became the first of a long line of glorious pantomimes, all of which were put together by Bures, Vosátka, and Kerholec.

Their novelty consisted in the fact that they were based on well-known events. All over the whole world the great powers were on the move: Russia marched into Central Asia, the French moved in the Far East and the Pacific, England in Africa and the Indian Empire; exotic lands had suddenly appeared on the horizons of the readers of newspapers, and each year Umberto's Circus came out with a slogan under which unknown lands and their wonders were presented to the hungry sight of the great public.

After the spectacle of the American Civil War came the Conquest of Mexico, then the Japanese Flower Festival, the Emir of Bokhara, the Princess of Annam, Across Africa, and the Romance of the Hindu Dancing Girl. To this they added heroic motives from European war: the Night Watch at Sedan, Haji Loya, the Cossacks on the Shipka. All of these were cut out of the same cloth, but the public crowded in. Frau von Hammerschmidt had sold-out houses for days on end, and with the mounting receipts Berwitz bought more and more animals, purchased costumes and settings, improved his tents, and hired exotic artists for the circus. These last were given special parts to play in the pantomimes.

A large share in the composition of these librettos was played by the Sailor's Bride. But one evening when they went there to drink Malina's keg of beer and to scatter some of Berwitz's fifty marks to the four winds, Moesecke's hoarse voice did not rasp out its usual greeting; in his stead a woman turned round from behind the bar. Moesecke had caught a cold and had had to take to his bed, and his place had been taken by his wife. None of the gang had ever seen her before, and Moesecke himself had never mentioned her. It was a great surprise to them and, as they had to admit, quite a pleasant one. In place of the burly bartender there smiled at them a plump being with dimples in her cheeks, dark flashing eyes, and black curly hair.

"How did that brute Moesecke find such a treasure?" was the first involuntary question of all of them. But these seasoned globe-trotters did not rack their brains long over the mystery. Kerholec was the first to shove his hat on the back of his head and sit up with Vosátka at the bar to give Mrs. Moesecke a proper look-over. Soon Vosátka was winking at Kerholec; this woman was no fool. She knew her stuff—"Lord, she could give you an answer like a whiplash." And Kerholec agreed with him—"This woman's been around, Vosátka, she's been around"—and soon they were clink-ing their glasses and toasting her beauty, soon they were tapping their fingers on the edge of the counter and ordering more.

And somehow or other, the stuff tasted better that day, when in place of the sallow old Moesecke such a plump, pretty little thing was in charge! That evening they swilled up their beer in bliss. Sergeant Vosátka, in particular, was in the seventh heaven; he spoke only American Spanish, called Adéla Moesecke "Na Misia" and *"dulce pebete"* and *"mío damasco,"* and began to sing, into the bargain. His scar reddened and his eyes half closed as he bent over to Adéla and softly hummed some foreign song. It was a slow *tango milonga,* one of those *tristes* which are sung on the pampas in endless, constantly improvised stanzas which celebrate a woman's beauty.

> Death comes to me in your fair eyes,
> Your gemlike eyes which are my foes;
> Death lurks inside your opened eyes,
> Yet you would kill me if they close.

They had never seen their Sergeant in such a mood before; suddenly he had become a Mexican wild beast, a puma which sought its prey; everything was alive in him, everything burned in him as if electrified, and it was plain to see that this dark woman, who had suddenly reminded him of some beauty in New Granada, was conscious of the sparks which flew from him, and was kindling under them. Kerholec, too, was a wild man with the woman, but with the Sergeant as his opponent he unconsciously yielded. What else could he do? Vosátka marched straight forward as if he were going to jump the *batoude* over sixteen horses, no matter at what cost to horses or to his own neck! Now he stood with the glass in his three good fingers, a scarred but unconquerable warrior who began a new stanza in Spanish:

> Should I your magic beauty tell?
> That evil thing in which I glory—
> For my eyes heaven, for my soul hell,
> And for my wallet purgatory.

Crash! The drained glass flew against the floor and the Sergeant ordered, "A bottle of aqua vitae!"

"For God's sake," Malina cried in a smothered voice, "this will kill me! It'll end badly. Spanish singing and Swedish liquor— there may be a couple of dead and wounded!"

Karas too was worried, and both of them now slipped out and hurried off down the Reeperbahn, where they said good night. As Malina passed the side entrance to the circus the door half opened and someone looked out. Malina stopped and recognized goldenred hair.

"Alice! Carrothead!" he called softly. "What are you doing up so late?"

"Is that you, Papa Malina?"

"Yes, in all my beauty. But you're not waiting up for me?"

"No, not that. But Mr. Kerholec isn't home yet."

"Kerholec? Oh, that's right, he told me himself he was moving into the building this year. He's in the night watchman's room, right?"

"Yes. Across the passage from us. Mr. Kerholec has always been so punctual, and tonight he hasn't come in for the first time. I was afraid that something might have happened to him. . . ."

"No, Alice, so far nothing's happened. But don't wait up for him."

"Where is he?"

"Well, you know, a man . . ."

"What . . . he's with girls?"

"No, not that. He's with the gang. But how it will all end, I don't know."

"They're with girls somewhere?"

"Not yet, I tell you. And even if they were, it should be all the same to you. Go to bed, let's not wake Harwey up."

"Good night."

The door closed and Malina made his way through the darkness to wagon Number Eight. The window in Alice Harwey's tiny room did not light up; the girl slipped in on tiptoe, sat down on the bed, and in the dark listened to detect whether or not her father in the next room was sleeping. It was quiet, only the throbbing of her own heart could be heard. Why, ever since the time when Kerholec began to sleep on the other side of the passage, could she not fall asleep, but lie and wait for him to return? How many years they had lived near each other and she had never before felt any disturbance! Why, she had even grown up with him; he was already superintendent when she began to ride. How many times he had helped her onto her horse in place of the groom, how many times he had stood by the curtain and watched her vault, and then teased her because of her red hair!

He had some sort of strange expression in his own language, something like "Redhead, redhead, what's ruffling you?" Alice remembered it well, for he had said it the first time he met her and she had pinched him for it on the arm. My God, all that had been so innocent, so friendly, no one could have thought anything of it; why then a week ago did she suddenly begin to tremble at the thought that he was entering the door across the passageway? They had wintered here for many years, and always some man whom the owner of the building had hired as night watchman had slept there; but now that Mr. Berwitz had bought the building he had dismissed him as unnecessary and turned the cubbyhole over to Kerholec.

Why had it never interested her before that someone slept there? She had never even wondered who it might be, and yet on the first night that Kerholec had moved in such agitation seized her that she double-locked her door and listened till long after midnight to every rustle, every crackling which sounded in the old building. And today, when for once he did not come, today some strong feeling had seized her, today she suddenly saw that something was happening to her that perhaps ought

255

not to happen. Was it a disgrace to submit to such agitation? Ought she to resist it? But how could she defend herself against something which was possessing her like a feverish whirl-wind?

My God, where had she got this feeling from? From her mother, perhaps? Perhaps this was the same fever which had once caused her mother to disappear with the Irishman while her father lay ill covered with bandages? Perhaps it was the blood that she had inherited from her mother which was demanding its own. . . . Was someone coming? . . . Yes . . . It was he.

Alice Harwey jumped up quickly and without even thinking, at the vehement command of her instinct, she rushed to her little dressing table and seized a bottle of perfume and sprinkled it on her bodice. Then she slipped out to the front door of the building.

It was Kerholec returning. He and Vosátka had come to the point with that black minx where Kerholec felt that he would not stand in his comrade's way. When he left with Bures his head was foggy from the effect of the drinks, but after a few breaths of air, pleasantly cool in the moonlit night, his intoxica-tion blew away. Only his passionate, aroused desire remained.

"Where are we going?" He turned to Bures.

"Nowhere, Karel. You have too much money on you."

"Nonsense. I know what I'm doing. We might have gone to the Bunch of Grapes. There are nice girls there. . . . But it's too late now . . . they'll all be in their rooms by now . . . Phooey, it's a disgusting life. . . . Whores, whores, and nothing but whores. . . . But Adéla was nice, clean, pretty. . . . Vosátka is a dirty dog! . . . As ugly and as savage as a devil. . . . My God, Bures, we won't meet one single girl tonight! All of them are taken already in hand, delivered, sold—Christ, it's enough to make a man scream. Where shall we go, Bures? Say where we can go, where we can find beautiful, pure women. Think, Bures, Lord, you're supposed to be a cultured man. . . ."

But Bures stuck to his opinion that it was too late now for them to go anywhere, that they would find only depraved left-overs, and that the only sensible thing was to go home. So he got Kerholec halfway up the Reeperbahn, led him across the

256

street to the open space in front of the circus, patted him on the shoulder, and sent him off to bed.

Kerholec headed toward the circus, but he stopped when Bures had disappeared.

"It really isn't possible," there buzzed in his brain, "for me to be left alone after such an evening. At least let's stand here a bit . . . at least wait here . . . perhaps something will come along by chance . . . white, beautiful, perfumed . . . perhaps she's coming this way, and it would be a sin to let her go by . . . At least count up to a hundred; if you're lucky she'll come . . . one . . . two . . . three . . . fo-ur . . ."

Kerholec stood in the moonlight; behind him lay the building with its lights extinguished, before him stretched the empty street, along which only drunkards staggered here and there. Kerholec counted; he counted slowly, stretching out the numbers: twen-ty se-ven . . . but his vision of happiness did not appear. He did not finish counting the hundred; he waved his hand, shoved his hat back on his head, and turned toward the building. A dog's life, this one, and now he would have to wake up old Harwey into the bargain to get him to open the door.

But what is this? The door is open! Kerholec's eyes brighten —yes, the door's not closed! And someone stands on the doorstep . . . someone in white . . . Kerholec raced over the last few steps. . . .

"Carrot-top! What are you doing here?"

"Waiting for you!"

"For me!"

"Yes, so that you won't have to wake Father."

Alice stands in the darkness of the passage, tall and slender, and her whisper strikes him like a tender caress. Kerholec smells a waft of her perfume. His arm rises involuntarily and embraces her, and clasps her at the back of her neck under that mass of hair. Alice stands stiffly, as if frozen; for a short eternity he holds her thus, and all at once her rebellious spine softens and without a word she bends toward him and suddenly she clings to him passionately, with her arms, her lips, her breast, with everything.

Slowly, slowly Kerholec reaches for the latch of his door,

257

slowly, slowly he moves toward it with this warm body which hangs on his. And when he crosses the threshold he feels light and ecstatic, and there flashes through his brain the triumphant "Ninety-eight, ninety-nine, one hundred!"

At that moment Sergeant Ferenc Vosátka was sitting with Adéla Moesecke behind the locked doors of the Sailor's Bride, running his hand through her black hair and singing:

> Your eyes inquire, though thus they burn me,
> Your eyes seek me, with hope they fill me,
> Your eyes find me and now they spurn me,
> Your eyes wound me and soon will kill me.

CHAPTER FIFTEEN

GAUDEAMUS had arrived unexpectedly from Berlin and had come straight from the railway station to see Director Berwitz.

"The business is already on foot," he said as soon as the two of them were alone together. "Kranz has bought the building on the Friedrichstrasse in Berlin where the French riding clubs used to be. It's a wonderfully suitable building, and good business could be done there this spring if you could come to an agreement with Kranz. He'd like to come to Hamburg for a week, and is willing to lend you his building in Berlin in exchange."

Berwitz became excited at once. To go to Berlin, at least for a time, had been his dream, but there was always someone established there who received special concessions, and competition dared only to enter the outskirts of the city. But at the same time there bristled up in him the pride of a man from an old circus dynasty against a man who had climbed up the ladder from nowhere. It could not matter that Kranz had now become owner of his own building, or that Berwitz had been master of his for half a year longer—still Berwitz was an old resident here in Hamburg, and to him this fellow seemed to be a mere upstart and vagabond. Now Berwitz found himself involved in a conflict so weighty that he felt he must light a cigar before coming to a decision.

He drew out a great black, real Hamburg cigar, bit off the tip with a rustling sound and, licking the wound which he had inflicted on the tobacco leaves, slowly and ceremoniously puffed on the flame of the match. He told himself that he thus gained time to think, but actually he thought of nothing more than the fact that he was gaining time, and that it made a good impression when he looked as if he were thinking.

"Good, Baron," he finally pronounced. "I understand Kranz is trying to get a guest performance in my building. And I'm to appear in his. Well, Baron, let's suppose we accept. But is his building big enough and suitable enough for Umberto's Circus to appear there? I've seen it . . . I never took much interest in it . . . and this year I've got a great program: I've worked out a realistic pantomime, a gigantic success—you must see it. North versus South—no one could hit on an idea of that sort but me. I appear in it as a marksman and as a sheriff—well, Baron, in a word, you really will have to see it. And then it's a question if Kranz is big enough yet to appear here at all. You know, the public here's used to things which are quite out of the ordinary, to having something new all the time . . . it won't be easy for him to keep up with Umberto's Circus. . . ."

To this Gaudeamus replied with a good-sized bit of figurative tightrope-walking. He praised Kranz, but kept admitting that, to be sure, one could by no means compare him with Berwitz. He spoke with enthusiasm, for Kranz had promised him a thousand marks if he, Kranz, could appear in the Hamburg circus building and show that stuck-up Berwitz what a real circus was like. Gaudeamus was fond of such diplomatic missions, especially when they had a financial point to them.

For years he had lived in touch with the circus, it was his daily task to praise the artists of the ring and their art; he possessed a whole stock of fine expressions and intriguing comparisons for the very purpose, but he himself regarded the circus folk as mad, foolhardy children. For him there existed but one true, worthy and exalted art; the art of living. He had heard it said in Viennese society that all great and true artists work their way up to fame only by hard practice, suffering, and want. And what else had those cursed years of exile in Halicz been for him? There he had learned to appraise each beautifully and completely lived moment and to value unfettered freedom in life.

This was the reason he loved his endless travels in the service of Umberto's Circus. Then he was his own master, he could measure his abilities in daily battles with obstacles, and whenever he wished he could throw aside the mask of Gaudeamus and appear on the scene with a grandee's gesture as Knight and Baron von Schönstein. He played a dual rôle, he played it with pleasure and he played it with all that it implied: Mr. Gaudeamus never neglected to provide enjoyable evenings for the Baron. The income Umberto's Circus provided him with of course did not suffice for both rôles; it was enough for Mr. Gaudeamus's way of life, but for the Baron it was on the skimpy side. And here the higher aspect of his art had to be brought into play, the foundations of which had been laid down in his office in Halicz.

Gaudeamus well knew how to pay off the authorities with a grand gesture, on behalf of Umberto's Circus, but with no less elegance did he accept the bribes of entrepreneurs on his own account. And with this same flexibility he could rely on his charming appearance to enchant those friends who were happy whenever they were permitted to entertain him and to overwhelm him with presents; he could take advantage of all sorts of entanglements and speculations, out of which inevitably some kind of share would always materialize for him. If it had not been for his rôle as Baron he would already have had a considerable fortune put away for the future, but the Baron in him could scatter with an easy hand all that Mr. Gaudeamus so skillfully amassed. But Gaudeamus was not vexed at this; it was life's charm to climb and fall so quickly and easily, and in the last analysis it was always the dashing Max, the Baron and Knight, who had the greater success.

It was in this rôle that Kranz knew him, and in his deep, un-concealed, and adoring respect for the aristocracy this stable hand who had started out from "scratch" was in raptures when-ever he could pay the Baron's expenses and when at times he was permitted to offer even greater assistance, which the Baron accepted with a lordly gesture and without the least intention of returning it. The idea of an exchange of guest performances by the two enterprises was Gaudeamus's inspiration. First he had talked Kranz into it, and now he was trying to win Berwitz over. It seemed to him that greater harmony between the two circuses would result in a multitude of benefits for him which he could reap from both sides.

He did not have to struggle with Berwitz's prejudices and antipathies for long: Berwitz's own vanity and egoism gave him his chief weapon against them. Why should he fear such a competitor? How could he back out when it was Kranz who had humbled himself and come forward with an offer? In point of fact, it ended just as Gaudeamus wished: they agreed that Kranz was to come to Hamburg to visit Umberto's Circus and that the two directors would then meet in a hotel to talk the matter over. Gaudeamus was to make the trip with Kranz and act as his second. For his confidant Berwitz should choose one of the local people, someone who could comprehend the fact of Gaudeamus's double life and not do any unnecessary talking about it. After a brief reflection Berwitz decided that the band leader, Selnicki, would be the most suitable for the part.

No newspaper reporter was at the station to describe for the citizens of Hamburg this solemn and almost historic moment when the two circus kings met for the first time. It was a cere-monial occasion. Baron von Schönstein stood at Kranz's side with the lofty air of a Minister Plenipotentiary, and clad in his huge fur coat, Mr. Selnicki, at Berwitz's side, looked like a Privy Counsellor. And when, carrying their coats over their left arms, Kranz and Berwitz came to meet one another, for the first time in their lives the two of them were unconsciously in agreement as the same thought simultaneously flashed through the heads of both of them: "Look, the sly fox, he's gone and bought himself a new top hat, too!"

Director Kranz, a powerful athlete with broad shoulders, and a thick black mustache under his great nose, stretched forth his hand in its rough yellow pigskin, and Director Berwitz took it in his shining white glove. Their handclasp was a firm one, the gloves almost crackled, and after a couple of polite inquiries they went out in front of the station, where Hans awaited them, holding open the door of the carriage, drawn by two white horses. These were Orestes and Cardinal, the only two which ever pulled a carriage; and they produced a striking impression a mile off, because of their pace and their action. Originally Berwitz had considered the possibility of telling Kranz that they were two Kladrubaks he kept for his own personal use, but then he told himself that Kranz would have a good eye for horses and would be sure to spot the deception all too soon.

The gentlemen took their seats in the carriage with great ceremony and drove through the city with such a dashing air that even the older, more experienced policemen saluted them, taking them for high state officials. On their arrival they went at once to the stables. It was pleasantly warm, and the two directors clamped into their stiff, high collars had all they could do to keep wiping away the sweat which kept appearing on their red faces.

At home Kranz had told himself that he would not have to yield the palm to this conceited Berwitz over anything, but now when he came to the stables and looked at the floor, which was scoured, examined the mangers and found them washed, bent over to look at the bedding and found it to be fine, long, clean hay, he had to admit that this Turkish pasha kept everything in amazing order. The grooms and stable hands stood beside the horses in spotless liveries and saluted when the gentlemen went past. "He puts on a good show," said Kranz to himself, "but he won't catch me with such monkey-business." And he walked up to the nearest horse, stroked it, and looked at his glove inconspicuously.

Well, there was nothing to be said, not even dust could be seen on the glove. And then, of course, when he saw the Lipicans he had to admit that he had no such collection in his own stables. His own preference was for Trakheners, fiery, stubborn, good for all purposes; his needs were best suited by horses which were easy to train, intelligent, and patient; for their beauty he kept only a few. But here in Berwitz's stable he had to admit that the selection of one type of horse created its own special charm.

At last the gentlemen began to speak their own language, their top hats pushed back on their heads, their collars slowly bending out of shape; they walked from animal to animal, felt muscles, looked at teeth and hoofs, measured heights and lengths, argued as to whether white horses were really slow to react, black ones melancholy, and brown ones wild, whether the morning feeding or the evening one was more profitable, and how many quarts of water should be given a horse to drink after a performance.

In the midst of these debates, during which they were ready to forget all else in the world, the sound of music blared forth behind them: it was the beginning of the performance. Kranz took only a hasty look at the elephant Bingo and at the menagerie, which held no interest for him. He had no elephant himself, but he had four camels and a giraffe; and as for big cats, he was convinced that his Siberian tigers were more powerful and more striking than anything Berwitz had. Then suddenly he lost all interest in the cats; he began to sense that the public was "on the march," and he was too much of a director to want to miss seeing them.

When the public begins to arrive, when it, as they say, is on the march, there is no director in the world who can bear to miss the spectacle; each one places himself inconspicuously among the thronging crowds, somewhere between the gate and the circus itself, to "sniff the air" of today's audience, to find out if it is impatient or indifferent, hard to please or easy-going, made up of city people or people from the country. All this and much more has an influence on the course of the performance, and an experienced director and those of his subordinates who have been with him the longest recognize, at the very moment when the public enters the tent, what the dominant mood will be that day and which performers will have the greatest success. How they know this is a mystery; often they are in strange lands, in a strange city, among strange people of whose speech they cannot even understand a word, but it is enough for them to mix with the streaming crowds for half an hour to feel that magnetic force which the crowds generate.

This unobtrusive but careful and attentive mixing with the audience is the director's overture, which he never wishes to omit. And Kranz, filled with curiosity to know the mood of the Hamburg crowds, felt he had to experience it himself. He stood with Berwitz now in one corner of the main entrance, followed the cries of the ticket sellers and the ushers, and ran his eye over the people. When the main wave had passed and the last march was being played to usher the people in, he turned to Berwitz and said:

"A wonderful audience. First-class. The tamers and the High School will have the biggest success today."

Needless to say, the performance staged that day was a unique one. Berwitz allowed no external sign of this to appear, but to score a triumph over his rival he had arranged a steeplechase race and a program of thirty-two acts instead of twenty-one. The performance flew along at a stirring tempo from one surprise to another. With Baron von Schönstein, Kranz sat at ease in a box, but not even a single raking-up of the sawdust in the ring missed his eyes. And the top hat on his head now slid back onto the nape of his neck, now to the front of his forehead, the safest proof, according to Gaudeamus's quiet observation, that he was interested.

That evening both magnates and their escorts sat down to a mighty dinner at the Hotel Metropole. Gaudeamus had ordered everything: turtle soup, *saumon du Rhin grillé, sauce anchovis, bœuf salé à l'anglaise, légumes, poulard au consommé, sauce Béarnaise, talmousse au fromage de Parme, méringués à la crême, glaces, desserts:* a dinner worthy of the sovereign dynasty of Umberto. Everything was prepared, even the right sequence of drinks, and all the gentlemen had to do was to tuck their napkins underneath their chins. But when the gray-haired head waiter approached with a bottle of golden sherry to fill the first glasses, his left arm politely bent behind his back, Kranz put his powerful paw on his glass and jovially proposed:

"I think we might have some jampagne!"

Gaudeamus was of the opinion that there would be plenty of time left for champagne, that other wine was more suitable for the moment. But Peter Berwitz sided with Kranz.

"Champagne," he answered Gaudeamus majestically, "drink, Baron, whatever you wish, you needn't consider my pocket; I can afford champagne right from the start!"

Selnicki, desirous of drinking his fill of the priceless beverage, was likewise of this opinion; it would be better not to mix the drinks, he said, or they might stir up some digestive trouble. And so, to the silent grief of Gaudeamus's epicurean heart, the glasses for sherry, Moselle, and Burgundy disappeared from the table, and with the turtle soup they drank champagne.

With an eye to their drinking Gaudeamus sought as early as the fish course to have them settle the business which had brought them together. He explained their mutual situation so skillfully, so simply, with such discernment, that the two rivals, who had been boasting to each other continuously, now looked at him with amazement and admitted that all was as he said. The proposal was for a simple exchange of their buildings after the conclusion of the winter season, for a period of six weeks, with the right of prolongation. The start of the period was always to be determined by a separate agreement based on the plan of each of the two enterprises. For a short while they continued to discuss one thing or another, but before the next course was brought in Berwitz and Kranz had shaken hands on their bargain and Selnicki had quickly filled the glasses. Now they ate and drank more gaily and the conversation at once became freer.

Gaudeamus's selection of dishes was praised, especially the beef, which both magnates hugely enjoyed. But toward the end Peter Berwitz discovered that something had been forgotten which he considered indispensable at a gala dinner: caviare! Mr. Selnicki was of the opinion that what was not, might yet be, and at once rapped his fingers for the waiter. The head waiter was rather shocked that they should order caviare between the ices, but in an instant assumed the air of their choice being an obvious one.

After a while the "black groats," as Kranz called them, appeared on the table. And Peter Berwitz, breathing heavily on his overfilled stomach and red from food and drink, at last had the chance to tell this "Berlin groom" how he had eaten caviare that time in Petersburg when His Majesty the Tsar of all the Russias had come to see him. Only now with this magic word "tsar" did Berwitz get into his stride and, gulping down caviare by the spoonful, overwhelm his rival with boasting and bragging. By degrees it began to come out that Berwitz had known the Tsar well. Kranz expressed certain doubts that he and the Tsar had really been so intimate.

"What d'you mean?" Berwitz threw himself back in his chair. "There's even a written record of it in the archives of Umberto's Circus. There was some kind of old gray-haired professor there in Petersburg, a State Counsellor, who was all the time rummaging about and writing something. He came to see me and got me to tell him the history of Umberto's Circus and of our great art, and afterward he wrote letters to me several times. He said that our circus was really art, and not just a side show. And this professor knew that I had been the Tsar's favorite associate, and so on top of each page he wrote as a greeting, '*Carissime!*' You can see it at our place; Frans has saved it as a document."

"The old man's putting it on thick, eh?" Selnicki bent over to Gaudeamus. "Now he'll have to feed him the Persian Shah and the Turkish Sultan, and then they'll start calling each other names."

"The Persian Shah will do," Gaudeamus answered quietly in a half-whisper, "but the Turkish Sultan would be too much for Kranz. We'll have to go somewhere else before we get to Constantinople."

"To see the girls . . ." Selnicki pronounced, shedding a drunken tear.

"I have that number on the program," nodded the Baron.

Kranz tried in vain to out-trump Berwitz with his own successes and his own high-ranking nobles. What was a Hessian Duke against a Persian Shah? With clenched teeth he had to sit and listen to the Teheran epic. But during its course five bottles were consumed, and the gentlemen's heads were whirling a bit, so Gaudeamus proposed that they go out somewhere for black coffee.

"And for brandy," Mr. Selnicki added. "And perhaps a bit of plum brandy before it."

The gentlemen got up rather noisily, and even more noisily they entered the underground rooms of the Elysium, where they took a box covered with red plush, with a full-length mirror in the background, in front of which stood a bouquet of everlastings and two stands of artificial palms. In the room a quartet was playing, the leader of which bowed low to them. And beside the music stand there was a podium, and on it eight half-naked girls were dancing a quadrille, which then ended with a cancan.

"Look, Berwitz." Kranz pulled him over to the edge of the box. "That one, the third from the left, the red fox-colored one, she's the goods, isn't she?"

"Put a bottle of brandy on ice!" Mr. Selnicki commanded.

"She's a fine Juckers," Berwitz agreed with Kranz. "But how about that dun-colored one on the right—look at the high action of the knees."

"Yes, but when she stops she'll have them spread too far apart," Kranz objected.

"What of it, look at the width of those forelegs! She has legs like a Valencian mare!"

"Gentlemen, we're pouring out the brandy," Selnicki interrupted them from behind. "The finest Meunier! A hundred times more important than that female horse show of yours!"

"I think, gentlemen"—Gaudeamus raised his glass—"that first we should drink to the successful result of our business today, and then we should dedicate ourselves to the charms of the ring here. Prosit!"

They drank once, they drank twice, they drank a third time. Below the girls had begun to dance again, and Berwitz and Kranz decided that the flashing black one with hair bobbed like a Scotch pony looked like a real thoroughbred. But then the fawn-colored one on her right showed a fine figure; her ears were a bit mouselike, but she must be half a fist taller.

"They both have fire, Baron," Kranz asserted to Gaudeamus. "Look at that long step. Lord, that's a breed for you!"

"But that brown one," said Berwitz, "hasn't any wind. The black one's still going full tilt."

"We can invite them over," Gaudeamus proposed.

"Well, I don't know what we'd have to talk to them about," Berwitz weakly tried to object.

"Invite them over, Baron." Kranz nodded. "I'll pay for everything. I'd at least like to look at that brown one's back, to see if she's got an eel's stripe there. All fawn-colored fillies have a zigzag stripe on their backs."

"And which one will the Baron pick?" Berwitz guffawed. "How about that black one there, she looks like a Trakhener colt?"

"No, I prefer the Kladrubak type. I'll take that white one behind."

"And Selnicki?"

"Nothing, gentlemen, nothing. I won't disturb you. I . . ." and Selnicki got up unsteadily. "I'll play you the *Radetzky March*. It's like a war, the *Radetzky March,* a war waged by the first ballerina. The whole glory of the monarchy on tiptoes. Incomparable music, gentlemen . . . incomparable . . . champagne accompaniment for a regimental band. . . ."

An hour later Kranz was calling to Berwitz:

"Come here, you Turkish menagerist, come to my Pincgauerish breast!"

And because Berwitz, instead of falling on his breast, fell between the neighing fawn-colored filly and the exultant white one, Kranz turned to Gaudeamus, put his arm around his neck, and whispered with a terrible frown:

"Baron, I swear that when he goes bankrupt with that high art of his, I'll have him led out and exhibited as a Persian colonel!"

When, at half-past three in the morning, Peter Berwitz returned home, his new top hat was completely crushed, but his lips were wreathed with smiles from the wonderful evening. When he entered the bedroom Anna lit a candle and sat up in bed. In a second she took in the whole situation, but she did not utter a word.

"My dear," Peter slowly addressed her, tearing his clothes off, "we're really going to Berlin this spring. Everything's ready. . . . It was really magnificent. That banquet which I arranged . . . then the negotiations at the Elysium . . . really wonderful, magnificent . . . it had a grace of its own. . . . We showed that stable hand what a dynasty is."

"I see," Anna said slowly, "and you weren't at all rude to him?"

"No. Not the least bit." Peter shook his head. "I wanted to be, but I wasn't. Each time I told myself, 'Watch out, Peter . . . you're a horseman . . . you're a gentleman . . .'"

"Well, come to bed. But in the pantomime tomorrow you'll only shoot at the target. Tomorrow I won't hold the egg in my fingers."

"Nonsense . . ." muttered Peter, already in bed. "Why, I could shoot through a wedding ring with a pistol at this moment."

Nevertheless the next day for the first time during a performance he fired and the shot missed by a hair's breadth.

CHAPTER SIXTEEN

AFTER THE AGREEMENT Berwitz was in a wonderful mood, and Karas took advantage of this to wheedle an unheard-of thing out of him: a five-day leave for himself and Vasek. He asked for it for the dead week between Christmas and New Year, and Berwitz nodded. They departed the night after Boxing Day, for the first time in their lives by train. After Prague they had to go on by the old way, in a carriage, but even here Karas could permit himself an unparalleled luxury: they rode into Budejovice in the stagecoach. The closer their native mountains approached them the more agitated Karas became. He melted and softened;

for two years he had placed all his hopes on this trip, which he felt should decide Vasek's fate.

It was hard, very hard, for him, a simple man, to make such a grave decision. Your conscience was upset, he felt, and your reason was not enough. All around you people gave you advice, good people, perhaps, but that didn't take any of the responsibility off your own shoulders; only you and the dead woman were there to guard the boy. And if there were anyone else who had the right to give a word of advice, then it certainly was your own native village. A man's home had a natural claim, on all men. It was the village community, as well as our own mother, that brought us up. And Karas admitted this claim and respected it; why, God, it was even a relief to have that whole community of uncles and aunts behind you to advise you when you're full of anxiety, and to stop you when you contemplated some piece of foolishness.

That was Karas: quiet, thoughtful, stubborn at work, but dependent on others when there was a decision to be made. The main thing was that it went against his grain to step out of line in any way. He had never been so happy and contented in his whole life as he had been during these two years in the circus, but he would have considered it a sin to admit it. The thought constantly lay on his mind that at home they would not approve of it. And he was of the opinion that their disapproval would be enough to turn Vasek away from the tempting, but immoral, path.

They were going home now for this decision. Everywhere it was covered with snow, the weaker trees in the forest were bent beneath it, and everything was silent and somehow holy, just as when you go to confession. "And up there only a couple of steps, look, Vasek, there's Horní Snezná. . . . The Blahas' hut, the Cerhas', the Sembers' barn, the priest's garden, the mass of roofs and black trees and the church. God be praised that we've arrived safely. Look, Cerha has a new roof on his hut, and Blaha has bigger stables. But there's no time for worldly affairs just now; first we must go up there, up that hill to those poplars.

"Here it is to the right, Vasek, the last grave; but see, it's not the last, three have died since we were here before. And the larch tree's taken root and grown. Praise God, Márinka, now you have us here. Make the sign of the cross over Mamma's grave. Let's kneel, Vasek, never mind the snow. Our Father . . . Hail, Mary . . . I've brought him back to you, Márinka, in good health, he's a good boy, industrious, I can't say a word against him. And now, I ask you, you must help me to take care of him. I will do everything for his good, but please give me some sign here in the village as to what I should do. And accompany him on in life, Márinka, as his guardian angel, he is your child. Amen.

"Make three signs of the cross over the grave, Vasek. It's nice for Mamma here, isn't it? It's so quiet. Well now, wipe away your tears. We'll go along through the poplar trees to the village. Whose dog is that barking? Is that Opolecky's?"

"No, Father, that's Cerha's Vorech, I know it's Cerha's Vorech!"

"He must have scented us. And there's somebody looking out at us. Who could that be? Of course, it's old man Kromarik, you can be sure nothing would get past him. God keep you, Grandpa."

"Amen. By the Lord, look, it's Anton Karas! Where did you turn up from, man, you haven't been here for ages! Not long ago I was having a chat with Vasek Zelenka about you, whether you were still alive, or if you'd kicked the bucket and the devils had carried you off with them. Well, glad to see you, glad to see you, you've come back whole. And how about your kid here, he hasn't shot up much, but he's a fine fellow, by the Lord, he could split wood now, how about it, eh, Vasek?

"And I'd been wondering where you were coming from—but it's from the burial ground, for sure, from Márinka's, Lord, yes. So you will remember her, well, that's a good husband, Anton, that I won't deny, a wife's still a wife, even when she's under the sod. Well, how'd you manage your housekeeping without her, without a woman? Well, come on, here we're standing like three Turkish saints in the cold. It's blowing heavy today, the wind turned on Boxing Day and now the best thing to do's crawl into your corner by the stove.

"But Lord, people, you won't be able to go and see your relations, they both went off this afternoon with their work, of course, to the German side; they took baskets, dishes, rakes, and all kinds of things, they won't be back before eight. How are they? All sorts of things can happen during a year, Anton, you know, and if not by bucketfuls, then by spoonfuls. And these are hard times, good God, you can't turn pennies into dollars, that's one thing for sure. But your people have got a goat and some fowls and they have food for them, and they're getting on somehow. Well, good Lord, the best thing for us is to head straight to the inn, the Novotnys' place—they still keep it. But good Lord, get along with you, you're not going to stand there and be bashful—a circus man like you and afraid of beer? Come along; Vasek can drop in on the upper Cikharts, Jirka Cikhart'll roll his eyes to see him. And Vasek, tell Jirka's dad to come over to the Novotnys' for beer, we'll be there with your dad.

"God keep you, Mrs. Novotny, look, woman, what sort of customer I'm bringing you; good Lord, it's Anton Karas, circus man, sure it's him. Go along with you, you should have known him right off—why, he's as fat as a peasant from the knees down. Pour us out two mugs full, so that we can welcome him back, by the good Lord. There's a chair for you, Anton, make yourself comfortable. Here's to you, man, you don't even know how glad I am to see you."

Only the drink interrupted the talkative old man's speech. But he had hardly taken breath when he was off again:

"Mrs. Novotny, send somebody round the village, to Zelenka's hut and to Cerha's and Opolecky's and Padovec's and everywhere where there're masons. Tell them I said to come right off, there's a visitor here. What do you say? But go along with you, woman, I said to tell everybody except the peasants; we don't want any peasants. We want to be by ourselves. But the others'll come on the run, of course they will, the mason's never been born who won't come running when a keg calls. So, Anton, you circus man, they tell me that there're some eye-fetching women there, only they say they've got the evil eye."

"Wait, Grandpa," Karas interrupted him at last. "The thing I want to know is how you found out that Vasek and I were in the circus. I didn't write to anybody . . ."

"But, good Lord, Milner's boys came home with the news;

they rode in, thin as dried-up beanpoles and with as much money as a snake has hips. But they all told how Karas had landed on his feet; we went out to play music, they said, and he got a job in the circus . . ."

"But I didn't meet any of them!"

"Well, they must have got hold of it somewhere, good Lord, they didn't think it up by themselves, when it's really true. Why, we talked about it all one day, about how the mason's trade's down and out, and how you really got out of it at the right time. Well, and then the spring came and the boys got ready, and instead of building they went off to the circus . . ."

"What are you saying, Grandpa?" Karas shouted and caught Kromarik by the arm.

"Why, what would I be saying, I'm telling you, good Lord, how it was, the gang went off to join different circuses, for they didn't find any one that was big enough to take them all. Well, there they stayed from spring till winter; toward the beginning of November they came back, and good Lord, the stories they told, what and where and how, what the circus women were like and so on, so from them I know all about those circus women —how would I know by myself what sort of women they are? They told so much of it you couldn't have written it all down on an ox skin, and they all agreed in saying that Anton Karas has a head on his shoulders, he's a smart one, they ought to put up a memorial arch to him. . . ."

"Good God, Grandpa, what're you blathering about?"

"It's the living truth, Anton, why, you're the savior of the whole village, their benefactor when they were hungry; they wouldn't have talked about you otherwise, but you went and showed them how to make a living. . . ."

"And so they all went off to the circus?"

"All of them, Anton, all of them to a man, good Lord in Heaven, Cerha, Zelenka, Opolecky, Cikhart, Padovec, our Franta, the lower Blaha—well, all of them, no matter where you looked, all of them are circus men; to hell with being masons, that's no good. . . ."

"And how about Milner, the foreman?" cried Karas in almost painful surprise.

"Milner? Go along with you, he's no foreman, Milner's an ox like the rest of us. When things go well then there's nothing to it, but when they're standing still—then, comrade, a foreman should show the kind of stuff he's made of! But Milner, Lord, he turned out to be good for nothing. It wasn't till Cikhart and Blaha came to see him and told him, well, Milner, you're the boss, good Lord—are you going to fill the holes in our stomachs with rage, or what? Well, if *you* don't know what to do, Milner, then we'll tell you, by God, we'll go off to the circus like Anton Karas, where there's work for us for the summer."

Karas was not even listening to the loquacious old man. His arms fell to his sides. So this was the answer of his own native village which he had been waiting for, this was the salvation he had hoped would tear him away from his vagabond life on wheels! Here he had expected to find support for his inner struggle against the circus, and meanwhile the whole village had gone over to the same sort of life, had betrayed his conscience, had attacked him from the rear.

He did not even have a chance to straighten this thought out in his head properly, for here they all came, one after the other, Vasek Jirka, the lower Franta, the upper Franta, all of them good comrades of his, and already they were greeting him and embracing him and patting him on the back, already they were drinking his health and praising him and celebrating him —Goodgodinheavenabove, was it possible then that everything was all right and in order? The woman at the bar yelled as if she had been at a market, and each one outboasted the other in telling where he had found work: two had been with Kranz, one was traveling with Golowetzky, one was with the National Circus, one was a wagon driver for a menagerie. And all of them were happy and cheerful. That was the life—poles, ropes, stakes, women; a man could even play his trumpet. And you were the cause of it all, Anton, Tony, Tony, you clever old Karas!

At first he was overwhelmed by it all, but his unsuspected glory was sweet to him, he stretched himself out and blew up his chest, played the successful man, shouted the youngsters down, and again clinked his mug with the others. Little by little the burden which had lain on his shoulders disappeared;

he felt proud and cheerful, and now he wanted to embrace everyone all over again because they had eased his worries so much. Then Vasek ran in all excited: he had just shown the boys his trictrac and his monkey jump and his forward somersault, and how they had all stared at him! And then Karas's sister Karolina came to the inn; she and her husband had just returned from work and had heard who had turned up so unexpectedly. They took Vasek and him home for supper, and there, in their poor kitchen, the inner change in Karas became complete.

Both these hard-working people, his brother-in-law and his sister, sang his praises to the very heavens and told him how happy it had made them that he had taken up with the circus, of what poverty there was in the mountains and how scarce building work had become. God be with us, where would all these families be now if the young husbands hadn't taken Karas's example and brought back money they'd saved for autumn? All the village population except the peasants had to go out into the world somewhere, and even Karolina and her husband had to hawk about the countryside goods the latter had carved. How often had they sighed at the thought of how tiring and thankless their toil was! From their complaints and laments Karas saw how hard it would have been for them to make a living at home, and his carefree life on wheels now seemed to him to be a real paradise.

They went to bed rather late that evening, for it was a long time before they had finished talking. While Karas lay in the little bedroom under the cold, heavy, feather bed, he had already settled things quite definitely in his mind. He had asked Márinka to give him some sign in the village, and one had met him at every step. Grandpa Kromarik, the natives and workers of his own age, the village children, his own family: all had told him that he had done well when he found work, that there was no disgrace in it, that he would not be cut off from the village for what he had done.

"We cannot make our living here, we must go out into the world, into the struggle, nothing else will do, we cannot allow ourselves to perish through need and misfortune," thought Karas.

275

And the main thing was to remain true to home, not to lose himself in that great outside world, but to come back to his own people and help them. Yes, that was how it was, and Vasek would climb still higher, and surpass his father, that was certain, and God grant that he would not forget the nest which he had left to fly out into the world. This was the answer which Márinka had prepared for him. "God reward you for it, girl, now it's decided. Amen," said Karas.

The next day Karas had enough to do in his own hut to keep him busy all day long. He was moved when he unlocked it and entered the room which had been part of his life. But feelings come and feelings go; here the main thing was it was all full of dust and cobwebs, it was leaking a bit and he would have to look at the roof. Well, he and Vasek pitched in and did all of it, and by afternoon it was all in order. Then they went for more visits, to Márinka's relatives, to the godfathers and godmothers, and everywhere people greeted them warmly and embraced them and were full of joy to see them both healthy and getting along well.

And then one more night, and the next morning, while it was still dark, father and son again struck out down to the city, to Budejovice. Karas bade his village farewell:

"Huts of Horní Snezná, may your little lights stay burning and your chimneys never lose their plumes of smoke. Vasek, you and I will never forget them, even if we have to wander about like gipsies for the rest of our lives."

When they returned to Hamburg the inhabitants of Number Eight hardly recognized Karas, so much had he livened up and his tongue become loosened. It seemed to them that he must have had luck with some woman at home; they would never have suspected that he had only eased his conscience. In this joyous mood Lent quickly passed, winter was gone, and the first spring breezes again brought preparations for the new journey. This time they did not have Roméo with them. Berwitz found that with Vasek he now had enough tumblers in his troupe, and did not renew the contract. At this there was a great deal

276

of crying and wailing among Roméo's tiny ones, who did not want to part with their fine life in the great circus.

However, in a few days their watchful father had succeeded in pounding all their liking for the place out of their heads, and one Thursday the whole dark family stood around the blue wagon, to which Papa Achmed had again hitched his horses. Whoever was about now shook hands with them for the last time, and Achmed Roméo, son of Omar Roméo, the hadji, turned to the east and broke out into a loud melody which slid over halftones: *"La ilaha illa-lah, Muhummadun rasulu-llah!"*

Then he cracked his whip and sang the bee's sura:

"God made wagons to be your home and caused you to make your tents of leather, so that they shall be light when you move from place to place."

The children pushed against the wagon wheels, which during the autumn had sunk too far into the wet soil, and which now were hard to disengage from the frozen ground. Mrs. Roméo waved from the window with her kerchief, the circus people called, "Good-bye, *auf Wiedersehen, au revoir, a rivederci!*" and the blue wagon disappeared among the streets of Hamburg.

Vasek stood the closest to the wagon as it left. His first teacher was going away, and in spite of the fact that it had been more like torture than teaching, Vasek's soul was overflowing with grief when Achmed Roméo embraced him and kissed him on both cheeks. And he was sorry to lose the boys, too; they were ruffians, they were bastards—how many times Vasek had had to fight them! —but now, when they flocked round him and politely shook hands with him, one after the other, he was sad to see this rabble leaving, and to realize that he would never meet them again.

Involuntarily tears flowed out of his eyes, down his cheeks toward his mouth. He licked them off so that no one should see them, and was surprised at how salty they were. New ones welled up in his eyes, and he saw the wagon leave as through a distorted glass. Only when it was disappearing behind the corner did Paolo turn round on the backboard, wave his arms, and shout, "Double cow!" Like lightning Vasek stooped down to pick up a stone, but the ground was frozen and Paolo had disappeared before he could get one loose. Then he wiped his eyes, which suddenly stopped watering, and turned back to the building. Helen was running along in front of him unsteadily, and crying with her mouth wide-open.

"What are you howling about, Helen?" Vasek shouted to her.

"I . . . I was bringing . . . I wanted to give Paolo a piece of cake . . . but they're gone already!"

Vasek almost burst with anger, and then controlled himself.

"Don't howl, Helen. Paolo was a pig. And look, if you've got some cake, we can eat it together."

He walked into the unlit gallery, almost to the very place where Paolo had declared his love for Helen not long before, and both children consecrated their feast to the memory of the young African, for whom the girl was full of tenderness, the boy of scorn.

Several days later Umberto's Circus, too, set out. When the wagons had already started to move Vosátka came with the news that Hein Moesecke had died during the night. Three times that winter he had got up from his bed with the 'flu, and had gone back to his bar, but the third time he had caught pneumonia and had not recovered.

"And we won't even be able to go to the funeral." Kerholec nodded his head as he stood among the departing wagons.

"We couldn't have gone, anyway," Vosátka informed them. "The burial isn't going to be here. He asked them to bury him in the place where he was born."

"Where are they taking him, then?" asked Bures, already seated in the saddle and holding Vosátka's horse.

"To Buxtehude," answered the Sergeant as he tightened the horse's saddle-girths and swung into the saddle.

"Buxtehude . . . Buxtehude . . ." whispered Karas. From what far-off time had this weak wave of feeling come to him? That was it: Buxtehude had been the first town on their way into the unknown when they began this roving life. Then it had sounded to him like some mysterious voice of fate. All the concealed uncertainty which lay ahead was contained in the name. Today it came to him only as a wave of remembrance, and nothing more. Buxtehude . . . a name like any other. People were born there as they were anywhere else. They were born and they

278

died. Or they went back there to die. And even dead, they went back.

This was the last thought which came to Karas as he set off with his comrades:

"I must be like that fat Hein Moesecke . . . faithful to Horní Sneznà!"

PART THREE

CHAPTER ONE

IT WAS A beautiful Sunday in March, the sea gulls were flying over the embankment, and the clock in the tower of St. Paul's was sounding ten o'clock. Miss Rosa Langermann walked with long steps toward the gate to the city gardens. She was wearing a tiny hat set at an angle and a long skirt with a swelling train. She was hurrying, and smiled because the young man in the gray overcoat who was coming toward her was Vasek, the famous tamer of wild beasts of Umberto's Circus. It was he who had been waiting for her impatiently, and she was late!

What was it she had whispered to him yesterday: at ten, on the dot? A little more and she would have been late; they had had to finish three spring dresses today at the workshop so that they could be delivered that same afternoon. She had worked at them till ten the night before, and at half-past eight on Sunday she had gone back to work so that all of them should be finished. Usually the work seemed to flow along rapidly for her, but today her needle had dawdled; her heart was full of happiness, for at ten o'clock she could look forward to that beautiful, rapturous thing, her first rendezvous. . . .

But why, really, was it necessary for them to have to arrange a rendezvous? She had liked Vasek ever since childhood when he and his father had come to their flat and he had taken over the leadership of her innocent games. With what heartfelt sympathy she and her mother had followed his progress from the days when he began to learn to ride and to jump. Year after year he and his father had come back to them, and each time he had mastered something new, until at last he had roused the public's admiration as a great rider and unrivaled jumper.

It had been perhaps three years ago when Mr. Bures had told them that Vasek was already a finished artist and could do everything that could be expected from a first-class horseman. And only a couple of days later Vasek had come home and told them with much amusement about an upset that had occurred in the circus: the animal-tamer had run away, that gigantic French Captain; he had run away from fear of that Hammerschmidt woman. He had gone with his tigers in the fear that if he did not escape her he would have to marry her. The lions and bears were left—they were Berwitz's property—but who could take them over at such short notice, when Gambier had even taken his assistant away with him!

Of course it was Vasek who took them over; why, he had grown up with them in the circus, had fed them every day and had always looked after the two youngest ones, Sumatra and Borneo; as a boy he had carried them in his arms. Rosa well remembered how frightened she had been when she heard that Vasek would now go into the lions' cages every day; it was the first time that her heart had been pierced by the strange fear that something might happen to the boy. But Vasek only laughed and answered self-confidently that there was nothing to it, that lions and tigers were only great playful kittens and that you only had to know how to manage them. This answer by no means pacified her, and for the first time she had to confess to herself that she liked him as much as if he had been her own brother.

And she was pleased by the fact that Mr. Karas, too, was uneasy and tried to persuade Vasek not to play with the big cats, pointing out that there was a great difference between lions and horses. But Vasek would listen to nothing.

"Death lies in wait for all of us, Father," he had said then. "I could be killed on horseback or while jumping just as easily, and I can't ward it off. With lions I at least know what the danger is which lies before me."

And to that he had added that the circus could not close down, the show must go on, it was one's work, one's duty, the business must keep running. So he had taken over the lions and bears, and within a year he began to train the new tigers Berwitz had purchased. How much fear she underwent on his account, with what anxiety she waited each day until his step sounded on the staircase, how quickly her glance would fly to meet him to see if his arms were covered by a white bandage!

And when he and his father went away in the spring what loneliness seized her, what grief and sorrow!—Suddenly she realized how much she loved him; her own brother, perhaps, she would not have loved so much. She trembled all over at the thought of him, and was beside herself with joy when she and her mother received a letter which told them that the circus was on the way back and that Vasek was well.

He had no suspicion of her feeling when she looked at him. Year after year he came back to them just as tanned, well-muscled, calm as ever; he behaved to her with the same sincere friendship . . . but he had looked at her quite differently lately . . . she had felt unpleasantly warm and flustered under that look. And then once, when they were alone for a while, he had seized her by the arm and said, "You know, Rosa, you're a very pretty girl." And he had stroked her arm several times when they had met in the front hall or on the stairs.

And yesterday . . . yesterday he had slipped in behind her when she was cleaning his room, put his arm round her back and shoulders, and said softly: "Rosa . . . we two . . . might we two not have something to say to one another?" Her voice had faltered, and she did not even know how she managed to get the words out, "If you think so . . . Vasek. . . ." And he, the strong, self-confident Vasek, who mastered tigers and lions with a glance, looked about timidly and whispered, "Then come . . . to-morrow at ten . . . at the gate to the park . . ." and ran off quickly. And here he was, he was waiting for her, he had already caught sight of her and was coming to meet her; he took off his hat and said with emotion:

"It's good of you to come, Rosa!"

They clasped hands and Rosa told a bit confusedly how she had had to hurry with her sewing and how anxious she had been that she might have to deliver the dresses and would not be here on time, but that luckily the dressmaker had given them to the younger girls to deliver. And now as they walked through the park Vasek told her how nervous the beasts had been in their cages today, how spring was getting into their blood and making them irritable and excited. Rosa told him how her mistress, too, had been nervous the last few days, how she had thrown everything back at them to do again; perhaps spring was getting into her blood just as it was into the beasts'. Vasek thought that this was possible, that some people were just as sensitive as animals, but the majority were not, the majority were more phlegmatic than big cats or elephants.

"Are elephants so sensitive?" Rosa asked with surprise.

"Oh, elephants are the most sensitive of all animals," Vasek assured her. "Elephants are frightened by every tiny trifle. Once a squirrel got out of its cage and ran into the elephants' stable. You never saw such a rumpus as our six elephants kicked up. They roared, trumpeted, tore at their chains and shook with excitement, and we had no idea why they were doing it until we noticed the squirrel, bunched up on a girder overhead."

"What did Arr-Shehir say to that?"

"Arr-Shehir was angry. He said that elephants and geese were the guardians of real order in the world, and if everyone performed his duty properly his loved one would not have been upset. And then he demanded that the squirrel be executed as a lesson."

"But you didn't do that . . . ?"

"No, and Arr-Shehir told us that we were not of royal blood. He's getting old. This year he had to buy spectacles, and he has a lot of trouble with them; the two young elephants are always stealing them off his nose."

"What . . . do elephants steal?"

"Yes, everything they take a fancy to. Preferably the keys to their chains."

"And what do they do with them?"

"They either hide them in the hay or they eat them. Mostly eat them. Elephants make a lot of trouble."

Vasek was silent and Rosa, too, ceased talking. They walked along silently beside one another; they forgot the animals and the dress shop, and only told themselves inwardly how lovely it was to be walking together like this. Vasek took Rosa's arm and Rosa was amazed at how firm and calloused his palm was. But a current of warmth and pleasant excitement flowed from it and put an end to her thoughts. Only a feeling of pure well-being remained. With an effort Vasek told himself that he should say something tender now that he and Rosa were together at the rendezvous, but he did not know how to begin. Everything that occurred to him seemed terribly stupid, and whenever his eyes fell on Rosa's glowing face and shining glance her beauty seemed so heavenly to him that he became speechless.

No longer was she the Rosa of his boyhood games, she was an elegant young city lady. What was he beside her? A mere circus apprentice who worked with horses and animals. His unlimited self-confidence suddenly shriveled up. Should he speak now and tell her what he was thinking? But to break this sweet silence was harder than to climb into the cage with the lions and tigers. And what would he say? "Rosa, I love you? Rosa, you are beautiful?"

And then there was still one disquieting thing: what would she say to his confession of love? Would she not laugh at him? Would she not be annoyed? Vasek had the feeling that she would not be, that it was not possible for her to be, but what if . . . what if Rosa was already engaged, and she were simply meeting him out of friendship for him? Then he would say to her, "Rosa, I love you," and she, perhaps, would draw away and say, "Vasek, I am sorry, but there is already another. . . ."

But that was impossible. In that case he would have noticed something. Nor would she have consented to a rendezvous without saying something. But in spite of all reason he experienced terrible doubt. How many times had they talked of women in Number Eight, how many bits of advice, precepts and warnings, had they given him, and no one of them had ever really told him how a man should declare his love to a girl.

Of course they had discussed everything quite crudely, while Rosa was a tender and refined being, quite different from anyone in the circus. How could he tell her? And where, when there were so many people about, most of them lovers? These latter had already put this trial behind them, that could be seen from their looks of happiness; all of them were happier than he. Already they had been wandering about for a good half-hour without saying a word. God, what would she think of him? Perhaps he ought to amuse her somehow—but how? Surely not by telling her how that morning he had cut half a horse into portions for the beasts, or how the stallion Kismet had not wanted to eat the day before and had only played with his oats. . . . And nothing else occurred to him at the moment.

But just at that moment Rosa lightly pressed his hand and said: "Look, Vasek . . . how beautiful!"

He looked there where she was pointing, and truly it was beautiful: a whole clump of shrubs, already in bloom. There were still no leaves on the bushes, but they were already strewn with golden blossoms that shone and glittered like the purest gold. Vasek and Rosa went up to them and in among them—they were entirely surrounded by this flaming splendor . . . alone among the lovers . . . and suddenly Vasek's arm slipped round Rosa's neck and shoulder . . . Lord, how the girl trembled! Vasek did not know what had happened, but all at once he pulled her to him, he held her in his arms and was kissing her, kissing her with a long kiss, and, intoxicated, he smelled the cool scent of her body.

"Vasek . . . dear . . . dear one . . . beloved . . ."

Rapture, heat, confusion, a reddish mist; and then suddenly the overpowering feeling of triumphant certainty, of exultant self-confidence, of strength and faith. Where is the obstacle which he, Vasek, could not surmount? Look at his body, it was as if it were made of steel springs; look at his eyes before which wild beasts backed away, with all their strong will. "Why should I not win you, Rosa? I shall conquer all, I shall conquer the whole world for your smile, for your tenderness and devotion." Suddenly he was full of things he must say, must discuss; his heart was so full of them—they all meant one thing: that we . . . "say it, Rosa, it sounds sweeter from you" . . . that we are in love.

It was striking noon from the tower of St. Paul's as Vasek and Rosa walked, arm-in-arm, clinging to each other, home for dinner, to Frau Langermann, to Father Karas, to tell them the great and glorious news of their betrothal. It was spring, the circus would again move out into the world, and when autumn came round again they would arrange the wedding. And Rosa Langermann would become Rosa Karas, the wife of Vasek, rider and animaltamer in Umberto's Circus.

CHAPTER TWO

IT WAS A beautiful Sunday in March, the sea gulls were flying above the embankment, from the tower of St. Paul's ten o'clock was sounding. Miss Helen Berwitz was running out of her parents' home with short, quick steps. She was still buttoning one of her gloves when she reached the pavement. Round the corner, she stopped, opened her handbag and with an eager gesture pulled out a tiny letter. Did she remember exactly what he had written in it? It was so exciting and delightful that she must read it again and again.

"Beloved Helen! Do you still remember the promise which we once made each other in the gallery of Umberto's Circus? That was many many years ago—we were little children. But I have not forgotten it; all this time I have carried your sweet image in my heart, and the remembrance of you burns in my memory, no matter where my artistic career may take me in the world. Now it has brought me to your home; I have been engaged as *premier danseur* in the Hamburg Theater, and I arrived there today. My first memory was of you, the enchanting love of my childhood and the star of my life. Should you still feel any inclination toward me, come, I beg you, to the theater on Sunday morning at ten o'clock, and bring me a bit of luck and hope before my first appearance. Your faithful Paolo Roméo, who kisses you."

Yes, it had been frightfully long ago, already it was almost a dream. But Helen was awakened by this letter as if it had conducted an electric current. Paolo, handsome Paolo . . . What had happened to him, to that bronzed little boy who once had told her how to do the jockey jump? Had he actually become a dancer, just as he had then wanted? And how was it he was able to leave the circus and his family? And he said that he had not

289

forgotten her. From him that was so enchanting. It had only been a bit of childish foolishness, that promise of long ago, but yet it did bind them together a little. And was it true that he still loved her . . . ?

And why should he not? Men were so funny. For example, this one, now, with his white lilac. For three weeks he had been sending her a bouquet of white lilac every evening, though lilac was out of season and must be frightfully expensive. But he had never appeared, never even given any sign of himself, a letter, a visiting card, a note, nothing, nothing but the lilac, heavy and magnificent. Who was he? He must be rich and a man of wonderful taste, but was he old or young, handsome or ugly? Nothing could be guessed. Alice Kerholec said that he must be a decrepit and ugly old man who did not even dare to make an appearance, but that, too, was only a guess and Alice had said it as a joke to make Helen angry.

Alice was secretly piqued with Helen because she herself had not been made first rider when, in the course of time, Helen's mother had stopped riding. But that was nonsense. Helen had been trained from childhood for riding and for the High School, and it was obvious that the daughter of a director was more than a wife of a superintendent. And then that redhead should have more sense, too, for God's sake—the mother of three children couldn't have a body like a young girl's, everyone knew that. And that was the reason why Alice tried to make fun of Helen's unknown admirer, rather unkindly; Helen secretly believed that he was some lofty, supremely discreet personage who would one day present himself.

And if she had such devoted admirers, then why should not Paolo, too, have always been in love with her? Her parents told her that she had been a pretty little girl, and there would have been nothing surprising if she had left an undying impression on him. Various admirers wrote and told her that she was their dream, that they longed for her, that they could not forget her—why should this not also be true of that impulsive boy? But would she recognize him after so many years! That stout, bearded man under the theater chandelier couldn't be he, nor the one there in the overcoat, but . . . Paolo! She recognized him as soon as she saw him, and how handsome he was!

It was as if he were stepping out from some picture before her, slender and elegant, how elegant! The spring sun was so warm that he wore no overcoat, but a blue jacket with a tight belt, a brocaded waistcoat, and bright check trousers; a yellow cravat with red flowers and on it a great pearl tiepin; a brown hat with a bent rim over his black curls; in his hand he carried a thin bamboo cane and his hands are covered with heavy rings. But what is all this compared with his fine-featured brown face in which shine two large, dark, dreamy eyes beneath long silken lashes! His nose is chiseled to perfection, truly aristocratic, his mouth is beautiful, as if sculptured, and his gleaming teeth sparkle.

But Paolo, too, is evidently amazed at the charm of the young girl, involuntarily he half-closes one eye and examines her critically from head to toe before the fire again lights up in his eyes and he comes forward to her.

"Oh, *ma bella, bellissima* Helen"—he speaks in a soft and sweet tenor voice as he kisses her hand and then presses it to his heart—"now I see how infinitely weak my imagination has been; I was not able to imagine such beauty! You are delightful, child, truly delightful. Oh, I must have been mad when I dreamed that such a flower might bloom for me. . . . Or may I perhaps hope? You have no husband? No fiancé? No suitor? Oh, it is incredible."

And Paolo puts his right arm through Helen's and leads her with an even, self-confident manner as if it were his place to lead. And his soft fawning voice continues to sound in her ears, his heated glance draws her eyes to his every little while, and a light trembling seizes her; her head, arms, and side bend playfully as he touches her frequently to impart to her his eagerness.

"Your parents are well? The circus, I hope, is successful? And what about that stupid 'Double Cow'—did he go on with his career with the horses?"

"Don't talk so contemptuously, Paolo, I devoted mine to horses, too. And you helped me with a part of it—that time when you showed me how to do something."

"I showed you something about horses? I don't remember that —how could I have had anything to do with riding?"

"It wasn't exactly riding, it was a jump, the jockey jump, right onto the horse's back. You remember how Father struck you with the whip. . . ."

"Ah, it's beginning to come back to me. Yes . . . I hope that you didn't say anything about it to friend Double Cow, since it was I who taught it to him. He would have been terribly angry at me for interfering with things which he thought he understood better. Well, of course . . . I suffered that whiplash then for you, you know. And since then, I have suffered times without number, elsewhere as well. I always dreamed that we two could be a marvelous dance team. But you stuck to the saddle.

"As soon as I arrived here I heard of you. Straight off, like the beckoning of fate. Imagine, my partner and I came to the theater, to the dressing room to look round . . . and the wardrobe mistress there was an old woman, an Italian, Signora Delaglio. And when I started to ask her about you, she said at once she knew you, that she had given you ballet lessons. From her I learned how beautiful you were, and that you still were free.

"And Signora Delaglio also offered to take you a billet-doux, when my partner left . . . and she said that if we wanted to meet somewhere, undisturbed . . . that she has a quiet, discreet flat . . . where we could spend an intimate evening, or have tea, or only drink a bottle of wine. Imagine, Helen, what it was to receive such an offer just after having come to a city where I haven't been since I was a boy!"

"But it's horrible . . . I hope you turned that old procuress down?"

"Why?" Paolo laughed quietly, "I accepted her offer, Helen, I was delighted to accept it . . . and if you have nothing important to prevent you, we can go there now . . . to take a look at least and see how our future nest looks . . ."

"Paolo!" cried Helen, completely horrified.

"What? Perhaps you're afraid?"

They stood and looked at each other, Helen in confusion and despair, Paolo with a frivolous smile on his face, which now began to change into a more fixed look at her.

"Surely, Helen, you won't tell me that you, a circus rider, cling to old-world prejudices which are well enough for a daughter of the bourgeoisie, but which are quite out of place with a modern artist? That would surprise me greatly . . . and it would be something which I have never run up against, not even with girls from the best society."

"Paolo," Helen mastered her agitation, "I don't know with whom you associate or how you live. But the plan you have made for me was at least presumptuous. Of course we are circus people, riders, tamers, grooms—choose whatever term you find most contemptuous. We have no home, it is true we rove all over the world, but in spite of that our family is a decent one, do you understand? And none of us is so low that anyone, just by raising his finger, could . . ."

A cloud suddenly crossed Paolo's face. The gleam in his eyes was extinguished, his smile disappeared, his eyelids, with their long lashes, sank. Only for a second did a searching look appear in his face. And then, after a time, when he looked up again, his eyes were full of sorrow.

"Oh, forgive me, Helen, only now do I see what a cursed mistake that old witch Delaglio has made me commit. For God's sake, I beg you to forgive me. I would never have allowed myself . . . if she had not misled me . . . Ugh, it's vile even to speak about it. . . ."

"Delaglio. It's like her!"

"She's to blame! I swear to you that I myself . . . My God, you must realize, it was my childhood memory which moved me to try and find you. That pure image! Those innocent feelings! Oh, let us try to forget that hellhound and her work! There are other ties between us, and I would not wish to lose any one of them. For so many years I consoled myself with them . . ."

"How was it you went into the theater, Paolo?" asked Helen, longing to put the shameful episode behind them.

"Oh, the theater!" Paolo shone with joy at the change of conversation. "Who was it who once aroused the longing for the ballet in little Paolo? Have you already forgotten the little girl who was then studying her first steps in Hamburg and who showed them to Paolo? It was you, dear one, who led me to this. You taught me how close ballet was to my own knowledge, and how much more beautiful it was than those lifeless handsprings

293

and somersaults, performed on a square of carpet, which I felt I was doomed to all the rest of my life!

"And then one day the time came which awaits every tumbling family—the boys grow up, and their father can no longer toss them into the air with his feet. Papa Roméo began to complain that we were too heavy for his soles, that he would have to revise the whole act. We were in northern Italy at the time, in Milan, and I made the suggestion that he revise the act without me. There were some quarrels over it, but he gave in and I ran off to the theater to try my luck with the ballet. They gave me a tryout, and the ballet master found that I wasn't trained right, of course, but that in some of the leaps and pirouettes I outdid all the others. They accepted me, and soon I was dancing solos; they even wrote special parts for me. And my fame began to grow . . . no longer was I poor little Paolo, but the renowned and celebrated virtuoso of leaps and pirouettes. . . ."

"And you travel from theater to theater, or have you a permanent engagement?"

"I always try to get a fixed engagement which will leave me as free as possible. You know, be engaged in one city for so many performances during a season, and then be able to make guest appearances elsewhere."

"And now your main job is in Hamburg?"

"Yes. I hoped that we might see a great deal of each other here."

"I don't know, Paolo, that that is possible. Father is getting ready to leave."

"Ah, that's sad news for me. Helen, my dearest one, I have sinned against you deeply. But only because of our childhood promise, I beg you, I swear to you. Give me a chance to make it up to you!"

He stopped her with a light touch of his arm and looked straight into her eyes with a long supplicating look. And when she looked into the deep, mournful eyes of the Oriental it was as if an abyss opened beneath her.

"Promise me, Helen, that tomorrow we will see each other again. Even if only for a short while. For half an hour. For a quarter. For any length of time. I need you, I long for you. You mean far more for me than you suspect. You, Helen, you are the only one . . . who can save me."

He said it quietly, with firm insistency. His hand was hot. His eyes were afire. Helen's head whirled. She could not imagine what it was that she could save him from, nor how. She only sensed that she was yielding to his great charm and that she must save herself.

"Look, Paolo, first I must go home. We've stayed too long. And about tomorrow, I don't know . . . I'm afraid . . . they'll find out about it at home, and then I have a rehearsal. . . . But if you think so, then here perhaps . . . at three. . . ."

"Here at the theater, like today? Thank you, Helen, thank you. Let me kiss your hand for your kindness. Good-bye, my lovely Helen!"

"Good-bye, Paolo!"

From the tower of St. Paul's noon was striking as Helen Berwitz hurried home to arrive in time for dinner. And Paolo Roméo, dancer, walked in the other direction, whistling, twisting his cane, which he suddenly struck against the ground.

"*Allah il Allah*—I never saw a lovelier girl. And the fire's burning in her. She will be mine."

CHAPTER THREE

IT WAS A beautiful Sunday in March, the sea gulls were flying over the embankment, from the tower of St. Paul's ten o'clock was sounding. A young man was crossing the hall of the Hotel Réunion, a very stylishly dressed young man with a high top hat on his curly hair. From time to time he irritatedly asked the personnel if the messenger whom he was expecting had not arrived. At last a uniformed boy ran in at the door carrying a bouquet wrapped in rose-colored paper; the young man seized it, rushed out, jumped into a waiting carriage and drove off down the Reeperbahn toward Umberto's Circus.

Sunday-morning rehearsals were held in the circus only when it was most urgent. At this moment Berwitz was unoccupied and was sitting in his office. During the last few years he had turned gray, grown considerably stouter, and his powerful back was bent. He had to wear spectacles to read his letters. In the midst of this Frau von Hammerschmidt interrupted him. (The latter now had hair as black as coal.) Some gentleman would like to speak with Mr. Berwitz. He looked very "charming." Berwitz took a hurried glance at the visiting card and nodded his head. Frau von Hammerschmidt showed in the gentleman from the Hotel Réunion with a pleasant smile and disappeared.

"What can I do for you, Count?" asked the director, removing his spectacles with a dignified gesture.

"Mr. Director," answered the young man with the bouquet in his hand, "I have come to you . . . on a . . . on a very delicate matter. I should like to be certain that I have . . . that I have found you in a thoroughly good mood, so that you could . . . listen undisturbed to what I have to say."

The young man was very excited; a tremor could be heard in his voice, and some words he almost stuttered.

"Please, Count, be seated," Berwitz answered with a quiet nod. His experienced glance rested on the excited visitor, and he decided that this young man must be about twenty-four, that he had a pale, handsome face, but that he was a weakling, whose nerves were not completely under control. He was dressed faultlessly.

"I would like to . . . to speak with you as man to man . . . frankly and openly. What brings me here . . . what my business with your honored enterprise is, I will state. . . . Perhaps I should state it as briefly as possible, by showing you . . . this bouquet."

His trembling hand tore open the rose-colored paper and handed the director several branches of heavy white lilac.

"Ah, Count, so you are the mysterious stranger who has so distinguished our circus with his noble attention?"

"Yes. Your circus . . . or, more exactly, one person . . . one individual in it: your daughter. You know . . . I have not words

296

enough to express . . . what Mademoiselle Helène is for me
. . . for me she is a dream, truly a dream. I do not know what
happened to me from the moment when I saw her. I came to
Hamburg only by chance . . . for a visit . . . and that evening
we happened to remark: 'Well, let's go somewhere, how about the
circus?' . . . But you would not believe me if I told you . . .
what I experienced there, what I felt . . . Mademoiselle Helène
. . . It was a great shock. . . ."

"You didn't fall ill? We would have been concerned to hear
that!"

"Ill? Worse . . . much worse, dear sir. I fell into a trance . . .
into dreams . . . I don't know, the word which I am going to
use is proscribed . . . but I fear it is the only one which ex-
presses what I mean . . . I fell in love. *Comprenez-vous?* I have
no idea how you look on love in the circus . . . but I always
laughed at the word. But now I know what it is. Torment, sir,
torment and pain and torture and fear. Because of it I cannot go
away, I cannot speak . . . I cannot write home. It is as if I were
paralyzed and could do nothing but go to see your performance
every evening. And so, in my confusion one idea took root in me
. . . to speak . . . to ask advice . . . to talk it over with the
man who can decide the whole matter. That man is you, of
course, Mr. Director. You know . . . it would be a terrible complicated thing from one side . . . a morganatic marriage, disin-
heritance, loss of estate and position . . . On the other side, if I
were to risk it, I would be a millstone around your neck. What
could you do with me? I can only ride in a saddle; without a
saddle I would fall off, that is clear to me. And I don't know how
to jump or anything . . . but life without her I cannot imagine.
I beg you, advise me—dare I ask for the hand of your daughter in
such circumstances?"

"It's certainly a difficult case, Count," Berwitz answered. "You
want me to decide something which a man must always decide
for himself. Tell me, have you spoken to Helen yet?"

"No, Mr. Director . . . not a word . . . I would not dare . . ."

"And you haven't said anything to your family, either?"

"No, the old Count isn't here, you understand? He's at home,
in Hogy-Mezö-Vasarhely . . . you know, near Szegedin . . ."

"Near Szegedin?" Berwitz cried out and began to look around for the visiting card he had put down. "What is your name, may I ask?"

"Herbert Remigius Maria, Count Pallachich . . ."

"And you breed Lipicans on your estate."

"Yes, we have a *secundogeniture,* as they call it, from the stallion Dahaby. How do you know that? . . . And why are you laughing?"

Berwitz had indeed begun to laugh. At first he did it quietly so that the guest would not observe it, but then he could not control it, the tears welled up in his eyes and Berwitz roared with mighty guffaws.

"This is an amazing coincidence, Count, a unique coincidence . . . when you understand it. . . ."

Count Herbert Remigius Maria Pallachich fidgeted nervously in his chair.

"But I don't understand, Mr. Director!"

"No, but I'll tell you. The joke is that you're not the first Pallachich who's fallen in love with Umberto's Circus. The first was your father. And do you know whom he fell in love with? With me, Count, with me, Peter Berwitz! Isn't it funny?"

"What . . . the old Count? Count Edmund Maximin Bruno Pallachich?"

"Yes. His Excellence Count Edmund Maximin Bruno Pallachich was carried away by a mad love for the star of Umberto's Circus, and that star, ha, ha, ha, that star was myself!"

"How was that possible, Mr. Director?"

"He wanted to kiss my delicate hands, ha, ha, ha, and here they are, Count, these paws, ho, ho, ho! . . ."

"Forgive me, I don't understand. . . ."

"He admired my slender legs, ha, ha, ha, and you see them here, Count, these stiff old pegs of mine, ho, ho, ho! . . . He raved about my whitened skin, this pigskin you see here, Count, ho, ho, ho! . . ."

"For the Lord's sake, tell me . . ."

"My golden hair intoxicated him, but that, Count, was not these wiry bristles you see, but a wig. I was a boy disguised as a girl rider, you understand. . . . God, what fun we had in

298

Szegedin with him! Every day I had a bouquet and a basket of wine and some days even jewelry . . ."

"Yes, Papa was always better at it than I was!"

"And every day he took a box . . . and when I came on he turned as red as a lobster . . . and I flirted with him, I blushed in front of him, I pretended I was embarrassed, ha, ha, ha, ha, I hemmed and hawed and then I winked at him; all the boys in the circus were in the joke."

"Was his infatuation so strong, then?"

"Strong! Gigantic! Grandiose! Enormous! An infatuation like a thunderstorm! And that's what they call the unerring instinct of love!"

"But how could the old Count . . . ?"

"But he wasn't the old Count then, he was your age. Only he didn't end up in such a polite manner as you, he didn't come with a bouquet to have a discussion, but with a pistol, and he almost shot me."

"That's frightful. . . . I thought about a revolver myself, but I didn't dare. . . ."

"But your father, Count, did dare, and only escaped being locked up by a hair's breadth. So that's the history of Count Pallachich and me in Szegedin, and you understand why I have to laugh now when, on my last legs, I'm visited by the son of the old Count, who comes here to declare his love for my daughter. Why, man, you don't even know if she really is a girl! Suppose she's a man in disguise again? We circus people are scoundrels, we do all sorts of tricks to bamboozle the world!"

The young Count Pallachich sat in his chair, his eyes staring wildly, and wiped the sweat from his forehead with his silk handkerchief. This sudden revelation had completely dampened his spirits and the fire of all the persuasive speeches which he had spent a whole week preparing for this moment.

"Mr. Director . . . you've put me in complete confusion . . . in cruel confusion . . . truly . . . it's desperate. . . . I beg of you, what am I to do?"

Berwitz had already quieted down and now looked at the young man with a certain sympathy.

"Look here, Count, it's a complicated question. I can't permit any scandal to touch my daughter. If you were already master of your own estate . . . and you came to me with the announcement that you loved each other . . . well, then I'd give you my blessing. But under the circumstances you've described to me, the matter is hopeless. Just consider that if you were to see her and confess your love, as soon as you mentioned the name of Count Pallachich she would laugh in your face, for she knows the story about your father just as well as I do. And everyone here would laugh, too, because it's a story which keeps making the rounds of all the dressing rooms. In no case could the outcome be a happy one.

"If I may advise you, go home and let the old Count tell you how he got over his love for Miss Satanella. It was a great love, a real shock, just as yours was; but you can see for yourself that it passed away and the Count found his happiness elsewhere, and still lives contentedly. So it is in life, you understand? Evidently you yourself are not responsible for it; the Pallachichs seem to have it in their blood, this inclination for the circus."

"It must be. I can't say about Father, but they say that Grandfather was a great admirer of circus artists, and even made presents of horses to them."

"That's true, I could tell you a whole story about that. But that certainly can't be called a bad practice; it's a beautiful gesture I recommend to you when you are lord of Hogy-Mezö-Vasarhely."

Pallachich sat sadly in his chair and looked into empty space.

"I felt that it would not work, somehow . . . I sensed it, and that is why I was agitated. But to fail so completely . . . How shall I extricate myself?"

"That, Count, I cannot say. Such things are not done here in the circus. Or rather, only among the spectators, of course. The director can't be held responsible for his public. I can only give you one piece of advice: go home and resort to the family recipe by which the Pallachichs have evidently cured themselves of their love for circus people. That is all I can say to you. And as for the bouquet . . . if you permit me, I'll have it sent to Helen as your parting gift. All right?"

"As my parting gift," Pallachich whispered. But since Berwitz had stood up and made it evident that the conversation was already at an end, the young Count, too, arose, yielding to the other's more dominant nature.

"As my parting gift," he repeated. "You are very kind. But how can I reconcile myself with the fact that I must suffer for a stupid mistake of my father's?"

"That's what they call 'visiting the sins of the fathers.'" Berwitz laughed as he gave him his hand. "Give Miss Satanella's greetings to your father, I beg you. Tell him that you met her and that the great beauty had become an old father who has a great concern for his daughter—and for her admirers. Good-bye, Count, it was a pleasure. Good-bye."

Peter Berwitz remained standing in his office; for a while he continued to smile at the recollection of how he had kicked up his skirts in front of Pallachich. Then slowly his smile disappeared as, in place of himself, he saw his daughter on the back of the horse.

When he went home for dinner at midday Helen had still not come in. He called Anna, closed the door of their room, and told her what had happened that morning. She shook her head in amazement at the strange coincidences which occur in the circus.

"But this story only shows me," said Berwitz, "that the time has arrived to do something with Helen. We've overlooked the fact that she's already a grown woman. . . ."

"Perhaps you've overlooked it," Anna answered, "but I haven't."

"Well, now we must think about the future. Ours, Helen's, the future of Umberto's Circus. I should be very happy if a suitor for Helen turned up whom I would be glad to accept. Perhaps Helen has some inclination or other?"

"No, Peter, she hasn't. At least I haven't noticed anything. And it's better to keep her away from men whom chance throws in her way."

"Hm, for her the best thing would be someone in the profession. Isn't there a young circus or menagerie proprietor anywhere?"

"That's what I've thought of, too, but there's no such man. I've already gone over all the families. Everywhere all the young men are married. Or they're still boys."

301

"That's annoying, Anna. Umberto's Circus is such a great firm now that I cannot take on anyone whom I can't rely on completely."

"I know one person. But he's not a director."

"Who is it? Do I know him too?"

"Of course—Vasek!"

"Vasek! The son of a staker . . . hmm, of course, Vasek . . . yes, there's nothing wrong with him. Vasek's a first-class chap. Vasek started out from scratch, he understands everything in the circus. He's a good steady boy, and not a vagabond. Do you think Helen would take him?"

"Well, I can't guarantee it, but they've been friends since they were children, and the boy's pleasant and obliging. I think Helen would let us consider it. She has too much common sense to bring just anyone from the street into the business."

"Vasek. Yes, Vasek," Berwitz nodded, "it's not such a bad idea. We must prepare the ground, Anna. And better now than too late."

And with this decision they went to dinner, where Helen already awaited them, her head full of Paolo.

CHAPTER FOUR

"My dear, my most darling Rosa!

"First of all I must greet you a hundred thousand times and kiss you, and send my greetings to your dear mother. Father and Mr. Bures, too, ask to be remembered to you. We have been in Zurich now for three days, and will stay here for several more days, so that now I have time to write to you.

"How are you, dear Rosa? I hope that you are well and that your mistress isn't giving you too much work to do. It makes me sad to think of your dear little hands and how they must work with a needle every day from morning to night. But God grant that all that will soon be changed when I come back and we set the date for the wedding.

"Not much has changed since we left Hamburg. I now spend days on end with my animals. When we aren't performing or practicing I sit by the cages and watch these pets of mine, especially the new tigers. You know this is the whole secret of the art of taming: a man must know the animals through and through. And you can never know everything about them. Each one has a different nature and reacts differently to different things. Take Nero, for example, the big heavy lion from South Africa with the brownish mane. He's a natural sluggard; his favorite pastime is stretching—if he is disturbed he complains by giving a thunderous roar. His only interest is his food; he gets to his feet a quarter of an hour before feeding time and is the first to raise his front paws to pull his share of meat off the pitchfork. He knows the time just as well as if he had an alarm clock in his cage. So I don't have to worry about that; as soon as I see him get up I know it's time to cut up the meat.

"But he's a goodhearted beast by nature; the worst he ever does is roar. All he wants is for everything to be orderly and quiet. But Borneo and Sumatra, whom I brought up myself, are worse-tempered. They're already fairly old now, and are irritated at every trifle; at each command I give them they sulk and growl; when they see me reach for the whip they jump onto their places and then snarl at me. They try to fight with Ramona and Negus, and if we don't separate them soon enough the cage is full of torn-out tufts of hair. Sometimes Nero will restore order among them if he's irritated enough, but most often we let Fifina have a go at them. That's the female fox terrier Mr. Hamilton put with Borneo and Sumatra when they were still cubs.

"She's already a respectable old dog, her chin's all gray, her stomach's puffed out, she's had six litters of pups, and she's so fat that she can't run much now, she hasn't enough breath to. But when the lions start fighting she jumps into the cage at once, rushes at them, bites them on the ears, the legs, and the chin, and then barks so and scolds them that the great beasts are always frightened and crawl into their corners, and Fifina walks over and drinks all their water, because she's tired out from fighting. That fox terrier is supreme over them, and none of them dare to do anything to her. She's a poor old shabby dog now and has lost almost all her teeth, but her heart's brave.

"The lions are great lubberly sheep, they follow Nero like a ram, because he's the strongest, and in general they recognize his authority, but Fifina won't give way to him. Several times a day she jumps into their cage, sniffs over their straw, and jumps out again, like a real directress. Those Great Danes the director recently bought for the act are downright old women beside her; they're put in the cages just for the look of the thing. People think they protect me, but if it came to anything, which God forbid, I would have to protect the Great Danes.

"But now it dawns on me that there's a great piece of news which I haven't written about yet. We have a new cage for the lions' performance; it really isn't a new cage, but iron bars they mount round the ring just before my act. In France and elsewhere they've had the same thing for a long time. You should see how wonderful it is now that I can let all my beasts out and work with them in the open. Of course I have to learn everything over again now that there's more room for the jumps and the figures and for all the tricks. The beasts seem to like it, since the only thing they've missed up to now is the chance to move about; and now they can run and jump to their heart's content. Every morning before the rehearsal I let them run about there for a full half-hour, while I do nothing but sit and watch them play.

"I'm convinced that the old training with whips and force was worthless. I think tigers and lions are just like people and each individual has some special talent and other things which he cannot do, and a good trainer must know all about that. Why should I beat Ramona to force her to walk on a ball when I see that she is terribly frightened of it and that she'll jump off it the second that the ball moves in the ring? Evidently it seems mysterious and suspicious to her, and she is afraid of it just as in childhood we were afraid of our shadows. But Borneo, on the other hand, knows that a ball is a plaything and jumps on it at once; that shows me that Borneo can be taught to stand on it and to roll it along underneath him, himself. In general, it seems to me that the best-performed tricks are those the animal himself is fond of.

"Dear Rosa, I wrote this to you last evening before the gang came back from the tavern. Today I'm alone again and can continue it. First of all, I must tell you that I dreamed of you last night. It was an uncertain dream. I was on the point of going into a cage, and you were standing beside it in your rose-colored dress, and were crying and calling to me not to open the door, that something would happen to me. It was such a vivid dream that this morning I really had an unpleasant sensation when I opened the lock on the big cage. But I overcame it, and only tried to be extra careful. I think the tiger Sheik, the royal Indian, wanted to jump at me—at least he crouched and his eyes shone like two green fires. But then I yelled at him and began to crack the whip, and he crawled away.

"That sort of thing doesn't mean anything really. Sheik is a hunter, he always wants to jump at something, it's in him. The main thing is that I'm like one of them. Among the tigers I'm the biggest Siberian tiger, and among the lions the oldest Ethiopian. Some of them love me, especially the lionesses, who're always showing their love for me. The others feel respect for me and are afraid. The only bad thing is that they're jealous of one another, and are ready to fight with each other for my favor. I have to be fair in everything with them, equally fair to all of them, otherwise I'd lose the game.

"Anyway, they're better than the bears. The bears you can't rely on for anything; they're hardened scoundrels, who are always begging for a spoonful of syrup, and are always ready to bite you when they get it. You can't say to yourself that you're one of them; you have to dominate them by talking to them continually. I know when a lion or a tiger's irritated or when he's in a bad mood, but with those brown villains you can't tell: a bear always looks perfectly calm, performs its somersaults or dances, but suddenly it will snap. I like the lions and tigers much, much better; they at least give some warning before they jump, and a man can keep an eye on them.

"The most comical is the tigress Cambodia, she's so much in love with me that you would actually be jealous. Whenever she can she rolls over in front of me and licks my boots. And when she has to look me in the eye she trembles all over and purrs so caressingly, and then turns her head away and licks my hand, almost hurts it with her rough tongue. She is a magnificent, slender beauty from Sumatra, and that's quite surprising. At least Gambier always said that tigers from there are the most treacherous, because they live in the dark of the jungle.

"But oh, what are all the beasts of the jungle compared with people! At first I didn't want to write this to you, but there can be no secrets between us, and therefore I will tell this too. I don't know how it started, but lately there has been pressure on me from all sides to court Helen Berwitz! Rosa, beloved! By all that is dearest to me I swear to you that I have never even given a thought to Helen Berwitz. I've known her ever since I came to Umberto's Circus, we met in the ring when we were small children, we made our first appearance together and had a great success. And then we grew up together as friends, she worked as a rider and proved that she had talent, I worked at tumbling and at the *batoude* and so on, and so we were together every evening.

"But neither she nor I ever behaved to each other any differently than one artist would behave to another. Now that I'm an animal-tamer these contacts have lessened; sometimes we don't see each other all day long. And when we do meet at rehearsals or during the program and exchange a few words it's always as if both of us were men. You would really have to know what this circus life is like to appreciate how men and women can be together and think only of their tricks and their success, and not about stupid love affairs. For that there's neither the time nor the inclination.

"Therefore I was greatly surprised when people began to hint about Helen and me. . . . When I heard it for the first time I simply laughed and paid no more attention to it. But that didn't stop them, the hints became more and more frequent, and now the whole circus is whispering about it. For me it's a terrible thing, since I wish to hear nothing about it. What is Helen Berwitz to me when I have my Rosa, my own darling, my only undying love, to whom I shall be true my whole life and whom I will not allow anyone to take away from me!

"If I only knew who's spreading this stupid rumor! I thought at first that Kerholec might be starting it, and I took him to task for it. He answered, 'I spread no rumors, but I tell you frankly and openly what your duty is. Berwitz is getting old, and if he doesn't find a reliable successor in time it could mean an end to Umberto's Circus and misfortune for dozens of families.'

"I went to see Bures, you know what an idealist he is. He put both hands on my shoulders, looked straight into my face and said, 'Vasek, I know what sacred feelings burn within you. Young friend, I have boundless respect for them. I too once burned with love and was ready to sacrifice everything for it. But after all the experience of life I can tell you that there are some things which are more important than love. To be head of a great enterprise like this is no small thing. And for our people it would have great value. I do not wish to try to persuade you, but I advise you to reflect well on it!' I was completely crushed; I would never have expected such a thing from Bures.

"Without thinking I complained about it in front of Father, and Father nodded his head and said, 'Yes, these are hard questions to decide. I won't try to interfere with your future, to be sure. I know what a good girl Rosa is, and that the two of you would be very happy together. But you would work with wild beasts your whole life, and I fear your life would not last long . . . you understand . . . some brute would put an end to it. If you were head of the circus you wouldn't have to do such dangerous work. Think about it, Vasek . . . I beg you. . . .'

"And so it goes on and on, like tunes on a barrel organ, each piece is different, and yet all end the same—marry Helen Berwitz. Even old Malina, just think, told me at great length how Bernhard Berwitz, the father of our director, married into Umberto's family and from a simple juggler rose to be master of the whole enterprise. But I won't listen to such speeches! It's all stupidity and nonsense, and they are only making me miserable by harping on it. I have already made my decision, for me there is no one but you, my dear, dear Rosa. I think of you constantly, I dream of you, and without you life would be a torment.

"How much I long for us to be together again! I am already counting the days, and when we turn toward the north and when the leaves turn gold on the trees it will be like a new spring for me, in which I shall again be able to see you! Now that I have actually written on paper all these things which have been persecuting me, now that I have shaken off these nightmares and got rid of them, I feel much happier and more cheerful. Oh, how happy I am that I have you to confide in! You alone understand me, you alone comprehend me, you alone open your heart to me because you know how much I love you and that I shall never, never part from you.

"A thousand kisses, a hundred thousand kisses, my dear one, my only one, my beloved, my beautiful bride!

"Your Vasek, who ever longs for you

"p.s.—Before I could send this letter off, Cambodia clawed me on the left arm and tore open the flesh a bit. They dressed the wound at the Berwitzes'. Don't worry, it's nothing; you see I can write to you. Farewell, my beloved!"

CHAPTER FIVE

THE HOT SUMMER passed; day after day it flowed away down the silvery waters of the River Rhine. The blessed autumn was coming, and on the hills the grapes were turning golden and blue. Fog swirled along the water in the morning as Berwitz's caravans trailed along one after another. Wherever the road dipped a little it was impossible to see more than ten paces ahead. The stream of horses and wagons lost touch with each other, and Kerholec rode at a quick trot from the rear group forward, to tell each section where to stop in case it should lose contact with the one in front of it.

The horse on which he rode was named Admirable, a Trakhener stallion whose pace was a trot which was like soaring in the air. Kerholec passed the front division, but did not stop.

What a pleasure it was to fly thus through the cool, fresh morning! And Admirable, too, felt the pleasure of movement, he snorted and tossed his mane. Only when they were far ahead, alone and quite lost in the fog, did Kerholec straighten up and Admirable obediently change over to a walk. Behind them clattered the beat of hoofs at full gallop.

Kerholec edged his horse over to the right side of the road. From the gray curtains of fog Anna Berwitz came forth on Chérie. As she passed Kerholec she changed over to a trot, and a bit farther on stopped her horse. Turning round in the saddle, she waited until Kerholec came up.

"Why, it's Admirable. Peter and I couldn't make him out in the fog, and we guessed that it must be Sirius. He trots magnificently; I thought only Sirius could trot that way."

"Admirable is neglected, madame," Kerholec answered. "The stallion needs more exercise."

"So I see. Well, what's the news with Vasek?"

"Nothing, madame. He's holding back. As soon as Helen began to nurse his wound, it had a great effect on him. And he fully admits the force of our arguments. But he won't give in. He says he's in love and that he's given his promise. He's a bit stubborn about it, like he is with everything else."

"Vasek has character. That's the most wonderful thing about him. A rare boy. The more I see him the more I respect him. Where are we stopping this evening?"

"In Honnef, madame. It would be too expensive to spend the night in Bonn. And tomorrow we must appear in Cologne."

"In Honnef. That's near the Seven Mountains, isn't it?"

"Yes."

"What a marvelous coincidence!" Anna's keen, shining face lit up. "In Honnef. That's excellent. . . . Please, Karel, tell Vasek to come and see me soon after four o'clock. And tell him to put on his best clothes, we're going somewhere on a visit."

"Right, madame, I'll see to it."

The director's wife turned her horse round, but before she urged it forward she added:

"And please—you have an eye for everything—if you could buy some nice salmon along the way, send it to our wagon."

"With pleasure, madame," Kerholec agreed, and Anna galloped off.

In Number Eight at dinner that day they racked their brains to discover what there could be that was so unusual in Honnef, why Vasek should get all dressed up, who it was that they were going to visit, and for whom the fine salmon was intended. But they came to no conclusion, and with his hair combed Vasek set out for the director's wagon at four o'clock. The ordinary noises of camp life sounded round him, the horses stood in their canvas stables and the elephants were pushing some wagons with cages over into a better position.

The camp had been pitched on a dry meadow beside a wood, and here the living wagons formed a square. Behind them and behind the wagons with the animals a smithy had been set up, and here they were already building a fire. This was an innovation Berwitz had added when he discovered how much money blacksmith's work and shoeing were costing him on the road, and how often the horses suffered because of bad country workmanship. Beside the smithy stood a wagon with a clanking engine, which drove the pump for the water line.

The director's wife, whom they were all used to seeing dressed in a semimasculine costume, now appeared on the steps of her wagon wearing a very elegant town frock with a tight black bodice, the only adornment of which was its white collar. She was more than fifty now, and her hair was heavily streaked with silver, but she still had eyes like a lynx. Behind her Helen appeared in a summer dress, with a parasol in her hand, an incomparably beautiful sight amid these rough, gipsylike surroundings.

"Good-day, Vasek," Anna greeted the young man, who bowed. "How is your shoulder—is it still hurting you?"

"No, madame, thanks for asking, but my arm is quite all right. Helen is a wonderful nurse."

"Well, I've taught her how to put on and tie bandages; at any time one may have to practice first aid in a circus. The main thing is for you not to get blood poisoning. The claws of the big cats are a real hotbed of infection."

"Luckily I was wearing something on my shoulders when

Cambodia clawed me. And she struck only once. As soon as I looked round at her she turned her head and mewed for a caress."

"Did you hit her?" asked Helen.

"No—why, what sense would there be in that? She was driven by some instinct she couldn't help. Perhaps by love! Cambodia really loves me."

"That's right," the director's wife agreed. "When we take it into our heads to live with wild beasts we can't blame them when they follow their own natures. But let's set off for Honnef. Someone lives there whom you must meet, Vasek. And Helen too. I'm sure that you both will be grateful to me for it."

Of course Vasek asked who it was, but Madame only smiled and said that it would be a surprise for both of them. And now they went into town, where Anna asked the way from a woman. She willingly pointed out a side street to them.

"The last house on the right, madame, the one covered with creepers."

They turned in that direction and entered a little garden where roses and dahlias were blooming. The front door was closed and the director's wife rang. A light step could be heard. The green door opened. A slender, very old man stood before them, his back bent, but with a noble face and a white mustache under an aquiline nose. He raised his eyebrows in surprise, in a high arc.

"Pardon us for disturbing you," said Anna, herself somewhat confused. "I'm Mrs. Berwitz, wife of the director of Umberto's Circus. By chance we camped here for the night, and I did not want to pass through Honnef without visiting you."

"Oh, madame, you do me an extraordinary honor. Please, I beg you, come in. If you will permit me I will go before you and open the door. This way, please. . . ."

They entered a small drawing room, the broad window of which looked out on the valley of the Rhine and which now shone with sunlight. In one corner by the window there stood an old black piano; elsewhere the walls were hidden by bookcases filled with a multitude of books. Tiny figures of horses and riders were set at various places on the bookcases, most of them

311

bronze copies of classical and Renaissance sculpture. Over the piano old English and French engravings and etchings of race horses hung in their narrow frames.

"I am truly happy at your delightful visit, madame," the old man began when Anna had seated herself on the chaise longue and Helen and Vasek in armchairs. "Here one seems far away from the world, sunk in oblivion; and then suddenly you honor me with your attention. Even a hermit would be glad of such a pleasant interruption. Are these your children, madame?"

"Only the girl, Mr. Director, Helen. She's been riding ever since she was a child, as has Mr. Vasek here. He isn't of our family, but he is our protégé. He's our best rider, Mr. Director, but at the moment he's working as an animal-tamer. I told myself that he would be grateful to me should I give him the opportunity to meet you."

"Oh, madame." Their white-haired host bowed. "You are too flattering to an old man who has outlived his fame. These children of a younger generation can hardly have heard of me. And I'm quite used to bearing a name which has lost its splendor and which now is no more than an empty sound."

"By us, Mr. Director, your name is spoken quite often. Permit me to tell them whose house they are in. I wanted to surprise them, so I kept it to myself. Helen, Vasek, this is Eduard Wollschläger."

Helen knew that her parents had often pronounced this name at home, but she could not remember in what connection. Now she rose, made a charming curtsy, and looked at Wollschläger with a polite smile. But Vasek almost gaped in his surprise. Wollschläger, Wollschläger . . . so this was the man about whom they spoke over and over again in the stables and the wagons, the man who had trained Hans; this was the famous circus director about whom they said that he had owned the finest horses in the world, and that he had worked miracles with them.

"You speak a dead name, madame." The old man smiled with unconcealed grief in his voice. "What can you know, young sir, of a man who disappeared from the public eye long before you were born!"

"But nonetheless I do know, Mr. Director." Vasek gathered

strength for the answer, with one hand clasping the arm of his chair. "You are . . . the Arab and his horse!"

Wollschläger blinked several times quickly.

"It is a strange thing, madame, how poorly we are armed against the spell of fame! Look, I am becoming sentimental! The Arab and his horse! My greatest creation! How many times has it been imitated—even in the renowned Umberto's Circus! The part of the dying Arab was my favorite rôle. Not because it was a big part. I had more spectacular ones: I played, for example, Julius Caesar, galloping to his death with Brutus's dagger in his breast.

"The part of the Arab was not so gripping—but that gray Hippolyte, how he enjoyed playing the scene! He pricked up his ears when he felt that I was losing my strength, he lowered them when I lay on the ground, he neighed with tail raised when he called for help, and then, carefully, he picked me up with his teeth. Madame, Hippolyte did not act that scene, he lived it with all the anxiety of his faithful horse's heart! It was for him that I was dying, and each day he was ready to give his life for me!"

"Is he still alive?"

"No, madame, ten years ago he was gathered to his ancestors. I kept him here, and I rewarded him for his faithfulness by letting him finish his life in peace and quiet. And not far from here I bought a little field by the woods and there between three oaks I buried him. He was my most faithful friend. Ever since then I have been alone—except for those old friends whom I betrayed and deserted in my wild youth, and whom I have now found again: Virgil, Horace, Martial. They say a man always returns to his first loves. Especially to those whom, in his foolishness, he then failed to understand. Human loves are fulfilled only in dreams, but two well-beloved things will greet a man even when his hair is gray: books and his native land."

"You're from the Rhine country?"

"Yes. And you, I believe, are from elsewhere?"

"Yes. I'm Belgian. I wasn't even born in the profession. My father was a high official, and I grew up in the home of Count d'Ascensons-Létardais. Perhaps you knew him in Brussels?"

"Tall, slender, with a full beard parted in two? Yes, I remember him—a handsome figure. He was a true aristocrat. He had the highest quality a man can possess: a perfect harmony between spirit and heart. I used to attend his hunts, and a supper at his summer residence was a real experience. And the Countess—did she marry?"

"No, she didn't. It was her strange passion to marry off all her friends, including me, according to their hearts' desire, but she herself refused to marry. She corresponds with all of us and is now passing through her tenth "marriage," as she calls it, with all its joys and none of its disillusions."

"It looks as if she's going to remain the true daughter of a philosophic father. And your daughter here, you said, rides?"

"Yes. I've become a complete circus woman myself, and there can be no question about her. She was born in a circus wagon."

"And young Mr. . . . Mr. Vasek . . . is an animal-tamer now?"

"Yes. But since he was seven he's been riding for us. He and Helen began on ponies, but at ten he had already passed on to horses. He's expert at everything, even free style. And he's a reliable performer at the *batoude* and at all sorts of jumps on horses and on the ground. And he even understands elephants."

"Excellent, young man. Circus life is a beautiful career, but it demands perfect knowledge. I do not wish to blaspheme, but the circus always reminded me of the Holy Church: it marks its devotees with its imperishable symbol and demands that they be faithful to it until the grave."

The old man sat opposite Anna, with his legs gracefully crossed, and conversed, turning at intervals from one young person to the other.

"You have to know it all and you love it all. But remember that you will never find a more noble animal than the horse. Wife, husband, lover—believe an experienced man—no one will compare to a faithful horse in devotion and wisdom. And the beauty of a full-blooded animal! You can do many miraculous things with him. There is no trick which an intelligent horse cannot understand and participate in. This very attribute leads circus people into errors. They prefer to show neck-breaking stunts and strength. But remember that there is but one thing which will raise a performance to the height of art: a sense of poetry.

"Perhaps you do not understand me. I am a man of a bygone day, which loved beauty above all else. And I speak to you, to the children of another age, who try to win success before all else. Success—success before stupid crowds—how little it requires to achieve! A bit of routine, a few trite tricks! I know what goes in the ring today, and I tell you they are heading for their downfall. We old men always had to keep one ideal before us. And whoever was heedful of his honor sought to find such an ideal and express it as beautifully as possible. There are no more ideals, my friends. An ideal is a sublime thing; it is the duty of the artist who comprehends sublimity to clothe it in a form which is worthy of it."

His guests sat opposite him and were silent. In him Anna saw that great creator of circus enchantments who had so amazed the people of Brussels in her youth, and whom they could never forget. Everything he touched had a special stamp. Beautiful horses, beautiful equestriennes, and how much harmony in every performance! Wollschläger's costumes were never mere rags used to clothe the rough body of a rider; with him they transfigured people, and always created some new spectacle. Even his horses performed as if they knew that they were creating a new sight for the world which it had never seen, as if they were creating beauty such as people had never before encountered. Fire seemed to blaze from everything; each creation of Wollschläger's was suffused with flame.

In artists with some higher talent he had been able to infuse a sort of tenseness. Tension flamed from the fiery eye of his stallion and from each of its stiffened muscles; you felt tension between the rider and his horse, between the rider and the public; everything mounted constantly to a climax, grew more powerful, was filled with a sense of triumphant, passionate conquest. Wollschläger had mastered the old French school of artificial riding, had carried it to new heights, had filled all of it with a new refinement, taste, and grace—but his true artistic soul had not been able to master finance as well. Crude and insensitive competition had won over the undiscriminating crowds; its blatant gaudiness had undermined his quiet, patient work.

For a number of years Eduard Wollschläger had gone on struggling, but when he found that he had come upon times which were losing all taste and understanding for beauty, and that he could only hold on by making great concessions to the baser preferences of the public, he had renounced such success, disbanded his company, and with a small income settled down as a private citizen in his own native land, where he gave himself over to cultural pursuits.

Helen did not understand all he expounded with such emphasis. But her eyes remained fixed on his well-preserved skin, on his blazing eyes, on his carefully kept mustache and his faultlessly worn white riding plastron. To her he resembled one of those old men, one of those noble marquises, whose patronage was a legend in the circus. At one moment the mad thought flashed through her head that she would have been ready to marry an old man like this at once. And Vasek, too, could not have said that he understood everything. But with all his concentrated attention he realized that he was sitting beside a true genius of the royal art of riding and training. With pious admiration he hung on his words and took in each one of them.

"You know, Fillis once had the clever idea of putting signs with numbers on them round the necks of horses, of giving one horse a sign with plus on it and another the equals sign, and then teaching them to group themselves in various combinations while on the run, so that each combination would form a correct problem in addition. For example, one plus two equals three, or two plus three equals five. It took a great deal of work, but Fillis carried it out and it was extremely successful with the public. But I didn't like it. It was a new idea, true, but there was no poetry in it. You know, I always hated mathematics. And to shame magnificent creatures by subjecting them to the strict pattern of a mathematical equation always seemed distasteful to me."

"And what was your most beautiful production, maestro?" Anna asked.

"The most beautiful . . . Hmm . . . Once I trained four young girls. You know, I wasn't content merely to train horses, I trained thoroughbred women, too. It was more difficult and more dangerous, and that tempted me. And once fate gave me a collection of the four loveliest women that the world has ever seen. Each one of them had magnificent black hair, great, dark eyes, and red lips, and each one of them carried herself as gracefully as a Crown Princess. And each one bubbled and overflowed with youth. I felt that it was my duty to create something unique from such priceless material. At first I tried them out in light peasant costumes, in a quadrille, but that was not right.

"Little by little I hit on the right method. I had four dark-red costumes made, with long skirts which lay in rich folds along the side of the horse, with slender bodices, above which the girls' white shoulders and heads gleamed like dazzling exotic flowers. Then I mounted them on four English stallions, as black as coal. That alone was enough to produce a bewildering effect; the skirts lay on the horses like ruby trappings and under their mantle the black horse and the white girl were like a single fabulous, magnificently living organism. Then I trained them to do a slow Spanish bolero. The girls had castanets in their hands and the horses wore dark-colored bells on their slender legs. Basically it was a quadrille, but what passionately moving beauty grew out of that quartet of rearing stallions and the triumphant mistresses who controlled them, out of their glances, their smiles, and their dance! No longer was it riding—it was a perfect equestrian poem!"

"How long did the ladies ride for you?" asked Helen.

"Ah, only for a short time. I think it was less than a year. It was too intoxicating. Before the year was out all four were married. Outside the circus, of course; two to nobles, one to a banker and one to a diplomat. That's the bitter outcome when you create beauty from human material. Madmen fell in love with my dark thunderstorms and each one tore away a piece of a thundercloud. And then they were amazed that afterward their marriages didn't turn out particularly exciting. But for me . . . for me they destroyed an act. . . . I gave up training girls then. It was thankless work. It is necessary that your passion for the circus be a strong one, or it will yield to the temptations of love and forget its duty."

"So then, maestro, you do not recognize the supreme right of love?" Anna asked quietly.

"I do not recognize it, madame, as soon as it takes us away from our world. Perfection can be achieved only through the greatest self-sacrifice. We people of an ancient art must have the strength to forswear everything which takes us away from it. We have forsworn our homes, society, domestic life, peace and comfort, safety and security of life, convention, and the Lord knows what else. We have set ourselves a goal beyond the world. This is a proud thing, but it is also a curse. We have made other laws for ourselves than those which govern ordinary people, and so we have lost our right to private happiness. Every one of us gambles daily with death in one way or another, and probes daily to find to what extreme he may carry his wager.

"That is no normal life, madame. Neither the medieval knight nor the soldier in battle repeats a wager with death day after day, month after month, year after year. Only members of that special order which is called the circus do that. And whoever has dedicated his life has no right to love. He has no right to violate the social order which binds us together. None of us is independent; each is interlinked with others, and will either strengthen the whole or weaken it. In our brotherhood love can only be justified when it does not weaken the whole, but strengthens it. That is the law of the man who is set apart from the crowd. If it is not kept our art will fall. The men who have succeeded in sacrificing everything are dying, and the artists of today are growing up to desire normal social life. But whoever longs for that opens the door in his heart to that which is most fatal: fear of his life."

Completely pale, Vasek listened to the unexpected turn in the conversation. If he had not been a witness to the fact that the meeting had been a chance one, he would have taken the whole incident for a malicious intrigue. But he saw before him this great man whose words he believed from the very start, and the latter unsuspectingly thrust a dagger into the most tender spot in Vasek's breast. Vasek was sick with agony, and it

318

seemed to him that he had ceased listening and that the other's voice sounded from far away in the distance, was pronouncing sentence of death. His heart stood still at the thought of how the director's wife would seize on this. But to his surprise and wonder he saw her stand up and heard her answer with a slight tremor in her voice:

"Mr. Director, forgive me if I interrupt what you have to say. But evening is drawing near—perhaps you would like to look at our stables? I am sure they would interest you. And after your inspection you could dine with us, and eat once more in a circus wagon. My husband would be greatly delighted if he could meet you again."

"Madame, you could not offer me a more welcome invitation. We old idealists place a totally different interpretation on the cry 'A horse, a horse, my kingdom for a horse!' "

When they reached the camp Peter Berwitz welcomed his parents' rival with all the grandiloquence of an Emir of the White Horses. At once Wollschläger began to call him by his Christian name. Anna and Helen excused themselves to go and attend to matters in the kitchen and Vasek hurried off to the cages to prepare for the feeding. Berwitz and his guest now headed toward the stables. When he pulled the curtain before them aside, a sudden cry resounded.

"My God! Herr Wollschläger! Can it be possible? Maestro . . . maestro!"

The white-haired groom Hans ran to meet the guest with his arms outstretched and his face aglow. Wollschläger stopped, looked keenly at the old man, slowly searched his memory, and suddenly broke out:

"Hans! I'm not mistaken? Hans! How are you, old fellow? So you're still in the business. Well, it's good of you to recognize me."

"Why shouldn't I recognize you?" Hans stammered, all excited. "How could I forget the time when I worked for the Maestro! Why, the Maestro took an interest in me . . . the Maestro trained me . . . I'll be grateful as long as I live. . . . Such a great honor for our stable! Such a visit, and I haven't even got my red waistcoat on!"

319

Wollschläger patted him on the shoulder and said that it didn't matter, and he turned away toward the stable. His eyes shone when he caught sight of the long lines of horses, and with the expertness of a connoisseur he headed straight for the finest. Berwitz puffed out his chest with satisfaction; Wollschläger had chosen those whom he himself considered the most valuable.

In the stable it was at once evident that a master had entered. He clucked at the horses and called to them, and the restless stallions stood motionless in concentrated attention. Their flashing eyes fixed themselves on his slender figure, and when Wollschläger came up to them none of them moved, not one of them was frightened. He ran his fingers along their manes, he patted each on the neck, stroked its muzzle, glanced at its teeth—even the wildest among them endured the touch of his firm, masterful hand. As they got to each one he asked the horse's name, which he repeated caressingly several times. And when he walked past they all turned their beautifully arched necks toward him, and more than one stretched out his head and neighed lightly.

The supper was a luxurious one. Anna put all her culinary skill and ability as a hostess into it. She was amply rewarded by the fact that she was entertaining a guest who appreciated every subtlety of her cooking. As at any meeting of circus people, the conversation turned on recollections of persons, cities, and beasts. Wollschläger was an accomplished narrator, and especially enchanted Frau von Hammerschmidt with his polished manners. But everything he said was suffused with a note of grief for the declining star of the circus.

"I do not wish always to sing the praises of old times. It is sad enough that I must say with Horace, 'Alas, Postumus, they flee away, our years.' Rather would I glorify this lament of mine with a glance toward the successful growth of new strength. The poet teaches me that the brief span of life does not permit one to entertain hope for the final outcome, but nonetheless I did have hopes for the distant future, for I believed that new growth might start up where the old had been cut away. And now that I am very, very old, I see but one thing and that constantly: the great, versatile riders of the past are dying out, and with them their performances.

"The new people execute what they have learned mechanically, and in no way raise the level of art. I jumped through a flaming hoop when it measured only twenty-two inches in diameter. Today it would not occur to anyone to try to overcome an obstacle as difficult as that. When I jumped on a running horse I would put my slippers on in mid-air; today such a trick is unheard-of. In place of that they prefer to enlarge the program.

"I have seen your elephants, lions, tigers, and bears. In time there will be ostriches, camels, and giraffes, and perhaps even walruses and seals, and kangaroos with pouches on their stomachs—always more animals, always different ones, always new sensations—but the conception of the noble beauty of a horse in all its postures is passing. The nobility is dying out, the riders are dying, the critical public is dying. There are left only the crowds, whom you must drum up and deceive. Your work is not easy."

"But what of it?" Peter, stimulated by the wine, objected. "It will last during our lifetime. And what happens after that others can worry about."

When they came out of the wagon to accompany their guest home the great full moon swam along above the pine trees and the meadow shone with its silver light. Yellow and red strips of light gleamed from the windows of the wagons; from somewhere the sound of muffled conversation could be heard; near the smithy someone was playing an accordion.

"Might I look at the horses once more before I go?" Wollschläger turned to Peter. "You know, this may be the last time that I shall ever see such a choice collection."

The gratified Peter was delighted to grant him the favor. Kerholec, Hans, and Vasek were sitting near the stable, and Hans was puffing at a pipe and telling of the tricks Eduard Wollschläger could do with horses. Now he jumped up and, taking his pipe from his mouth, announced to the director that all was in order in the stable—but that none of the horses had gone to sleep; they were all standing up as if waiting for a performance.

"They're waiting for me." Wollschläger smiled and went in. Both rows of horses turned their heads toward him and a light wave of movement passed through the stable.

"Sirius! Daimon! Admirable! Cyrus! Kismet! Heros!"

Wollschläger called each of their names, and each one pranced at the sound of his name, some even neighed.

"*Mon Dieu, mon Dieu*"—the old man spoke with emotion—"if I could only take the whip in my hands once more . . ."

"Vasek!" Anna, who stood beside him, called: "Run over to Number One and bring both whips!"

"Madame"—Wollschläger turned to her joyfully—"do you think it would be possible . . . ?"

"I beg you to, maestro," she answered quickly and firmly. Peter Berwitz looked at her hesitantly, but under her energetic look all he could do was nod in consent. Wollschläger bowed, walked toward the horses, and let out twelve of the most beautiful ones. At the same time he stroked each one, whispering its name in its ear and pressing its face against his. Vasek brought both the long and the short whip. The old man held them, weighed them in his hand, and nodded to Berwitz with satisfaction.

"The right kind! I managed my own horses without a whip . . . but I wouldn't dare to try it the first time with strange ones."

He walked out into the moonlight to the center of the bright illuminated clearing and cracked with the larger whip three times. In the stable the clatter of hoofs resounded.

"Open the door! *Avanti!*"

Hans and Vasek pulled the curtain aside and the freed horses, wearing nothing but their halters, rushed forward with waving manes and raised tails straight toward the man who called them. But the old man stopped them a whip length away and turned them toward the left. The great whip flew through the air like a flashing snake as Wollschläger's gentle calls of encouragement and coaxing mingled with the quick sound of the whiplash. The stallions and mares trotted with extreme tenseness, their ears and eyes concentrated on his every command. People began to run out of the wagons but before they could come up all twelve magnificent animals were trotting in a perfect circle.

"*Potztausend!*" a quiet oath resounded, and Vasek felt someone press his arm tightly. Beside him stood Berwitz in complete amazement.

322

"By all the thunders . . . look at them . . . look at them . . . They're running clockwise!"

It was truly an incredible miracle, for the horses had been trained all their life, in his circus as elsewhere, to run in a counter-clockwise direction; now suddenly, at Wollschläger's command, they ran the opposite way.

Again the slender old man cried out, waved his whip, and the horses stopped, turned on their hind legs toward the center and stood with their foreheads toward Wollschläger. Twice he made a circle in the air with the whip to give them a chance to rest and to concentrate. And then, after he stood still for a second, he stretched out his arms and cried:

"Aloft! *En parade!*"

At once nine horses raised themselves up on their hind legs in the air; three, untrained for the High School, neighed and reared up; it was evident how the desire to obey was struggling in them with fear and uncertainty, but in the middle of the circle the old man stood with his eyebrows contracted, his commanding will darted forth from his eyes, his hands stretched up as if by themselves they could support and lift up the horses' bodies, and after a moment of deliberation all twelve stood up in the moonlight, their manes blown to one side, their ears raised, their eyes agitated, their front hoofs beating the air, their flashing bellies arched beneath them.

Around them the onlookers were captivated by the magnificent spectacle and, themselves experienced circus men, began to applaud. Wollschläger bowed, gave a command, and the horses again turned in a quarter-pirouette, as if doing a curvet, and let themselves down on all fours. The whip sailed through the air and the whole troop again began to circle in a counterclockwise direction.

"Cyrus! *A gauche!*"

The whip lightly cracked and Cyrus, finding himself right in front of the stable door, turned and ran to his stall. One after another they thus dropped out of the formation, until finally Kismet had run into the stable, where all the horses stood neighing.

"Madame"—Wollschläger spoke to Anna with great emotion—

323

"I shall never forget this evening with which you provided me."

"Nor shall we ever forget you," answered Mrs. Berwitz.

"I am afraid," said Berwitz, "that I won't believe it until I've had a good night's sleep. To parade horses you've never handled before in the opposite direction to which they've been trained, and to get them to raise their forelegs in the air like that are things which seem like an impossible dream to me. You are a true maestro, Eduard."

"You are very kind to an old man. I wish all of you the very best of good luck."

They parted with great emotion. The director's wife asked Vasek to accompany Wollschläger home. The old man made a gesture of refusal, but nonetheless gave in. Vasek was very glad to go with him. Never in his life had he had such a feeling of respect, of admiration, of devotion, for a person. Inwardly he repeated what Hans had said that evening, "He is no director, he's a magician!" And for himself he had no other longing than to be like this enchanter, to do just such wonders, to bring his art to the same peak, and be able to look at the whole world with just such wisdom. Vasek hoped that this "old idealist" would once more start to talk to him about the circus, and that he would be able to ask him about the secrets of his magical influence. He would have been ready to listen to him all night and to believe every word in advance.

But Wollschläger was silent. Wollschläger walked along at his side through the moonlit night as if Vasek had not been there. Once along the way he stopped, looked in front of him, and smiled. Vasek felt that now he would say something. Now some beautiful, great truth would leave his lips. And, in point of fact, Wollschläger's lips trembled and three times was ecstatically sounded a phrase of which Vasek understood nothing:

"*Non omnis moriar! Non omnis moriar! Non omnis moriar!*"

And Eduard Wollschläger took off his hat and made a grand bow of thanks to the moon in the heavens.

He said nothing more until he stood in front of the gate of his house. He unlatched it, opened it, and standing between the gate posts, he suddenly turned toward Vasek. Raising himself to his full height, as when he had succeeded in raising the stallions onto their hind legs, he concentrated his eyes in a glance which penetrated to Vasek's very brain, speaking precisely and in a voice of command:

"You stand before a dual treachery. If you marry the girl in Hamburg, you will betray your art. If you wish to serve your art, you must betray the girl. There is no other way. Either one or the other. You must fight it out within yourself. All great men have had to pass through some painful sorrow, for greatness cannot grow out of an idyll. I have heard and seen enough to say to you that you are one of the chosen ones. You are one of the chosen! And for the chosen only struggle and strife are appointed, and never the peaceful contentment of love. Our art is rushing toward its destruction. Your own circus is threatened. Berwitz cannot hold it off. Berwitz is old. And Berwitz is foolish. For the times which are coming a man of quite different qualities must be at the head of things. If you wish to save Umberto's Circus, marry Helen Berwitz."

Vasek stood aghast. Wollschläger looked at him and his glance became softer.

"Poor, poor boy, I know your pain. And I have no ointment with which to soothe it. You will throw away your happiness and find nothing but heavy care in return. Fortune will not await you, nor comfort, nor peace and security from fate, only struggle, struggle, struggle. But only thus will you find yourself. Good night!"

Wollschläger closed the gate and turned the key. His light step resounded on the crunching sand as he walked toward the little house and disappeared. And Vasek Karas stood there motionless, and then leaned against the post of the gate and wept.

CHAPTER SIX

"I would like the wedding to be a quiet one," declared Anna Berwitz.

"What do you say, Baron?" Berwitz questioned Gaudeamus, pouring him out a glass of wine. "We've been fighting over it for a whole week now, and have only succeeded in agreeing that your word should decide the business."

"Thanks for the unexpected confidence you show in me," smiled Gaudeamus. "Though actually it's not so pleasant, for I must contradict a lady. In the circus the only thing which can be quiet is a bankruptcy. Everything else must be pounded out on a drum."

"There, what did I tell you?" Berwitz interjected. "You know, Baron, if it were done my way, I'd arrange the whole wedding like a pantomime. I would play a sheriff, Helen would be the sheriff's daughter, Vasek would be the cowboy in love . . . no, he'd be the young rancher from across the border, and ride up to do his wooing with a whole stampede of horses. I would refuse him my daughter, he'd carry her off, I'd shoot after him . . ."

"And then you'd kill him, of course!" Anna interrupted him. "Did you ever come across such a madman, Baron?"

"Be quiet, Anna. The main part would be getting the parson . . . you know, lassoing him and dragging him off to the deep forest to consecrate the marriage there. And if that parson were a real one, then the marriage, too, would be real, I think. . . ."

"And do you think, Mr. Berwitz"—Gaudeamus laughed—"that you could lasso the Archdeacon of Hamburg?"

"Well, if you paid him enough. . . ."

"You will have to pay him enough even without the lasso. A showy, well-staged wedding will be good publicity for Um-

326

berto's Circus. But you have to have the publicity outside, in the Hamburg streets. . . ."

"A big parade! Of course! That's a wonderful idea, Baron. It's terrible that it didn't occur to me right away. A procession of all the animals. . . . But I must buy a pair of camels at once. The wedding won't be complete without camels. I'll telegraph Hagenbeck immediately."

"What are you thinking of with your camels?" Anna interrupted him. "Rather think of a gift for the young couple, if you're not going to give them a dowry."

"The camels will be my gift. Forgive me, Anna, but you don't feel as strongly as I do what a disgrace it is that we still have no camels. Nowadays every side-show man has his own dromedary. And we, an old-established family, are to go into the streets with no camels? What would people think of us? How would we look? I tell you, a wedding without camels is impossible."

If walls have ears, the ears of the wagons were deafened during the next few days with debates over the coming event.

"I can just imagine," said Alice Kerholec to Frau von Hammerschmidt as the wagon housing the treasures and the wardrobe mistresses rattled along from Lüdenscheid toward Iserlohn, "I can just imagine how sweet our Helen will look in a wedding costume trimmed with ruffles. Her waist is so slender, and if she's laced up a bit besides . . ."

"Costume?" Frau von Hammerschmidt paused. "What costume? Helen must have a long wedding gown with an immense train, as is proper for a girl of good family."

"I'd much rather see her in something more clinging; that sort of thing is coming into fashion now. A clinging costume, fitting closely to the front of the body . . ."

"I know, I know—a new depravity. My dear Alice, believe me, there was nothing better than a wide crinoline. Then the body was well hidden, as in a bell, and wasn't always put on display for the eyes of the men."

"Yes, but when you were dancing and your partner pressed you tight, the crinoline would stand up on the other side, and the Devil could see right through the church to the altar."

"Yes, and we used to do just that, and pretend we knew nothing about it. It was easy with a crinoline: you pushed it to the right, to the left, and it stood up behind, in front—the men went mad, and the women looked as if nothing were happening."

"But dear lady, how much worry you had with it! And especially here, when you tried to get through the narrow doors of these wagons . . ."

"Never mind, it was a beautiful fashion. I always pictured Helen as a bride in a great white crinoline, on which we would sew tiny wreaths all round, roses and lace. But today I wouldn't try to persuade her to wear it; today the fashion is going over to bustles, and one person doesn't know what all must be sewn on behind to make it stand up and look better. But I hope they give her a train that will flow nicely."

"In her place I would do without a train. That would be modern."

"Please, I beg you, don't invent anything extreme for Helen. Helen must look like a girl of good family. A heavy bustle behind, décolleté in front, and a train of course; ruffles and ribbons round the skirt, a lace tunic on top, and over everything a veil, so that people can see that her family has money."

"Poor girl, she won't be able to drag a mile-long train like that!"

"That doesn't matter, Alice, the director can easily afford to have two pages walk behind and carry the train for her."

That evening in the stable it came to a hot argument between Hans and Malina.

"You whippersnapper," cried the quiet Malina to the rest of the stable hands, "hardly dry behind the ears yet, and already you think you're the boss!"

"You're an old fogy," the gray-haired Hans abused him, "ready to dry up and blow away like a leaf! But still you want to get in the way of young people!"

"You crawled out of a bankrupt outfit; we took pity on you and took you in for the sake of charity, and now you start giving orders!"

"You've been taking care of goats and monkeys all your life and now you think you're so good you can take over the horses! For you, Grandpa, there's Bluebeard. You can hitch him up and paint his whiskers!"

"What are you saying, you lout, you piddling stable hand! If I'd take a whip to you . . ."

"What's all the fuss about?" Kerholec spoke from the entrance. He had arrived just at the moment when both old men were ready to have a go at each other, to the delight of the whole stable.

"I beg to inform you that Malina's calling me names," startled Hans spoke up.

"Why shouldn't I call you names?" Malina bridled up. "Did you ever see such an upstart, trying to decide what should be done and what shouldn't be!"

"But what is it you're fighting about?"

"I'm not fighting," proclaimed Malina. "I only told him to brush up his best rig for me, as I'm taking the bride to the church. But this garbage-hauler has the cheek to tell me, Vendelín Malina, right to my face, that *he* is taking the bride! Did you ever see such impudence? *I* took her mamma, I'll take the girl; that's as plain as daylight!"

Hans again bridled up and said that Malina would cut a poor figure on the coachman's box, and that such a disgrace couldn't be permitted on a great occasion like this.

"So I'll cut a poor figure!" Malina crossed himself. "You conceited ass, I've seen how they drive the Pope himself. Before you were born I drank with the Turkish Sultan's coachman! I'll cut a figure good enough to take the Empress Elizabeth and the Archbishop themselves out for a drive! You should have tried telling Old Man Umberto that Malina couldn't cut a good figure!"

"Wait, you two kids!" Kerholec shouted with energy. "Here you're ready to fight each other, and all over nothing. The arrangement is that Malina will drive the bride . . ."

"Well, that's exactly what I said—I'm almost a member of the family."

". . . and Hans will take the groom. He trained him himself, he will drive him himself."

"Why, of course." Hans nodded his head. "I didn't think of that; there'll be a groom at the wedding, too."

Everybody took part in the festivity, from those in the director's wagon down to the stable hands. Only the bridegroom walked about, serious and pensive.

"What's the matter with you, Vasek?" his father said to him one day as they met in front of Number Eight. "You decided in favor of this, and now you're walking round as if you're expecting a burial and not a wedding."

"I don't know, Father, what's the matter with me. I decided in favor of it, you're all happy, everyone commends me for my decision, Berwitz is joyful, Rosa released me from my promise of her own accord, Helen is nice to me—everything is working out for the best, but it all lies over me like a nightmare: have I really chosen the right thing? You know, sometimes I think that you . . . and the others . . . and all of us, that we are men, and that it's all correct from a man's point of view, but that if Mamma were . . . perhaps Mamma wouldn't think that way. She had quite a different outlook on things from ours."

The elder Karas stopped in complete surprise. Márinka! God, how long ago and how far away she seemed now! Before, during the first years after he had lost her, his head had been full of her; everything about him, especially all that concerned the boy, he had measured in terms of his memories of her, by what she would have said and how she would have judged. But then, when he had given up the idea of leaving the circus, when he had already grown to be a part of it, bit by bit, as if on tiptoe, she had slipped out of his mind. Well, a living person can't live with a dead one. Little by little he had lost all thought of her; other women had turned up, life had been gay, he had seen a bit of the world here and there, had been free as a bird, and was no longer tormented by the reproaches of his conscience.

And now suddenly, after so many years, the lad reminded him of her, and in what a way! He was tormenting his own conscience in exactly the same way that he, Anton, had once tormented his. The fact was that he was a wonderfully good boy, resolute, courageous, sensible, and with a heart! Lord, he had a heart like his mother's! God knows what pain was in store for him! What was he to tell him—God, what was he to say to comfort him? Irresolutely Karas the father searched for a word as a salvation, but nothing came to his mind, no idea, no inspiration; only from somewhere far away a song, his favorite song, hummed in his head . . . the maidens come from the forest . . . that wouldn't do . . . Why, of course, that was it, that was Vasek's sorrow. . . .

But suddenly a burst of common sense jerked him out of this mood. He found the right word, the everyday word of comfort, smoothing over any excitement.

"When we go back to Hamburg, Vasek, we'll go on living in the wagon."

"Yes, Father, I had thought of that myself. We can't go to the Langermanns'. And it wouldn't pay to go anywhere else. Mrs. Berwitz is counting on Helen and me to live with them. But how about you? Will you stay on in Number Eight?"

"I'd stay, it doesn't matter so much where I'm concerned. Maybe I'll find something with Bures. Only there's still the problem of whether I ought to stay at all."

"Why? What's the matter with you?"

"Well, it's this way. Maybe the Berwitzes won't be so happy when they have a plain workman for a relative. You're much more important to them than I am, that's no secret. And then I might get in your way. Director and tent-staker—that's no kind of relationship."

"Until Mrs. Berwitz thinks of that, you're not to, either. That woman is very resourceful, and knows how to manage Berwitz. We only have to act a bit for the old man's benefit. His chief concern is how things look on the outside. As for the inside, tent-pitcher or whatever you are, he can't say much, for it's no different from his own history. But we can oblige him as far as appearances go. I'll order a dress coat for the wedding from the best tailor, and you'll have a black morning coat made, and buy a top hat."

"A top hat! Have you gone mad?"

"No, not mad. If you were to jump over the gallery it wouldn't impress him so much as if you come to the wedding in a top hat."

"Me in a top hat? Me in a top hat! Vasek, Vasek, you don't mean that seriously. Me with a stovepipe on my head! Me, Anton Karas, mason and tent-pitcher, balancing a stovepipe on my dome! Why, it'd fall off my head, man; I'd bump into everything with it, I wouldn't get through the door, I wouldn't be able to climb into the wagon, the wind would carry it off, I'd crush it, I'd get it dirty, I wouldn't know how to hold it, I'd sit on it somewhere. Boy! Son! I'd make muddle after muddle and everyone would laugh at me. . . ."

"Nonsense, Father," Vasek interrupted him sharply, "I mean it: morning coat and top hat—to that I'll stick and further speeches are useless."

Vasek walked off and left his father in complete bewilderment.

"The devil take your fancy director's airs!" Karas gave vent to his feelings. "You haven't quite wormed your way in yet, and you're giving your old man orders already. Hey, Malina!"

The inhabitants of Number Eight were gathering for dinner, and the first to approach was Malina.

"Malina, what'll you wear on your head for the wedding?"

"What'll I wear, Anton? I'll wear a top hat!"

"A top hat?" Karas rolled his eyes.

"Of course. How could I sit on the box without a top hat? And that fool Hans doesn't know I have a top hat, from the time of Berwitz's wedding, a beautiful, shiny one, with a white ribbon and a cockade on the side. Old Umberto fell for that kind of thing. When he didn't care what things looked like, he'd say, 'Vendelín, hitch up.' But when he came along to some big estate, he'd say, 'Vendelín, drive up.' When he said, 'Drive up,' that meant with top hat and gloves. And when he said, 'The first coachman will get the carriage ready,' I'd always put on white stockings, short breeches, and a three-cornered hat with a tassel.

"What does a fellow like Hans know about what difference there is between coachmen? There was such a difference, fellows, that if I were to be driving the carriage properly and happened to meet myself out driving just so-so, I wouldn't even shake hands with myself. Hans may say I don't cut a figure, but Old Umberto would always say, 'Never forget, Vendelín, to cut a good figure. A gentleman can look as if he's just crawled out of a stable, but a coachman must look like a nobleman.'

"And that's the sacred truth. Once a Prince's coachman from Kynzvart, from the Metternichs, worked for us for a year. That was beauty for you—I can't even tell you. It was as though he was made of stone; he didn't even wink. When he'd join the parade in front of the arena people would come up and stick pins in him, to see if he was alive or just stuffed. And he bragged that he came from ten generations of Metternich coachmen, that he had it in the blood, and that each mother in his family had had her first child by one of the Metternichs. The finest coachman's blood you can imagine."

"And how did he get on in the circus?" asked Bures, who had come up in the meantime and was listening inquisitively.

"He never really wanted to join the circus. He always wanted to be an actor. But he couldn't make a go of it. No matter what he acted, he always stood there stiff, like a statue. He showed me a newspaper clipping where it said that his Hamlet would make a good tombstone for Hamlet's grave. He was terribly proud of that, but I think it's the real reason why they kicked him out. Where he disappeared to, I don't know. . . ."

"Maybe he went back," speculated Bures, "married, and had a son who was really a Metternich."

"Maybe so," Malina nodded, "if the Metternichs are still such a sturdy family."

"Well, the family traditions of our best-born nobles are still being preserved." Bures grinned. "How did you happen to be talking about this coachman?"

"Because of that blockhead Hans," Malina answered.

"No, we were talking about top hats," Karas corrected him. "Vasek ordered me to buy a top hat for the wedding. What do you say to that, Bures?"

"Well, if you want to look appropriate," Bures grinned, "buy yourself a straw hat with a big ribbon and a veil. Or a Scotch cap and bagpipes to match."

"I'm talking seriously. Shall I buy it?"

"When in Rome, do as the Romans do. My old cap would be all right for me. But your Romans wear top hats. Buy yourself a stovepipe; let's have some fun out of it. And if you have hard times, you can pull flowers and rabbits out of it. A top hat's always a good thing for a circus man to own."

"Only don't let things happen to you the way it did to that magician in Saint-Omer," another recollection slipped out from

Malina. "His name was Gianini, he had a booth right beside us. One day his assistant ran off and he took on a young fellow from the country who happened to be loafing around in front of his booth. He showed the fellow what he had to do before the act and then went off to beat up an audience. Among other things, the fellow had to stuff a live rabbit into a secret drawer in the magician's table. The drawer was narrow, of course; the rabbit couldn't squeeze in, and began to squeal. The fellow was from the country; he liked animals, but he was stupid. So he said to himself, 'Poor little fellow,' he says, 'why should I cram you in there, and why should you suffer? . . . The gentleman's a magician . . . he'll conjure up another one. . . .' And he took the rabbit and put it back in its cage. . . ."

"And during the show . . . ?" asked Bures.

"I don't know what happened, I wasn't there. But after the show I saw what happened. The boy kept hollering, 'The gentleman's a magician . . . he can enchant . . .' and Gianini kept yelling, 'The gentleman's a magician, he'll enchant a couple of punches onto that mug of yours!' "

"And did he?"

"Not a couple, man, it was a whole fireworks display of blows. The slaps rained down like rockets."

Bures chuckled, but Karas remained gloomy and lost in thought over the problem of the top hat. And when they were back in Hamburg, the circus people would go secretly to watch him at those times when, believing that no one could see him, he would come out of the wagon with the top hat on his head, walking as carefully as if he were balancing a ball, climb down the steps and back again, always with his neck convulsively tense in the fear that the tall stovepipe would fall off his head.

But the wedding, the glorious wedding, was perhaps not so magnificent as Berwitz had imagined it would be. The magistrates refused to allow a parade with elephants and camels through the streets, but had no objection to a cavalcade of horses to accompany the coaches of the wedding party. Again the most expensive costumes were brought to light and the Sunday-morning crowds strolling through the streets saw a host of magnificent horses with glittering trappings, bearing fantastic riders on their backs.

334

After them came the strings of coaches, their drivers with white bows on their whips and green rosemary in their buttonholes. And the last coach, all beribboned in white, was drawn by four white horses, which stepped high in Spanish style, astonishing the crowds with their precisely even gait. Four pairs of glittering reins came together between the deft fingers of the man on the box, who aroused great admiration by the pompousness with which he sat on the decorated coachman's box, like an ancient patriarch on a throne.

When this coach reached the cathedral the bride alighted, clad all in white, slender under her misty veil, and majestic as a young queen. Two little boys dressed in white jumped down behind her and carried her train as she climbed up the steps to the cathedral door. The bridegroom's tail coat was perfection itself; it had been tailored under the personal supervision of Baron Schönstein by the Viennese specialist in formal attire, Jan Václav Koblizka. And the top hat which the Baron had selected shone with its obligatory eight reflections no less brilliantly than did his father's, though the latter was a bit battered here and there. The bride's father, wearing a chest full of exotic medals, shone with respectability. Her mother appeared a bit upset. She stood apart from the other women of the bridal party in the striking simplicity of her attire. Her sister-in-law, on the other hand, was swimming in lace, ribbons, ruffles, and cockades no less than in tears and sobs.

Peter Berwitz, leading his daughter, stopped on the threshold of the cathedral and quickly glanced over the throngs of people crowding into the church. Then he turned to Anna, who walked behind him on the arm of Karas the tent-staker, and whispered with satisfaction:

"A full house!"

"What did he say?" asked Frau von Hammerschmidt, who walked behind her, led by Baron von Schönstein.

"That it's a full house."

"A full house!" echoed Frau von Hammerschmidt with emphasis. "May God bless them, since they fill the house so well for Him. And then, Baron, you must bear in mind that it's a matinée, and fine weather, besides!"

"Yes, but the advance publicity was extraordinary. Cheap and to the point. That debate they had in the City Council whether elephants and camels could be let into the cathedral . . ."

"It's a full house," the voice of Frans Steenhouwer repeated behind them. He escorted Mrs. Alice Kerholec, and was talking to the couple behind him.

"What are they saying?" Conductor Selnicki asked Kerholec.

"The Lord has a full house," answered the ringmaster.

"What good is that?" sighed the band leader. "There's no buffet."

"Fifteen hundred people at three marks fifty apiece," calculated Steenhouwer on his way to the altar. "That would come to 5,250 marks. A beautiful gate for the management. A minister, a sexton, two acolytes, and not a single animal. I'd like a business like that myself."

"If they weren't all here on passes." Alice Kerholec smiled.

"The bride's in the ring already," the rear couples were saying as the procession stopped. And in fact, Berwitz's family and Karas the elder had formed a circle around the bridegroom and the bride, and Mrs. Kerholec was hastily smoothing out the latter's veil.

"Ready?" asked Peter Berwitz.

"All right," answered Helen.

"*Allez!*" Berwitz gave the command, and in his mind he cracked his whip. The bridal couple knelt down at the altar rail, and the minister entered from the sacristy.

"She is so splendid, and his suit becomes him so well," sobbed Fran von Hammerschmidt. "They're a beautiful couple, Baron. Vasek has a good heart, and how well formal clothes suit him. . . ."

"Well, he has a good figure," whispered Gaudeamus. "Every animal-trainer has a good figure."

"I beg of you, Baron, don't mention animal-tamers to me. There are some atrocious people among them. And when he settles down to married life, he won't have to think about wild beasts and taming."

"You're right there." Gaudeamus grinned. "That might well be dangerous. A man should think of that before it's too late."

"You're a terrible cynic, Baron. If I didn't have to cry so much

336

I'd pinch your arm. But I can't see which arm is yours and which is mine, I'm crying so much."

On the other side Peter Berwitz bent over to Gaudeamus and, covering his mouth with his top hat, whispered:

"You were right, Baron. That parson is so fat you couldn't catch him with a lasso. It would slip right off him. But the staging is good, isn't it? Look at old Karas, how magnificent he looks in his morning coat and top hat. If he had a gold chain around his neck he'd look like a senator. I must make a note of that—a gold chain. The circus has never had that—a doorman in a black suit and a gold chain. A wonderful idea, don't you think?"

During this time Karas the elder forgot his morning coat and top hat. He was a simple man who was seeing his son married. He stood with bowed head and asked the Lord for the couple's happiness. Beside him stood Anna Berwitz with clasped hands, quietly whispering a prayer.

The ceremony over, Vasek and Helen stood up and the crowd threw itself at them to embrace them, kiss them, and shake their hands. Again the two pages picked up the train.

"Pay attention, boys, don't stumble on the steps outside," Kerholec enjoined them under his breath, "or I'll give it to you when we get home."

On the steps leading up to the cathedral they were met by the costumed riders, who formed into a double row. When Vasek and Helen came out they raised their riding whips in the air to form an arch, and the newly-weds walked underneath. The surrounding crowd began to applaud. On the top step Peter Berwitz stopped and pointed at the throngs.

"Look, what a success!"

And when he reached the bottom of the steps he clapped his hands and announced in his sturdy director's voice that, at the suggestion of Ringmaster Kerholec, they would all adjourn now for a bit of refreshment, and that the costumed riders must make their way there as soon as they could change their clothes. The members of the party returned to their carriages or remounted their horses, and the great cavalcade again began its slow movement along the main boulevards until it reached the Reeperbahn. Here the riders on horseback turned off toward the circus, but the carriages continued forward, turned to the left down a crooked street and stopped in front of the Sailor's Bride. When, at the head of the party, Vasek and Helen approached the entrance, the doors opened wide, and on the threshold there appeared the swarthy Sergeant Ferenc Vosátka and Mrs. Adéla Vosátka and pelted the couple with confetti and rice.

The Sailor's Bride was no longer a mere bar. The shops on either side of it had been bought up, their walls knocked out, and the bar converted into a restaurant with a number of off-lying rooms. Outside, over the entrance, hung a great sign depicting a young girl in a crinoline. She was standing on the shore and waving her handkerchief at a boat which made its way through the high waves toward a sailing boat in the background. Round the picture were the words: *Zur Seemans-Braut, La Novia del Marinero, La Sposa di Marinaio,* The Sailor's Bride, *A la Fiancée du Marin.*

The Spanish inscription was given first place, for ever since that day when the circus hand Vosátka had married the bartender Moesecke's widow, he had gone every day to the port and had welcomed every boat from South and Central America. Great transatlantic steamers from Buenos Aires, Montevideo, Rio de Janeiro, Pernambuco, ships with their home ports in New Orleans, Tampico, Vera Cruz, big-bellied ships taking on cargo in Cayenne, Paramaribo, Georgetown, Maracaibo, and Cartagena, ships stopping at Colón, Havana, Kingston, Port au Prince, ships on which people sailed from Argentina, Brazil, Guiana, Venezuela, Colombia, Costa Rica, Nicaragua, Honduras, Guatemala, Mexico, Texas, and Arkansas, people from the Antilles and Yucatán—all these would recognize the scarred Ferenc Vosátka, who spoke like a fellow countryman to whites or to blacks alike, babbled Spanish, French, English, Dutch, the five Negro tongues and the ten Indian dialects, inviting everyone to his nook, the Sailor's Bride.

Gradually the old rendezvous of the Czech workers looked as if it lay somewhere between the Tropics of Cancer and Capricorn, and in less than a year two more rooms had to be added, one named the Caribbean Sea, the other the Gulf of Mexico, while the bar at the entrance was called Providence Street. Mrs. Adéla, who had been learning Czech cooking during her first months there, now had to reorient herself to Spanish and American cuisine, to prepare "fiery" beefsteaks with paprika and wine, meat balls *à la criolla* with tomatoes, paprika, and onions, pot roast with mushrooms *à la Mexicana,* to cook *callos con chorizo,* tripe with paprika, bacon, onions, parsley, and a mass of spices, or *pepitoria de pollo,* chicken with pepper, garlic, and egg yolks. The most important was *olla podrida,* beef cooked with peas, beans, saffron, and a host of other essential ingredients.

The Caribbean Sea and the Gulf of Mexico soon hummed with all the dialects from La Plata to the Mississippi, and Providence Street wasn't big enough for all the newcomers. Of course, there were days of low tide, when boats raised their anchors and steamed away, and new ones had not yet docked. But this only made the occasions when the crews of ten or fifteen boats would congregate there all the wilder. This whole wild gang was ready to pull out their knives at the drop of a hat, but Sergeant Vosátka ruled them with an iron hand.

He was the lord and master of all, with but one exception: the buffet cupboard with its liquors, which Adéla Vosátka had moved from the bar to the kitchen, from which she personally supervised what was given out and to whom it went. She evidently did not want liquor to reawaken in her husband that wild passion with which he had once won her heart.

Here now, to the inn of his old wagon mate, Kerholec brought the wedding party from Umberto's Circus. It was a day when other business was quiet. Sergeant Ferenc Vosátka welcomed his former boss with the grand manners of a Spanish viceroy. Beer and wine flowed, with the roast kidneys and the spicy hot dogs; the first toasts were pronounced, the first honor unanimously bestowed on the future chief. Even Hans came over to clink glasses with Vendelín Malina and to congratulate him on how perfectly he had driven the bride, and the reconciliation of the two old men wound itself into a long argument on whether, in Old Umberto's day, the mare Vendida should have been bred to the stallion Mashallah or to Vasco.

The "bit of refreshment" would have changed into a heroic feast in no time if Berwitz and Kerholec had not kept in mind the

339

fact that Sunday meant a double performance for the circus. So after a noisy hour and many speeches they deserted the Caribbean Sea, in which Leopold Selnicki remained alone, like a ship-wrecked Robinson Crusoe.

The real wedding reception was confined to the family. It was simple and heartfelt, and did not last long. The bride had still to perform her ride, straddling a pair of horses, with many jumps, while the groom had to prepare the lions, tigers, and bears for the show. Only late that evening, after all the animals had been fed and watered, the props packed away, and the sandy ring buried in darkness, did Vasek, alone with Helen, embrace her, and say:

"At last, Helen, we have a little time to ourselves."

"Yes," said Helen. "You know, there's nothing more terrible than being a bride in a circus and having to give a double performance."